Introduction to
Physical Metallurgy

McGraw-Hill Book Company

New York   *St. Louis*   *San Francisco*

London   *Toronto*   *Sydney*

SIDNEY H. AVNER

Professor
City University of New York

Introduction to Physical Metallurgy

To

Judy, Kenny, and Jeffrey,

in whose hands

the future lies

Introduction to Physical Metallurgy

Library of Congress Catalog Card Number 63-20995

02495

789101112-HDMM-7543210

PREFACE

This book is written as a text to be used in the teaching of metallurgy to students who are not majors in metallurgy or as an introductory course to engineering students. It could also be useful for technician training programs in industry.

The core of this book is made up of notes developed during more than ten years of teaching the fundamentals of physical metallurgy to non-metallurgy majors. The fundamental concepts are presented in a simplified form yet as accurately as possible. The only background required is an elementary course in physics.

After a brief introduction to the field of metallurgy, some of the important tools and tests are discussed in Chap. 1. The properties of metals and alloys determine their suitability for a particular application. It is therefore useful to know how some of these properties are obtained.

Chapter 2 contains a simplified explanation of atomic and metal structure; it discusses crystal planes and the transition from the liquid to the solid state. Chapters 3 and 4 cover the fundamentals of plastic deformation and the effect of heat on cold-worked materials.

The study of binary phase diagrams is covered in Chap. 6 after the terms to be encountered are explained in Chap. 5. Wherever possible, actual alloy systems are used as illustrative examples. The relationship between age hardening and the appropriate phase diagram is pointed out. The chapter closes with a study of complex binary systems, using the principles developed in the chapter. Several actual complex binary systems are given as exercises for the student.

The next five chapters deal with the alloys of iron. The iron–iron carbide phase diagram is considered in some detail in Chap. 7, followed by the heat treatment of steel in Chap. 8. Alloy steels, tool steels, and cast irons are covered in Chaps. 9, 10, and 11.

Chapter 12 deals with the most important nonferrous metals and

v

alloys. Chapters 13 through 16 treat wear resistance, metals at low and high temperatures, corrosion resistance, and powder metallurgy. The final chapter covers the principles of extractive metallurgy and was added to broaden the scope of the book.

There is very little on the details of operation of heat-treating and testing equipment since they are covered in the laboratory course which is taken in conjunction with the theory course.

Numerous photomicrographs have been used to illustrate typical structures. Many tables have been included to present representative data on commercial alloys.

The aid received from the following people in reading portions of the manuscript or in preparation of photomicrographs is gratefully acknowledged: J. E. Krauss, G. Cavaliere, A. Dimond, A. Smith, A. Cendrowski, J. Sadofsky, C. Pospisil, T. Ingraham, J. Kelch, and O. Kammerer. Many companies have contributed generously from their publications, and the original sources have been credited wherever possible for all illustrations and tables.

The author would like to express his appreciation to Miss Barbara Worth for typing most of the manuscript and finally to his wife, without whose patience and understanding this book could never have been written.

Sidney H. Avner

CONTENTS

INTRODUCTION

Metallurgy is concerned with the study of metals. Metallurgy as an art has been practiced since ancient times. The worker of metals is mentioned in the Bible and in Greek and Norse mythology. The art of smelting, refining, and shaping metals was highly developed by both the Egyptians and Chinese. Iron does not seem to have been popular with ancient people because of its tendency to rust. They preferred working with copper, gold, silver, brass, and bronze. That steel had the ability to harden was also known to the ancient Egyptians.

Very little was written on metallurgical processes until Biringuccio in 1540. Knowledge was generally passed directly from master to apprentice in the Middle Ages, leading to an aura of superstition surrounding many of the processes.

The beginning of metallurgy as a science may be considered to be 1864, when Sorby reported on the structure of meteoric iron by use of the microscope. Sorby's work aroused little interest among scientists at first, but additional work by Martens (1878) and Sorby (1886) interested the iron and steel manufacturers.

In the early part of the twentieth century, Albert Sauveur convinced American steel companies that the microscope was a practical tool to aid in the manufacture and heat treatment of steel. This led to the rapid development of *metallography*, the field concerned with the use of the microscope to study the structure of metals.

More fundamental knowledge of the structure and properties of metals was added by the application of X-ray diffraction and wave mechanics, starting about 1925.

Metallurgy is really not an independent science since many of its fundamental concepts are derived from physics, chemistry, and crystallography.

The metallurgist has become increasingly more important in modern technology. Years ago, the great majority of steel parts were made

1

of cheap low-carbon steel that would machine and fabricate easily. Heat treatment was reserved largely for tools. Designers were unable to account for structural inhomogeneity, surface defects, etc., and it was considered good practice to use large factors of safety. Consequently, machines were much heavier than they should have been and the weight was considered a mark of quality. This attitude has persisted, to some extent, to the present time but has been discouraged under the leadership of the aircraft and automotive industries. They have emphasized the importance of the strength-weight ratio in good design, and this has led to the development of new high-strength–lightweight alloys.

In power generation by steam turbines and nuclear reactors, temperature and pressure levels are continually being pushed upward to extreme conditions requiring new alloys.

The metallurgical field may be subdivided into two large groups:

1. Process or extractive metallurgy—the science of obtaining metals from their ores. This includes the mining, extraction, and refining of metals and alloys.
2. Physical metallurgy—the science concerned with the physical and mechanical characteristics of metals and alloys. This field studies the properties of metals and alloys as affected by three variables:
    a. Chemical composition—the chemical constituents of the alloy.
    b. Mechanical treatment—any operation that causes a change in shape such as rolling, drawing, stamping, forming, or machining.
    c. Thermal or heat treatment—the effect of temperature and rate of heating and cooling.

Chapter 1

TOOLS OF THE METALLURGIST

The purpose of this chapter is to give the student an understanding of some of the common tools and tests that are used in the metallurgical field.

1·1 Temperature scales. In scientific research and in most foreign countries, the standard temperature-measuring scale is the centigrade scale. However, in American industrial plants, the Fahrenheit scale is used almost exclusively. Therefore, all references to temperature in this book will be in terms of the Fahrenheit scale since this is the one most likely to be encountered by the industrial technician. Conversion from one scale to the other may be made by the following equations:

$$°C = \tfrac{5}{9}(°F - 32) \tag{1·1}$$

$$°F = \tfrac{9}{5}\,°C + 32 \tag{1·2}$$

The accuracy with which temperatures are measured and controlled will determine the successful operation of some metallurgical processes such as casting, smelting, refining, and heat treatment. It will also have a profound effect on the strength properties of many metals and alloys.

TEMPERATURE MEASUREMENT

Pyrometry deals with the measurement of elevated temperatures, generally above 950°F, and instruments used for this purpose are known as *pyrometers*.

Thermometry deals with measurement of temperatures below 950°F, and instruments for this purpose are known as *thermometers*.

1·2 Temperature measurement by color. One of the simplest methods of estimating the temperature of a metal is by noting the color of the hot body. There is an apparent correlation between the temperature of a metal and its color, as shown by Table 1·1. Except

3

when applied by an experienced observer, this method will give only rough temperature estimates. The principal difficulty is that judgment of color varies with the individual. Other sources of error are that the color may not be uniform and may vary somewhat with different materials.

Table 1·1   Variation of color with temperature

Color	Temp., °F
Faint red	950
Dark red	1150
Dark cherry	1175
Cherry red	1300
Bright cherry	1475
Dark orange	1650
Orange	1750
Yellow	1800

1·3   Filled-system thermometers.   This type of temperature-measuring device consists of a bulb exposed to the temperature to be measured and an expansible device, usually a bourdon tube, operating an indicating pointer or a recording pen. The bulb and bourdon tube are connected by capillary tubing and filled with a suitable medium. The filled-system thermometers may be classified as follows:

1. Liquid expansion
2. Gas or vapor pressure

The liquid-expansion thermometer has the entire system filled with a suitable organic liquid or mercury. Changes in bulb temperature cause the liquid to expand or contract, which in turn causes the bourdon tube to expand or contract. Temperature changes along the capillary and at the case also cause some expansion and contraction of the liquid, and some form of compensation is therefore required. Figure 1·1 shows a fully compensated liquid-expansion thermometer using a duplicate system, less bulb, arranged so that motions are subtracted. The construction of all filled-system thermometers is essentially the same as shown in Fig. 1·1. Some of the liquids used and the temperatures covered by them are:

Mercury	−35 to +950°F
Alcohol	−110 to +160°F
Pentane	−330 to + 85°F
Creosote	+20 to +400°F

In the vapor-pressure thermometer a volatile liquid partially fills the bulb. Different temperatures of the bulb cause corresponding pressure variations in the saturated vapor above the liquid surface in the bulb. These pressure variations are transmitted to the bourdon tube, the pressure indications acting as a measure of the temperature in the bulb. By suitable choice of volatile liquid, almost any temperature from -60 to $+500°F$ can be measured. Some liquids used are methyl chloride, ether, ethyl alcohol, and toluene.

The gas-pressure thermometer is similar to the vapor-pressure thermometer except that the system is filled with a gas, usually nitrogen. The range of temperature measured by the gas-pressure thermometer is from -450 to $+1200°F$.

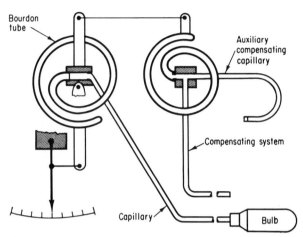

Fig. 1·1 A fully compensated liquid-expansion thermometer. (*From "Temperature Measurement," American Society for Metals*, 1956)

Filled-system thermometers are used primarily for low-temperature applications such as plating and cleaning baths, degreasers, cooling water and oil temperatures, and subzero temperatures in the cold treatment of metals. These instruments are relatively inexpensive but are not used where quick repair or exceptionally high accuracy is required.

1·4 Resistance thermometer. The principle of the resistance thermometer depends upon the increase of electrical resistance with increasing temperature of a conductor. If the temperature-resistance variations of a metal are calibrated, it is possible to determine the temperature by measuring its electrical resistance. The resistance coil is mounted in the closed end of a protecting tube and the leads are extended to a suitable resistance-measuring instrument, usually a Wheatstone bridge.

Resistance coils are usually made of copper, nickel, or platinum. Nickel and copper are most satisfactory for temperatures between 150 and $500°F$, whereas platinum may be used between -350 and

+1100°F. The resistance thermometer is very accurate and is of great importance in the laboratory. However, its industrial use is limited because it is fragile and requires many precautions in use.

1·5   Thermoelectric pyrometer. This is the most widely used method for metallurgical temperature measurement and control, and will perform satisfactorily up to about 3000°F.

The simple thermoelectric pyrometer, shown in Fig. 1·2, consists of the following units:

1. The *thermocouple*, composed of two different metals or alloys
2. The *junction block*, just outside the furnace
3. The *extension leads*
4. The *indicating instrument* or recorder

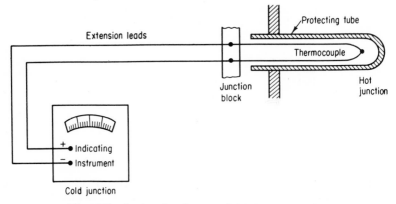

Fig. 1·2   A simple thermoelectric pyrometer.

The operation of this pyrometer is based upon two principles:

Peltier Effect. If two dissimilar metallic wires are brought into electrical contact, an emf will exist across the point of contact. The magnitude of the emf developed will be determined by the chemical composition of the wires and the temperature of the junction point.

Thomson Effect. If there is a temperature difference between the ends of a single homogeneous wire, an emf will exist between the ends of the wire. The magnitude of the emf developed will be determined by the composition, the chemical uniformity of the wire, and the temperature difference.

The total emf in a thermoelectric pyrometer, sometimes called the *Seebeck effect*, is therefore the algebraic sum of four emf's, two Peltier emf's at the hot and cold junctions and two Thomson emf's along each of the wires.

If the cold junction, or reference junction, is kept at a constant temperature, usually the melting point of ice, then the measured emf

Table 1·2   Temperature vs. electromotive force*

Emf in millivolts; cold junction 32°F

Temp, °F	Pt + 10%Rh vs. platinum	Chromel vs. Alumel	Iron vs. constantan	Copper vs. constantan
32	0.0	0.0	0.0	0.0
100	0.221	1.52	1.94	1.517
200	0.595	3.82	4.91	3.967
300	1.017	6.09	7.94	6.647
400	1.474	8.31	11.03	9.525
500	1.956	10.57	14.12	12.575
600	2.458	12.86	17.18	15.773
700	2.977	15.18	20.25	19.100
800	3.506	17.53	23.32	
900	4.046	19.89	26.40	
1000	4.596	22.26	29.52	
1100	5.156	24.63	32.72	
1200	5.726	26.98	36.01	
1300	6.307	29.32	39.43	
1400	6.897	31.65	42.96	
1500	7.498	33.93	46.53	
1600	8.110	36.19	50.05	
1700	8.732	38.43		
1800	9.365	40.62		
1900	10.009	42.78		
2000	10.662	44.91		
2100	11.323	47.00		
2200	11.989	49.05		
2300	12.657	51.05		
2400	13.325	53.01		
2500	13.991	54.92		
2600	14.656			
2700	15.319			
2800	15.979			
2900	16.637			
3000	17.292			

* By permission from P. H. Dike, "Thermoelectric Thermometry," p. 82, Leeds and Northrup Company, 1954.

in the pyrometer circuit will be a definite function of the temperature of the hot junction. By suitable calibration, it is possible to determine an exact relationship between the developed emf and the true temperature of the hot junction (Table 1·2).

Another useful thermoelectric law states that, if a third metal is introduced into the circuit, the total emf of the circuit will not be

affected if the temperature of this third metal is uniform over its entire length.

The purpose of the extension leads is to move the reference junction to a point where the temperature will not vary. Thermocouple wires are usually not long enough or well enough insulated to be run directly to the instrument. The extension leads are usually made of the same material as the thermocouple wires and are placed in a duplex cable with the individual covering color-coded for identification. Copper extension leads may be used in some cases, but then the cold junctions are at the junction block instead of the instrument and may be more difficult to maintain at constant temperatures.

1·6 Thermocouple materials. Theoretically, any two dissimilar metallic wires will develop an emf when there is a temperature difference between their junction points. Industrially, however, only a few combinations are actually used for thermocouples. These were chosen primarily for their thermoelectric potential, reasonable cost, grain-size stability, linearity of the temperature-emf curve, and melting points higher than the temperature to be measured. The first material in the combination is always connected to the positive terminal.

Chromel-Alumel. Chromel (90 per cent nickel, 10 per cent chromium) vs. Alumel (94 per cent nickel, 3 per cent manganese, 2 per cent aluminum, 1 per cent silicon) is one of the most widely used industrial combinations. It has a fairly linear calibration curve and good resistance to oxidation. It is most useful in the range from 1200 to 2200°F.

Iron-Constantan. Constantan is an alloy containing approximately 54 per cent copper and 46 per cent nickel. This combination may be used in the range from 300 to 1400°F. The primary advantages are its comparatively low cost, high thermoelectric power, and adaptability to different atmospheres.

Copper-Constantan. The constantan alloy used with copper differs slightly from that used with iron and may contain small amounts of manganese and iron. This combination is most useful for measuring low temperatures, down to −420°F. The upper limit is approximately 600°F.

The above combinations are known as *base-metal* thermocouples.

Platinum, 10 per cent Rhodium–Platinum. This is a "noble-metal" thermocouple. It is used for measuring temperatures which are too high for base-metal thermocouples and where radiation or optical pyrometers are not satisfactory. It is suitable for continuous use in the range from 32 to 3000°F but deteriorates rapidly in a reducing atmosphere.

Thermocouples are manufactured by cutting off suitable lengths of

the two wires; the ends are carefully twisted together for about two turns, or sometimes butted together, and welded to form a smooth well-rounded head (Fig. 1·3a).

The thermocouple wires should be in electrical contact only at the hot junction since contact at any other point will usually result in

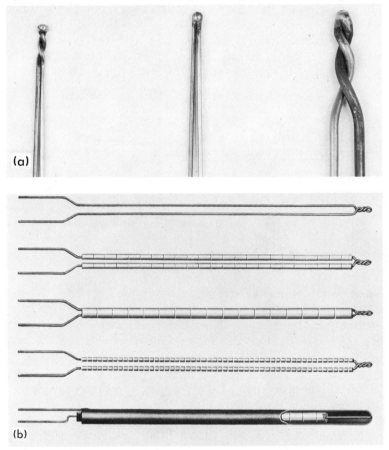

Fig. 1·3   (a) Examples of properly welded thermocouples.   (b) Different types of porcelain separators.   (*Leeds & Northrup Company*)

too low a measured emf. The two wires are insulated from each other by porcelain beads or ceramic tubes (Fig. 1·3b).

In most cases, thermocouples are enclosed in protecting tubes. The protecting tubes may be either ceramic or metallic materials. The tube guards the thermocouple against mechanical injury and prevents contamination of the thermocouple materials by the furnace atmosphere. A variety of metallic protecting tubes are available, such as wrought iron or cast iron (up to 1300°F); 14 per cent chrome iron (up to 1500°F); 28 per cent chrome iron, or Nichrome (up to 2000°F). Above 2000°F, porcelain or silicon carbide protecting tubes are used.

1·7   Measurement of emf.   The temperature of the hot junction is determined by measuring the emf generated in the circuit. The instrument generally used is a potentiometer or millivoltmeter, calibrated either in millivolts or directly in temperature. In the latter case, the instrument should be used only with the type of thermocouple for which it is calibrated. This information is always stamped on the dial face of the instrument.

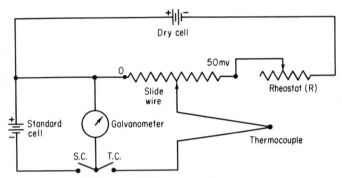

Fig. 1·4   A simple potentiometer circuit.

A simple potentiometer circuit is shown in Fig. 1·4. When the switch is closed in the standard cell (S.C.) position, the battery rheostat *R* is adjusted until the galvanometer indicates zero. This standardizes the potential drop across the slide-wire so that each ohm of the slide-wire is equivalent to a definite amount of millivolts. The slide-wire may now be calibrated in millivolts. When the switch is closed in the thermocouple (T.C.) position, the thermocouple emf is placed across the galvanometer and the movable contact of the slide-wire. The movable contact is adjusted so that the galvanometer reads zero. At this point, the drop of potential through the slide-wire up to the point of contact is equal to the emf of the thermocouple, and the millivolts may be read directly on the slide-wire scale. Reference to a suitable calibration table, such as Table 1·2, for the particular thermocouple being used will allow the conversion of millivolts to temperature.

Since the cold junction at the instrument is usually higher than the standard cold junction (32°F), it is necessary to compensate for this variation. The compensation may be made manually, or automatically by a temperature-sensitive resistor called a *cold-junction compensator*.

1·8   Recording and controlling pyrometer.   In most industrial installations, the instrument is required to do more than simply indicate temperature.   The pointer of the potentiometer may be replaced by a pen that moves over a traveling chart to obtain a complete record of the temperature.   This is called a *recording pyrometer*.   The instrument, through the use of electric circuits, may also be used to control the flow of gas to the burners or electricity to the heating elements, and thereby maintain a constant predetermined furnace temperature. This is called a *controlling pyrometer*.   It is possible to design the instrument to record and control the temperature from one or more thermocouples.

1·9   Radiation pyrometer.   The basic principles of the operation of the radiation pyrometer involve a standard radiating source known as a *blackbody*.   A blackbody is a hypothetical body that absorbs all the radiation that falls upon it.   Such a body radiates energy at a higher rate than any other body at the same temperature.   Radiation pyrometers are generally calibrated to indicate blackbody or true temperatures.   The Stefan-Boltzmann law, which is the basis for the temperature scale of radiation pyrometers, shows that the rate of radiant energy from a blackbody is proportional to the fourth power of its absolute temperature.

$$W = KT^4 \qquad\qquad (1\cdot3)$$

where W = rate at which energy is emitted by a blackbody

K = proportionality constant

T = absolute temperature of blackbody

The apparent temperature measured from non-blackbody materials will always be lower than the true temperature.   This is due to the emissivity of the material, which is defined as the ratio of the rate at which radiant energy is emitted from the non-blackbody material to the rate of that emitted from a blackbody at the same temperature. Hence

$$W = Ke_t T^4 = KT_a{}^4 \qquad\qquad (1\cdot4)$$

or $$T_a{}^4 = e_t T^4 \qquad\qquad (1\cdot5)$$

where T_a = apparent absolute temperature of non-blackbody measured by pyrometer

e_t = total emissivity of non-blackbody

Therefore, knowing the total emissivity of the material, the indicated pyrometer temperature may be easily corrected to the true absolute temperature that would be read by the pyrometer under blackbody conditions.

Figure 1·5 shows a cross section of a mirror-type radiation pyrometer.   Radiation from the target passes through window A to mirror

B and is focused to form an image of the target in the plane of the internal diaphragm *J*. This image is then focused by mirror *D* upon a group of thermocouples called a *thermopile E*. By viewing hole *C* through lens *H* it can be determined if the image of the target is sufficiently large to cover the hole and whether the pyrometer is properly aimed. The rise in temperature of the thermopile is approximately proportional to the rate at which radiant energy impinges on

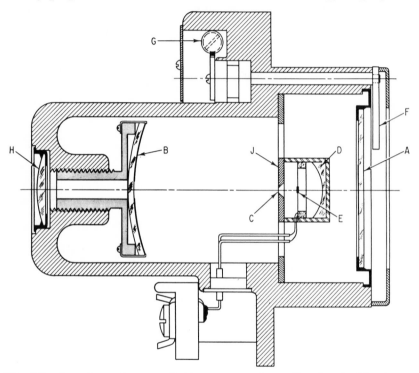

Fig. 1·5 A mirror-type radiation pyrometer. (*Leeds & Northrup Company*)

it, and the emf is therefore proportional to T^4. In actual practice, however, not all the radiant energy reaches the thermocouple since some will be absorbed by the atmosphere and optical parts of the instrument. Therefore, the Stefan-Boltzmann law is not followed very closely and the relation between the temperature of the radiating source and the emf of the thermocouple may be expressed empirically as

$$E = KT^b \qquad (1·6)$$

The constants *K* and *b* must be determined experimentally by calibration at two standardization points.

The radiation pyrometer does not require direct contact with the hot body, and therefore the upper temperature range is not limited by the ability of the pyrometer itself to withstand high temperatures. By using suitable stops in the optical system, there is no upper temperature limit. The lower temperature limit is approximately 1000°F.

1·10 Optical pyrometer. The general principles on which the optical pyrometer is based are the same as for the radiation pyrometer.

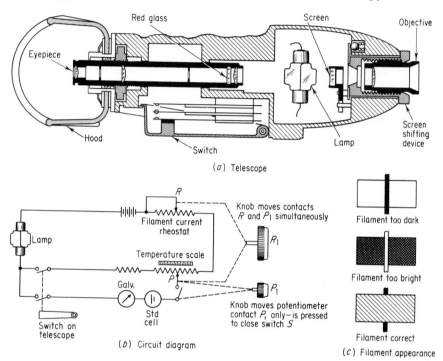

Fig. 1·6 The disappearing-filament type of optical pyrometer. (a) Telescope; (b) circuit diagram; (c) filament appearance. (*Leeds & Northrup Company*)

The optical pyrometer measures temperature by comparing the brightness of light emitted by the source with that of a standard source. To make the color comparison easier, a red filter is used which restricts the visible radiation to only the wavelength of red radiation.

The type most widely used in industry is the *disappearing-filament* type. This pyrometer consists of two parts, a telescope and a control box. The telescope (Fig. 1·6a) contains a red-glass filter mounted in front of the eyepiece and a lamp with a calibrated filament upon which the objective lens focuses an image of the body whose temperature is being measured. It also contains a switch for closing the electric circuit of the lamp, and an absorbing screen for changing the range of the pyrometer.

The control box contains the main parts of the measuring circuit shown in Fig. 1·6b. These include dry cells to provide the current to illuminate the lamp, a rheostat R to adjust filament current, and a potentiometer slide-wire, with associated standard cell and galvanometer, to measure the filament current accurately. This current is manually adjusted by rotating R_1 until the filament matches the brightness of the image of the object sighted upon and the filament seems to disappear (Fig. 1·6c). Accurate balance is then obtained by rotating P_1 until the galvanometer reads zero. A scale attached to the potentiometer contact P indicates the temperature directly.

The temperature range of the optical pyrometer described is from 1400 to about 2400°F. This upper limit is due partly to danger of deterioration of the filament at higher temperatures and partly to the dazzling effect on the eye of the brightness at elevated temperatures. The temperature range may be extended upward by use of an absorbing screen between the objective lens and the filament, thus permitting brightness matches to be secured at lower filament temperatures. The pyrometer can then be calibrated for the higher temperature range by using the lower filament temperatures. Thus, by using various absorbing screens, the upper limit of the optical pyrometer can be extended to 10,000°F or higher.

Some advantages of the optical and radiation pyrometers are:

1. Measurement of high temperature
2. Measurement of inaccessible bodies
3. Measurement on moving or small bodies
4. No part of the instrument is exposed to the destructive effects of heating

The principal disadvantages are:

1. Errors introduced because the photometric match is a matter of individual judgment
2. Errors introduced by smoke or gases between the observer and the source
3. Uncertainty as to the amount of departure from blackbody conditions

MICROSCOPY

1·11 Introduction. Microscopy or metallography consists of the microscopic study of the structural characteristics of a metal or an alloy. The microscope is by far the most important tool of the metallurgist from both the scientific and technical standpoints. It is possible to determine grain size and the size, shape, and distribution of various phases and inclusions which have a great effect on the mechanical properties of the metal. The microstructure will reveal the mechanical and thermal treatment of the metal, and it may be possible to predict its expected behavior under a given set of conditions.

Experience has indicated that success in microscopic study depends largely upon the care taken in the preparation of the specimen. The most expensive microscope will not reveal the structure of a specimen that has been poorly prepared. The procedure to be followed in the preparation of a specimen is comparatively simple and involves a technique which is developed only after constant practice. The ultimate objective is to produce a flat, scratch-free, mirrorlike surface. The steps required to prepare a metallographic specimen properly are covered in Secs. 1·12 through 1·17.

1·12 Sampling. The choice of a sample for microscopic study may be very important. If a failure is to be investigated, the sample should be chosen as close as possible to the area of failure and should be compared with one taken from the normal section.

If the material is soft, such as nonferrous metals or alloys and non-heat-treated steels, the section may be obtained by manual hacksawing. If the material is hard, the section may be obtained by use of an abrasive cutoff wheel. This wheel is a thin disk of suitable cutting abrasive, rotating at high speed. The specimen should be kept cool during the cutting operation.

1·13 Rough grinding. Whenever possible, the specimen should be of a size that is convenient to handle. A soft sample may be made flat by slowly moving it up and back across the surface of a flat smooth file. The soft or hard specimen may be rough-ground on a belt sander, with the specimen kept cool by frequent dropping in water during the grinding operation. In all grinding and polishing operations the specimen should be moved perpendicular to the existing scratches. This will facilitate recognition of the stage when the deeper scratches have been replaced by shallower ones characteristic of the finer abrasive. The rough grinding is continued until the surface is flat and free of nicks, burrs, etc., and all scratches due to the hacksaw or cutoff wheel are no longer visible.

1·14 Mounting. Specimens that are small or awkwardly shaped should be mounted to facilitate intermediate and final polishing. The mounting material may be either Lucite (thermoplastic resin) or Bakelite (thermosetting resin) (Fig. 1·7). The Lucite mold will be transparent so that the shape and location of the section will be visible.

1·15 Intermediate polishing. After mounting, the specimen is polished on a series of emery papers containing successively finer abrasives. The first paper is usually No. 1, then 1/0, 2/0, and finally

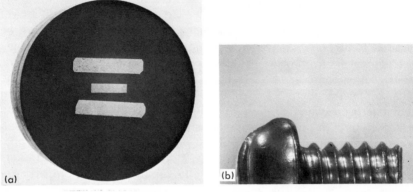

Fig. 1·7 (*a*) **Sample mounted in Bakelite, enlarged 3×.** (*b*) **Sample mounted in Lucite, enlarged 9×.**

3/0.   In some cases No. 4/0 may be used.   The intermediate polishing operations are usually done dry, but for the preparation of soft materials, the polishing papers may be wetted with a suitable lubricant. This will minimize smearing of the soft metals and also act as a coolant.

1·16   Fine polishing.   The time consumed and the success of fine polishing depend largely upon the care that was exercised during

Fig. 1·8   Scratch-free surface after final polishing, magnification 50×. Black spots are oxide impurities.

the previous polishing steps. The final approximation to a flat scratch-free surface is obtained by use of a wet rotating wheel covered with a special cloth that is charged with carefully sized abrasive particles. Abrasives that have been used with varying success on different materials are diamond dust, magnesium oxide, chromic oxide, and aluminum oxide. The choice of a proper polishing cloth depends upon the particular material being polished and the purpose of the metallographic study. Many cloths are available of varying nap or pile, from those having no pile, such as silk, to those of intermediate pile, such as broadcloth, billiard cloth, and canvas duck, and finally to a deep pile, such as velvet. Synthetic polishing cloths are also available for general polishing purposes, of which two, under the trade names of Gamal and Microcloth, are most widely used. A properly polished sample will show only the nonmetallic inclusions and will be scratch-free (Fig. 1·8).

1·17 Etching. The purpose of etching is to make visible the many structural characteristics of the metal or alloy. The process must be such that the various parts of the microstructure may be clearly differentiated. This is accomplished by use of an appropriate reagent which subjects the polished surface to chemical action.

In alloys composed of two or more phases, the components are revealed during etching by a preferential attack of one or more of these constituents by the reagent, because of difference in chemical composition of the phases (Fig. 1·9a). In uniform single-phase alloys or pure metals, contrast is obtained and grain boundaries are made visible because of differences in the rate at which various grains are attacked by the reagent (Fig. 1·9b). This difference in the rate of attack is mainly associated with the angle of the different grain sections to the plane of the polished surface. Because of chemical attack by the etching reagent, the grain boundaries will appear as valleys in the polished surface. Light from the microscope hitting the side of these valleys will be reflected out of the microscope, making the grain boundaries appear as dark lines. This is illustrated schematically in Fig. 1·9c.

The selection of the appropriate etching reagent is determined by the metal or alloy and the specific structure desired for viewing. Table 1·3 lists some of the common etching reagents.

1·18 Metallurgical microscopes. At this point it is appropriate to discuss briefly the principles of the metallurgical microscope. In comparison with a biological type, the metallurgical microscope differs in the manner by which the specimen is illuminated. Since a metallographic sample is opaque to light, the sample must be illuminated by reflected light. As shown in Fig. 1·10, a horizontal beam

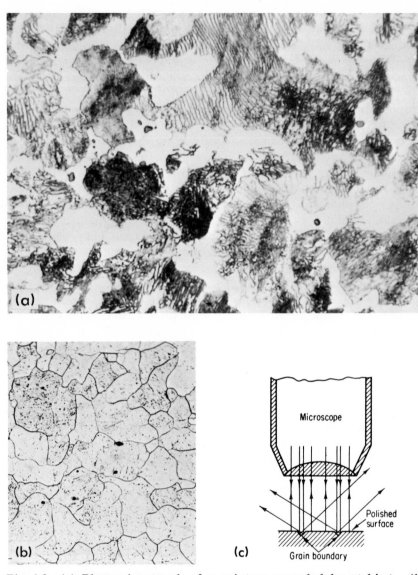

Fig. 1·9 (a) Photomicrograph of a mixture revealed by etching. (b) Photomicrograph of pure iron. (*The International Nickel Company*) (c) Schematic illustration of the microscopic appearance of grain boundaries as dark lines.

Table 1·3 Etching reagents for microscopic examination*

Etching reagent	Composition		Uses	Remarks
Nitric acid (nital)	White nitric acid Ethly or methyl alcohol (95% or absolute) (also amyl alcohol)	1–5 ml 100 ml	In carbon steels: (1) to darken pearlite and give contrast between pearlite colonies, (2) to reveal ferrite boundaries, (3) to differentiate ferrite from martensite	Etching rate is increased, selectivity decreased, with increasing percentages of HNO_3. Reagent 2 (picric acid) usually superior. Etching time a few seconds to 1 min
Picric acid (picral)	Picric acid Ethyl or methyl alcohol (95% or absolute)	4 g 100 ml	For all grades of carbon steels: annealed, normalized, quenched, and tempered, spheroidized, austempered. For all low-alloy steels attacked by this reagent	More dilute solutions occasionally useful. Does not reveal ferrite grain boundaries as readily as nital. Etching time a few seconds to 1 min or more
Ferric chloride and hydrochloric acid	Ferric chloride Hydrochloric acid Water	5 g 50 ml 100 ml	Structure of austenitic nickel and stainless steels	
Ammonium hydroxide and hydrogen peroxide	Ammonium hydroxide Water Hydrogen peroxide	5 parts 5 parts 2–5 parts	Generally used for copper and many of its alloys	Peroxide content varies directly with copper content of alloy to be etched. Immersion or swabbing for about 1 min. Fresh peroxide for good results
Ammonium persulfate	Ammonium persulfate Water	10 g 90 ml	Copper, brass, bronze, nickel silver, aluminum bronze	Use either cold or boiling; immersion
Palmerton reagent	Chromic oxide Sodium sulfate Water	200 g 15 g 1,000 ml	General reagent for zinc and its alloys	Immersion with gentle agitation
Ammonium molybdate	Molybdic acid (85%) Ammonium hydroxide (sp gr 0.9) Water Filter and add to nitric acid (sp gr 1.32)	100 g 140 ml 240 ml 60 ml	Rapid etch for lead and its alloys; very suitable for removing thick layer of worked metal	Alternately swab specimen and wash in running water
Hydrofluoric acid	Hydrofluoric acid (conc) H_2O	0.5 ml 99.5 ml	General microscopic for aluminum and its alloys	Swab with soft cotton for 15 sec

* From "Metals Handbook," 1948 edition, American Society for Metals, Metals Park, Ohio.

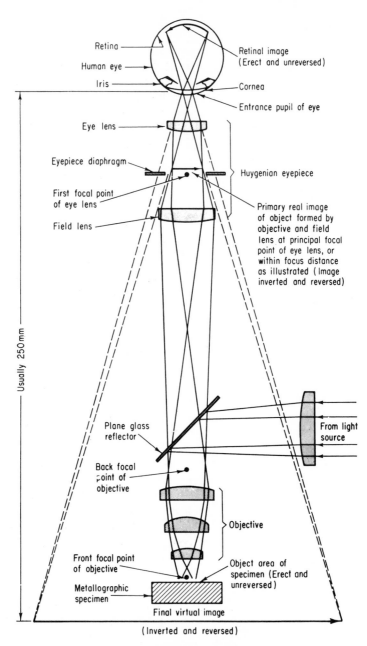

Fig. 1·10 Illustrating the principle of the metallurgical compound microscope and the trace of rays through the optical system from the object field to the final virtual image. (*By permission from G. L. Kehl, "Principles of Metallographic Laboratory Practice," 3d ed., McGraw-Hill Book Company, Inc., New York, 1949*)

of light from some light source is reflected, by means of a plane-glass reflector, downward through the microscope objective onto the surface of the specimen.   Some of this incident light reflected from the specimen surface will be magnified in passing through the lower lens system, the objective, and will continue upward through the plane-glass reflector and be magnified again by the upper lens system, the eyepiece. The initial magnifying power of the objective and the eyepiece is usually engraved on the lens mount.   When a particular combination of objective and eyepiece is used at the proper tube length, the total magnification is equal to the product of the initial magnifications of the two optical systems.   Figure 1·11a shows a table-type metallurgical microscope.

It is possible to mount a camera bellows above the eyepiece and use the table-type microscope for photomicrography.   However, the bench-type metallograph illustrated in Fig. 1·11b, which is specifically designed for both visual examination and permanent recording of metallographic structures by photographic methods, will give superior photomicrographs.

The maximum magnification obtained with the optical microscope is about 2,000×.   The principal limitation is the wavelength of visible light, which limits the resolution of fine detail in the metallographic specimen.   The magnification may be extended somewhat by the use of shorter-wavelength radiation such as ultraviolet radiation, but the sample preparation technique is more involved.

The greatest advance in resolving power was obtained by the electron microscope.   Under certain circumstances, high-velocity electrons behave like light of very short wavelength.   The electron beam has associated with it a wavelength nearly 100,000 times smaller than the wavelength of visible light, thus increasing the resolving power tremendously.   An electron microscope is shown in Fig. 1·12a.

Although in principle the electron microscope is similar to the light microscope (Fig. 1·12b), its appearance is very much different.   It is much larger because of the highly regulated power supplies that are needed to produce and control the electron beam.   The entire system must be kept pumped to a high vacuum since air would interfere with the motion of the electrons.

The lenses of the electron microscope are the powerful magnetic fields of the coils, and the image is brought into focus by changing the field strength of the coils while the coils remain in a fixed position. In the optical microscope the image is brought into focus by changing the lens spacing.

Since metallographic specimens are opaque to an electron beam, it is necessary to prepare, by special techniques, a thin replica of the surface to be studied.   The specimen is polished and etched following

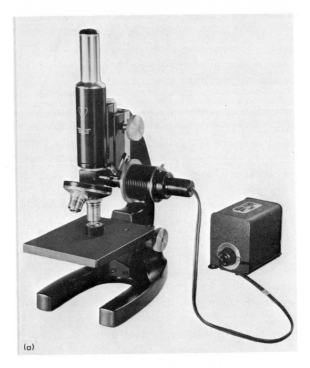

Fig. 1·11   (a) Metallurgical microscope.   (b) Bench-type metallograph.
(*Bausch & Lomb, Inc.*)

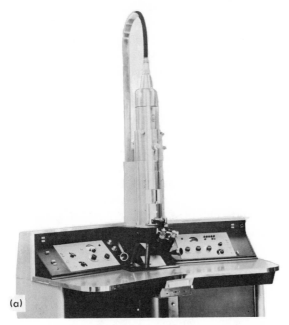

(a)

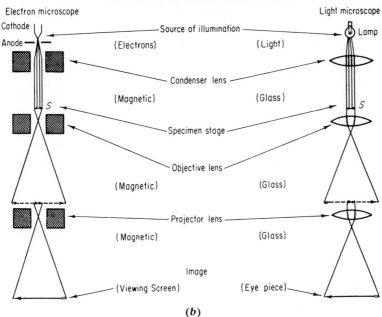

(b)

Fig. 1·12 (a) The electron microscope. (b) Similarity of light and electron microscopes. (*Radio Corporation of America*)

normal metallographic practice. It is then placed on a hot plate with a small pellet of suitable plastic on the etched surface. As the temperature rises, the plastic begins to flow and pressure is applied to ensure intimate contact between the plastic and the surface. After cooling, the replica is carefully peeled off. To improve contrast, a thin coating of carbon or tungsten is evaporated onto the replica at an angle and from one side. Since the shadowed replica is fragile, it is supported on a disk of very fine copper-wire mesh. The disk is then placed over the opening in the specimen holder, which is inserted in the column of the instrument.

The electrons emitted by a hot tungsten-filament cathode are accelerated, to form a high-velocity beam, by the anode. This beam is concentrated on the replica by the condensing lens. Depending upon the density and thickness of the replica at each point, some of the electrons are absorbed or scattered while the remainder pass through. The magnetic field of the objective lens focuses and enlarges the electron beam that has passed through the replica. Some of the electrons in this image are brought into a second focus on a fluorescent screen by the projector lens. The electron microscope shown in Fig. 1·12a has a basic magnification range of 1,400 to 32,000× which may be extended to 200,000× with accessory lenses.

TESTS FOR MECHANICAL PROPERTIES

1·19 Hardness. The property of "hardness" is difficult to define except in relation to the particular test used to determine its value. It is not a fundamental property of a material but is related to the elastic and plastic properties. The hardness value obtained in a particular test serves only as a comparison between materials or treatments. The test procedure and sample preparation are usually simple, and the results may be used in estimating other mechanical properties. Hardness testing is widely used for inspection and control. Heat treatment or working usually results in a change in hardness. When the hardness resulting from treating a given material by a given process is established, it affords a rapid and simple means of inspection and control for the particular material and process.

The various hardness tests may be divided into three categories:
Elastic hardness
Resistance to cutting or abrasion
Resistance to penetration

1·20 Elastic hardness. This type of hardness is measured by a scleroscope (Fig. 1·13), which is a device for measuring the height of rebound of a small diamond-tipped hammer after it falls by its own weight from a definite height onto the surface of the test piece.

The instrument usually has a self-indicating dial so that the height of rebound is automatically indicated. When the hammer is raised to the starting position, it has a certain amount of potential energy. When it is released, this energy is converted to kinetic energy until it strikes the surface of the test piece. Some of the energy is now

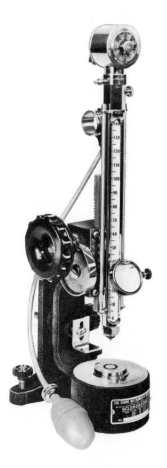

Fig. 1·13 Vertical-scale scleroscope. (*The Shore Instrument & Manufacturing Company*)

absorbed in forming the impression, and the rest is returned to the hammer for its rebound. The height of rebound is indicated by a number on an arbitrary scale such that the higher the rebound, the larger the number and the harder the test piece. This test is really a measure of the resilience of a material, that is, the energy it can absorb in the elastic range.

1·21 Resistance to cutting or abrasion

Scratch Test. This test was developed by Friedrich Mohs. The scale consists of 10 different standard minerals arranged in order of

increasing hardness.   Talc is number 1, gypsum number 2, etc., up
to 9 for corundum, 10 for diamond. If an unknown material is scratched
noticeably by number 6 and not by number 5, the hardness value is
between 5 and 6.   This test has never been used to any great extent
in metallurgy but is still used in mineralogy.   The primary disadvantage is that the hardness scale is nonuniform.   When the hardness
of the minerals is checked by another hardness-test method, it is
found that the values are compressed between 1 and 9, and there is a
large gap in hardness between 9 and 10.

File Test.   The test piece is subjected to the cutting action of a
file of known hardness to determine if a visible cut is produced.   Comparative tests with a file depend upon the size, shape, and hardness
of the file; the speed, pressure, and angle of filing during the test;
and the composition and heat treatment of the material under test.
The test is generally used industrially as one of acceptance or rejection.

1·22   Resistance to penetration.   This test is usually performed
by impressing into the specimen, which is resting on a rigid platform,
a penetrator of fixed and known geometry, under a known static load
applied either directly or by means of a lever system.   Depending
on the type of test, the hardness is expressed by a number that is
either inversely proportional to the depth of penetration for a specified
load and penetrator, or proportional to a mean load over the area of
penetration.   The three common methods of making penetration hardness tests are described below.

Brinell Hardness Test.   The Brinell hardness tester usually consists
of a hand-operated vertical hydraulic press, designed to force a ball
indenter into the test specimen (Fig. 1·14a).   Standard procedure requires that the test be made with a ball of 10 mm diameter under a
load of 3,000 kg for ferrous metals, or 500 kg for nonferrous metals.
For ferrous metals the loaded ball is pressed into the test specimen
for at least 10 sec; for nonferrous metals the time is 30 sec.   The
diameter of the impression produced is measured by means of a microscope containing an ocular scale, usually graduated in tenths of a
millimeter, permitting estimates to the nearest 0.05 mm.

The Brinell hardness number (BHN) is the ratio of the load in
kilograms to the impressed area in square millimeters, and is calculated from the following formula:

$$\text{BHN} = \frac{L}{(\pi D/2)(D - \sqrt{D^2 - d^2})} \tag{1·7}$$

where L = test load, kg
    D = diameter of ball, mm
    d = diameter of impression, mm

Calculation is usually unnecessary because tables are available for converting the observed diameter of impression to the Brinell hardness number (see Table 1·4).

(a)

(b)

Fig. 1·14 (*a*) **Brinell hardness tester.** (*Pittsburgh Instrument and Machine Company*) (*b*) **Rockwell hardness tester.** (*Wilson Mechanical Instrument Division, American Chain & Cable Company*)

Rockwell Hardness Test. This hardness test is a direct-reading instrument based on the principle of differential depth measurement (Fig. 1·14*b*). The test is carried out by slowly raising the specimen against the penetrator until a fixed minor load has been applied. This is indicated on the dial gauge. Then the major load is applied through a loaded lever system. After the dial pointer comes to rest, the major load is removed and, with the minor load still acting, the

Table 1·4 Approximate hardness relations for steel*

Brinell, 3,000 kg			Vickers diamond pyramid	Rockwell, using brale				Scleroscope	Mohs	Tensile strength, 1,000 psi
Diameter, mm	Standard ball	Tungsten carbide ball		C 150 kg	D 100 kg	A 60 kg	Superficial 30 N			
2.35	...	682	737	61.7	72.0	82.2	79.0	84		
2.40	...	653	697	60.0	70.7	81.2	77.5	81		
2.45	...	627	667	58.7	69.7	80.5	76.3	79	8.0	323
2.50	...	601	640	57.3	68.7	79.8	75.1	77	...	309
2.55	...	578	615	56.0	67.7	79.1	73.9	75	...	297
2.60	...	555	591	54.7	66.7	78.4	72.7	73	7.5	285
2.65	...	534	569	53.5	65.8	77.8	71.6	71	...	274
2.70	...	514	547	52.1	64.7	76.9	70.3	70	...	263
2.75	{ 495	...	539	51.6	64.3	76.7	69.9	..	...	259
	...	495	528	51.0	63.8	76.3	69.4	68	...	253
2.80	{ 477	...	516	50.3	63.2	75.9	68.7	..	...	247
	...	477	508	49.6	62.7	75.6	68.2	66	...	243
2.85	{ 461	...	495	48.8	61.9	75.1	67.4	..	...	237
	...	461	491	48.5	61.7	74.9	67.2	65	...	235
2.90	{ 444	...	474	47.2	61.0	74.3	66.0	..	7.0	226
	...	444	472	47.1	60.8	74.2	65.8	63	...	225
2.95	429	429	455	45.7	59.7	73.4	64.6	61	...	217
3.00	415	415	440	44.5	58.8	72.8	63.5	59	...	210
3.05	401	401	425	43.1	57.8	72.0	62.3	58	...	202
3.10	388	388	410	41.8	56.8	71.4	61.1	56	...	195
3.15	375	375	396	40.4	55.7	70.6	59.9	54	6.5	188
3.20	363	363	383	39.1	54.6	70.0	58.7	52	...	182
3.25	352	352	372	37.9	53.8	69.3	57.6	51	...	176
3.30	341	341	360	36.6	52.8	68.7	56.4	50	...	170
3.35	331	331	350	35.5	51.9	68.1	55.4	48	...	166
3.40	321	321	339	34.3	51.0	67.5	54.3	47	...	160
3.45	311	311	328	33.1	50.0	66.9	53.3	46	...	155
3.50	302	302	319	32.1	49.3	66.3	52.2	45	6.0	150
3.55	293	293	309	30.9	48.3	65.7	51.2	43	...	145
3.60	285	285	301	29.9	47.6	65.3	50.3	42	...	141
3.65	277	277	292	28.8	46.7	64.6	49.3	41	...	137
3.70	269	269	284	27.6	45.9	64.1	48.3	40	...	133
3.75	262	262	276	26.6	45.0	63.6	47.3	39	...	129
3.80	255	255	269	25.4	44.2	63.0	46.2	38	...	126
3.85	248	248	261	24.2	43.2	62.5	45.1	37	5.5	122
3.90	241	241	253	22.8	42.0	61.8	43.9	36	...	118
3.95	235	235	247	21.7	41.4	61.4	42.9	35	...	115
4.00	229	229	241	20.5	40.5	60.8	41.9	34	...	111

* Adapted from H. E. Davis, G. E. Troxell, and C. T. Wiskocil, "The Testing and Inspection of Engineering Materials," 2d ed., McGraw-Hill Book Company,

Table 1·4 Approximate hardness relations for steel (*Continued*)

Brinell, 3,000 kg		Rockwell								
		Brale				Superficial				
Diameter, mm	Standard ball	D 100 kg	A 60 kg	B 1/16-in. ball	E 1/8-in. ball	30 N brale	30 T 1/16-in. ball	Scleroscope	Mohs	Tensile strength, 1,000 psi
4.05	223	40	60	97	...	41	80.5	33	...	108
4.10	217	39	60	96	...	40	80.0	32	...	105
4.15	212	38	59	95	...	39	79.0	31	...	102
4.20	207	37	59	94	...	38	78.5	31	...	100
4.25	202	37	58	93	110	37	78.0	30	...	98
4.30	197	36	58	92	110	36	77.5	29	...	96
4.35	192	35	57	91	109	35	77.0	28	5.0	94
4.40	187	34	57	90	109	34	76.0	28	...	92
4.45	183	34	56	89	109	33	75.5	27	...	90
4.50	179	33	56	88	108	32	75.0	27	...	88
4.55	174	33	55	87	108	31	74.5	26	...	86
4.60	170	32	55	86	107	30	74.0	26	...	84
4.65	166	32	54	85	107	30	73.5	25	...	82
4.70	163	31	53	84	106	29	73.0	25	...	81
4.75	159	31	53	83	106	28	72.8	24	...	79
4.80	156	30	52	82	105	27	71.5	24	...	77
4.85	153	..	..	81	105	..	71.0	23	...	76
4.90	149	..	..	80	104	..	70.0	23	4.5	75
4.95	146	..	..	79	104	..	69.5	22	...	74
5.00	143	..	..	78	103	..	69.0	22	...	72
5.05	140	..	..	76	103	..	68.0	21	...	71
5.10	137	..	..	75	102	..	67.0	21	...	70
5.15	134	..	..	74	102	..	66.0	21	...	68
5.20	131	..	..	73	101	..	65.0	20	...	66
5.25	128	..	..	71	100	..	64.0	..	...	65
5.30	126	..	..	70	100	..	63.5	..	...	64
5.35	124	..	..	69	99	..	62.5	..	...	63
5.40	121	..	..	68	98	..	62	..	...	62
5.45	118	..	..	67	97	..	61	..	...	61
5.50	116	..	..	65	96	..	60	..	...	60
5.55	114	..	..	64	95	..	59	..	...	59
5.60	112	..	..	63	95	..	58	..	...	58
5.65	109	..	..	62	94	..	58	..	...	56
5.70	107	..	..	60	93	..	57	..	...	55
5.75	105	..	..	58	92	..	55	..	...	54
5.80	103	..	..	57	91	..	54	..	...	53

Inc., New York, 1955; based on "Metals Handbook," 1948 edition, American Society for Metals, Metals Park, Ohio. See ASTM E 48 for additional relations.

Rockwell hardness number is read on the dial gauge. Since the order of the numbers is reversed on the dial gauge, a shallow impression on a hard material will result in a high number while a deep impression on a soft material will result in a low number.

There are two Rockwell machines, the normal tester for relatively thick sections, and the superficial tester for thin sections. The minor load is 10 kg on the normal tester and 3 kg on the superficial tester.

A variety of penetrators and loads may be used, and each combination determines a particular Rockwell scale. Penetrators include steel balls $\frac{1}{16}$, $\frac{1}{8}$, $\frac{1}{4}$, and $\frac{1}{2}$ in. in diameter and a 120° conical diamond (brale) point. Major loads are usually 60, 100, and 150 kg on the normal tester and 15, 30, and 45 kg on the superficial tester.

The most commonly used Rockwell scales are the B ($\frac{1}{16}$-in. ball penetrator and 100-kg load) and the C (diamond penetrator and 150-kg load), both obtained with the normal tester. Because of the many Rockwell scales, the hardness number must be designated according to the scale used, for example, as Rockwell B or R_B or R/B and so on.

The performance of the machine should be checked frequently with standard test blocks supplied by the manufacturer. The operating crank should be returned gently to its starting position; snapping the crank to remove the major load may cause an error of several points in the dial indication. Care must be taken to seat the anvil and penetrator firmly. Any vertical movement at these points results in additional depth being registered on the gauge and, therefore, a false hardness reading.

Vickers Hardness Test. This instrument uses a square-based diamond-pyramid penetrator with an included angle of 136° between opposite faces. The load range is usually between 1 and 120 kg. The Vickers hardness tester operates on the same basic principle as the Brinell tester, the numbers being expressed in terms of load and surface area of the impression. As a result of the penetrator shape, the impression on the surface of the specimen will be a square. The length of the diagonal of the square is measured through a microscope fitted with an ocular micrometer that contains movable knife-edges. The distance between knife-edges is indicated on a counter calibrated in thousandths of a millimeter. Tables are usually available to convert the measured diagonal to diamond-pyramid hardness number (DPH), or the following formula may be used:

$$\text{DPH} = \frac{1.854L}{d^2} \tag{1.8}$$

where L = applied load, kg
 d = diagonal length of square impression

As a result of the latitude in applied loads, the Vickers tester is applicable to measuring the hardness of very thin sheets as well as heavy sections.

1·23 Accuracy of any penetration hardness test. Some of the factors that influence the accuracy of any penetration hardness test are:

Condition of the Penetrator. Flattening of a steel-ball penetrator will result in errors in the hardness number. The ball should be checked frequently for permanent deformation and discarded when such deformation occurs. Diamond penetrators should be checked for any sign of chipping.

Accuracy of Load Applied. The tester should apply loads in the stated range with negligible error. Loads greater than the recommended amount should not be used for accurate testing.

Impact Loading. Besides causing inaccurate hardness readings, impact loading may damage diamond penetrators. The use of a controlled oil dashpot will ensure smooth, steady operation of the loading mechanism.

Surface Condition of the Specimen. The surface of the specimen, on which the hardness reading is to be taken, should be flat and representative of sound material. Any pits, scale, or grease should be removed by grinding or polishing.

Thickness of Specimen. The specimen should be thick enough so that no bulge appears on the surface opposite that of the impression. The recommended thickness of the specimen is at least ten times the depth of the impression.

Shape of the Specimen. The greatest accuracy is obtained when the test surface is flat and normal to the vertical axis of the penetrator. A long specimen should be properly supported so that it does not tip. A flat surface should be prepared, if possible, on a cylindrical-shaped specimen and a V-notch anvil should be used to support the specimen unless parallel flats are ground, in which case a flat anvil may be used. If a Rockwell hardness test is made on a round specimen less than 1 in. in diameter without grinding a flat, the observed reading must be adjusted by an appropriate correction factor (Table 1·5).

Location of Impressions. Impressions should be at least 2½ diameters from the edge of the specimen and should be at least 5 diameters apart for ball tests.

Uniformity of Material. If there are structural and chemical variations in the material, the larger the impression area the more accurate the average-hardness reading. It is necessary to take many readings if the impression area is small to obtain a true average hardness for the material.

1·24   Advantages and disadvantages of different types of tests.   The selection of a hardness test is usually determined by ease of performance and degree of accuracy desired.   Since the Brinell test leaves a relatively large impression, it is limited to heavy sections.

Table 1·5   Wilson cylindrical correction chart*

Cylindrical work corrections (approximate only) to be added to observed Rockwell number

Diamond Brale Penetrator							
C, D, A scales	Diameter of specimen, in.						
	$\frac{1}{4}$	$\frac{3}{8}$	$\frac{1}{2}$	$\frac{5}{8}$	$\frac{3}{4}$	$\frac{7}{8}$	1
80	0.5	0.5	0.5	0	0	0	0
70	1.0	1.0	0.5	0.5	0.5	0	0
60	1.5	1.0	1.0	0.5	0.5	0.5	0.5
50	2.5	2.0	1.5	1.0	1.0	0.5	0.5
40	3.5	2.5	2.0	1.5	1.0	1.0	1.0
30	5.0	3.5	2.5	2.0	1.5	1.5	1.0
20	6.0	4.5	3.5	2.5	2.0	1.5	1.5

$\frac{1}{16}$-in. Ball Penetrator

B, F, G scales	Diameter of specimen, in.						
	$\frac{1}{4}$	$\frac{3}{8}$	$\frac{1}{2}$	$\frac{5}{8}$	$\frac{3}{4}$	$\frac{7}{8}$	1
100	3.5	2.5	1.5	1.5	1.0	1.0	0.5
90	4.0	3.0	2.0	1.5	1.5	1.5	1.0
80	5.0	3.5	2.5	2.0	1.5	1.5	1.5
70	6.0	4.0	3.0	2.5	2.0	2.0	1.5
60	7.0	5.0	3.5	3.0	2.5	2.0	2.0
50	8.0	5.5	4.0	3.5	3.0	2.5	2.0
40	9.0	6.0	4.5	4.0	3.0	2.5	2.5

* Courtesy of Wilson Mechanical Instrument Division, American Chain & Cable Co.

This is an advantage, however, when the material tested is not homogeneous.   The surface of the test piece when running a Brinell test does not have to be so smooth as that for smaller impressions; however, using a microscope to measure the diameter of the impression is not so convenient as reading a dial gauge.   Because of deformation of the steel ball, the Brinell test is generally inaccurate above 500 BHN.   The range may be extended to about 600 BHN with a tungsten carbide ball.

The Rockwell test is rapid and simple in operation. Since the loads and penetrators are smaller than those used in the Brinell test, the Rockwell test may be used on thinner specimens, and the hardest as well as the softest materials can be tested.

The diamond-pyramid hardness test operating under light loads will leave a relatively small impression and can be used for very thin samples, but a great deal more care is required to prepare the test surface. The surface is usually prepared by metallographic polishing. Since the surface impression is a square, it can be read more accurately than a Brinell impression.

The principal advantages of the scleroscope are the small impressions that remain, the rapidity of testing, and portability of the instrument. However, results tend to be inaccurate unless proper precautions are taken. The tube must be perpendicular to the test piece, thin pieces must be properly supported and clamped, the surface to be tested must be smoother than for most other testing methods, and the diamond tip should not be chipped or cracked.

1·25 Hardness conversion. The approximate hardness conversion between the various hardness-test machines is shown in Table 1·4. These data are generally applicable to steel and have been derived by extensive hardness tests on carbon and alloy steels, mainly in the heat-treated condition.

1·26 Stress and strain. When an external force is applied to a body which tends to change its size or shape, the body resists this external force. The internal resistance of the body is known as *stress* and the accompanying changes in dimensions of the body are called *deformations* or *strains*. The total stress is the total internal resistance acting on a section of the body. The quantity usually determined is the intensity of stress or unit stress, which is defined as the stress per unit area. The unit stress is usually expressed in units of pounds per square inch (psi), and for an axial tensile or compressive load it is calculated as the load per unit area.

The total deformation or total strain in any direction is the total change of a dimension of the body in that direction, and the unit deformation or unit strain is the deformation or strain per unit of length in that direction.

1·27 The tensile test. Next to the hardness test, the tensile test is most frequently performed to determine certain mechanical properties. A specifically prepared sample is placed in the heads of the testing machine, and an axial load is placed on the sample through a hydraulic or mechanical lever loading system. The force is indicated on a calibrated dial. If the original cross-sectional area of the specimen is known, the stress developed at any load may be calculated.

The deformation or strain is measured at a fixed length, usually 2 in., by a dial gauge called an *extensometer*. The unit strain may then be determined by dividing the measured elongation by the gauge length used. In some cases, an electrical strain gauge may be used to measure the total strain.

The relation between unit stress s and unit strain ϵ, found experimentally, is represented by the stress-strain graph in Fig. 1·15 for a ductile material and by Fig. 1·16 for a brittle material.

1·28   Tensile properties.   The properties which may be determined by a tension test follow.

Proportional Limit.   It is found for many structural materials that the early part of the stress-strain graph may be approximated by a straight line OP in Figs. 1·15 and 1·16. In this range, the stress and strain are proportional to each other so that any increase in stress will result in a proportionate increase in strain. The stress at the limit of proportionality point P is known as the *proportional limit*.

Elastic Limit.   If a small load on the test piece is removed, the extensometer needle will return to zero, indicating that the strain, caused by the load, is elastic. If the load is continually increased, then released after each increment and the extensometer checked, a point will be reached at which the extensometer needle will not return to zero. This indicates that the material now has a permanent deformation. The elastic limit may therefore be defined as the minimum stress at which permanent deformation first occurs. For most structural materials the elastic limit has nearly the same numerical value as the proportional limit.

Yield Point.   As the load in the test piece is increased beyond the elastic limit, a stress is reached at which the material continues to deform without an increase in load. The stress at point Y in Fig. 1·15 is known as the *yield point*. This phenomenon occurs only in certain ductile materials. The stress may actually decrease momentarily, resulting in an upper and lower yield point. Since the yield point is relatively easy to determine and the permanent deformation is small up to yield point, it is a very important value in the design of many machine members whose usefulness will be impaired by considerable permanent deformation. This is true only for materials that exhibit a well-defined yield point.

Yield Strength.   Most nonferrous materials and the high-strength steels do not possess a well-defined yield point. For these materials, the maximum useful strength is the yield strength. The yield strength is the stress at which a material exhibits a specified limiting deviation from the proportionality of stress to strain. This value is usually determined by the "offset method." In Fig. 1·16, the specified offset

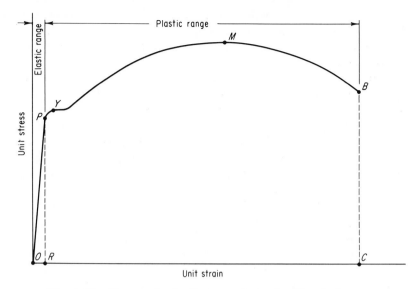

Fig. 1·15   Stress-strain diagram for a ductile steel.

Fig. 1·16   Stress-strain diagram
for a brittle material.

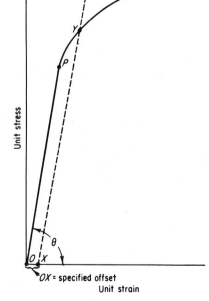

OX is laid off along the strain axis. Then XW is drawn parallel to OP, and thus Y, the intersection of XW with the stress-strain diagram, is located. The value of the stress at point Y gives the yield strength. The value of the offset is generally between 0.10 and 0.20 per cent of the gauge length.

Ultimate Strength. As the load on the test piece is increased still further, the stress and strain increase, as indicated by the portion of the curve YM (Fig. 1·15) for a ductile material, until the maximum stress is reached at point M. The ultimate strength or the tensile strength is therefore the maximum stress developed by the material based on the original cross-sectional area. A brittle material breaks when stressed to the ultimate strength (point B in Fig. 1·16), whereas a ductile material will continue to stretch.

Breaking Strength. For a ductile material, up to the ultimate strength, the deformation is uniform along the length of the bar. At the maximum stress, localized deformation or necking occurs in the specimen and the load falls off as the area decreases. This necking elongation is a nonuniform deformation and occurs rapidly to the point of failure (Fig. 1·17). The breaking strength (point B, Fig. 1·15), which is determined by dividing the breaking load by the original cross-sectional area, is always less than the ultimate strength. For a brittle material, the ultimate strength and breaking strength coincide.

Ductility. The ductility of a material is indicated by the amount of deformation that is possible until fracture. This is determined in a tension test by two measurements:

ELONGATION. This is determined by fitting together, after fracture, the parts of the specimen and measuring the distance between the original gauge marks.

$$\text{Elongation (per cent)} = \frac{L_f - L_0}{L_0} \times 100 \qquad (1·9)$$

where L_f = final gauge length

L_0 = original gauge length, usually 2 in.

In reporting per cent elongation, the original gauge length must be specified since the per cent elongation will vary with gauge length.

REDUCTION IN AREA. This is also determined from the broken halves of the tensile specimen by measuring the minimum cross-sectional area and using the following formula:

$$\text{Reduction in area (per cent)} = \frac{A_0 - A_f}{A_0} \times 100 \qquad (1·10)$$

where A_0 = original cross-sectional area

A_f = final cross-sectional area

Modulus of Elasticity or Young's Modulus. This is obtained by determining the slope of the initial straight-line portion of the stress-strain diagram or the tangent of the angle θ (Fig. 1·16). The modulus

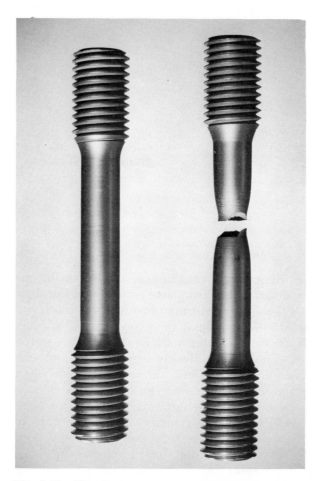

Fig. 1·17   Tension sample before and after failure.

of elasticity is the proportionality constant that connects stress and strain below the proportional limit. The modulus of elasticity is an indication of stiffness of a material. This property is important in the design of beams and columns.

1·29   True stress-strain. The conventional tensile test described will give valuable information up to the point of yielding. Beyond this point, the stress values are fictitious since the actual cross-sectional area will be considerably reduced.   The true stress is determined by the load divided by the cross-sectional area at that moment of loading.   The true strain is determined by the change in length divided by the immediately preceding length.   The true stress-strain diagram (Fig. 1·18) yields useful information regarding plastic flow and fracture of metals.

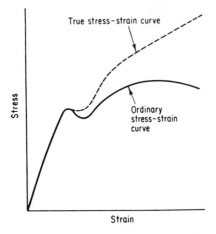

Fig. 1·18   True stress-strain and conventional stress-strain diagrams for mild steel.

1·30   Resilience and toughness.   It is possible to divide the stress-strain diagram into two parts as shown in Fig. 1·15.   The part to the left of the elastic limit may be called the *elastic range* and that to the right of the elastic limit the *plastic range*.   The area under the curve in the elastic range (area OPR) is a measure of the energy per unit volume which can be absorbed by the material without permanent deformation.   This value is known as the *modulus of resilience*. The energy per unit volume that can be absorbed by a material (the area under the entire stress-strain diagram) up to the point of fracture is known as *toughness*.   This is mainly a property of the plastic range, since only a small part of the total energy absorbed is elastic energy that can be recovered when the stress is released.

1·31   Impact test.   Although the toughness of a material may be obtained by the area under the stress-strain diagram, the impact test will give an indication of the relative toughness.

Generally, notch-type specimens are used for impact tests.   Two general types of notches are used in bending impact tests, the keyhole notch and the V notch.   Two types of specimens are used, the Charpy and the Izod, shown in Fig. 1·19.   The Charpy specimen is placed in the vise so that it is a simple beam supported at the ends.   The Izod specimen is placed in the vise so that one end is free and is therefore a cantilever beam.

The ordinary impact machine has a swinging pendulum of fixed weight which is raised to a standard height depending upon the type of specimen tested.   At that height, with reference to the vise, the pendulum has a definite amount of potential energy.   When the pendulum is released, this energy is converted to kinetic energy until it strikes the specimen.   The Charpy specimen will be hit behind the V

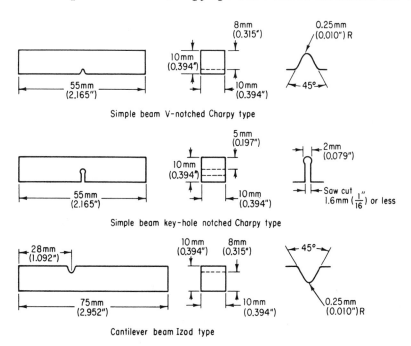

Fig. 1·19   Notched-bar impact-test specimens.   (*By permission from Tentative Methods for Notched Bar Impact Testing of Metallic Materials, ASTM Designation E23-56T*)

notch, while the Izod specimen, placed with the V notch facing the pendulum, will be hit above the V notch.   In either case, some of the energy of the pendulum will be used to rupture the specimen so that the pendulum will rise to a height lower than the initial height on the opposite side of the machine.   The weight of the pendulum times the difference in heights will indicate the energy, usually in foot-pounds, absorbed by the specimen, or the notched impact strength.

From the description of the test, it is apparent that the notched-bar impact test does not yield the true toughness of a material but rather its behavior with a particular notch.   The results are useful, however, for comparative purposes.   The notched-bar test is used by the aircraft and automotive industries, who have found by experience that high impact strength by test generally will give satisfactory service where shock loads are encountered.

1·32 Fatigue tests. The fatigue test is a dynamic type of test which determines the relative behavior of materials when subjected to repeated or fluctuating loads. It attempts to simulate stress conditions developed in machine parts by vibration of cycling loads. The magnitude of the stress may be changed on the machine, and the type of stress (tension, compression, bending, or torsion) is determined by the machine and the type of specimen tested. The stress placed

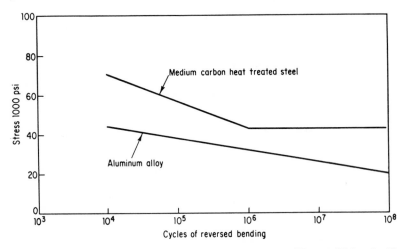

Fig. 1·20   Typical *S-N* (stress-cycle) diagrams.   (*From "Metals Handbook,"* 1948 *edition, American Society for Metals, Metals Park, Ohio*)

on the specimen during test continually alternates between two values, the maximum of which is usually lower than the yield strength of the material. The cycles of stress are applied until failure of the specimen or until a limiting number of cycles has been reached.

Those results are then plotted on a semilogarithmic scale with the stress S as the ordinate and the number of cycles N, to cause failure, as the abscissa. The "endurance limit" of any material is defined as the limiting stress below which the metal will withstand an indefinitely large number of cycles of stress without fracture. At that point on the *S-N* curve, the curve becomes parallel to the abscissa. For steel this will occur at approximately 10^7 cycles of stress. For some nonferrous alloys, however, the curve does not become horizontal, and the term *endurance limit* is often applied to the stress corresponding to some specific number of cycles. A typical *S-N* plot for heat-treated steel and aluminum alloy is shown in Fig. 1·20.

Fatigue tests are widely used to study the behavior of materials not only for type and range of fluctuating loads but also for the effect of corrosion, surface condition, temperature, size, and stress concentration.

1·33 Creep tests. The creep test determines the continuing change in the deformation of a material at elevated temperature when stressed below the yield strength. The results are important in the design of machine parts which are exposed to elevated temperatures. Creep behavior will be discussed in greater detail in a later chapter.

NONDESTRUCTIVE TESTING

1·34 Introduction. Although nondestructive tests do not provide a direct measurement of mechanical properties, they are very valuable in locating material defects that could impair the performance of a machine member when placed in service. Parts may also be examined in service, permitting their removal, in some cases, before failure occurs.

The most common methods of nondestructive testing or inspection are:

Radiography
Magnetic-particle inspection
Fluorescent-penetrant inspection
Ultrasonic inspection

1·35 Radiography of metals. The radiography of metals may be carried out using either X rays or gamma rays. Gamma rays are usually obtained from a natural source such as radium. Gamma radiation is more penetrating than that of X rays but the inferior sensitivity limits its application. There is no way that the source may be regulated for contrast or variable thickness, and the small quantity of radium which may be rented usually requires much longer exposure times as compared with the X-ray method.

X rays are produced when matter is bombarded by a rapidly moving stream of electrons. When electrons are suddenly stopped by matter, a part of their kinetic energy is converted to energy of radiation or X rays. The essential conditions for the generation of X rays are (1) a filament to provide the source of electrons proceeding toward the target, (2) a target (anode) located in the path of electrons, (3) a voltage difference between the cathode and anode which will regulate the velocity of the electrons striking the target and thus regulate the wavelength of X rays produced, and (4) a means of regulating tube current to control the number of electrons striking the target. The first two requirements are usually incorporated in an X-ray tube. The use of X rays for the examination of a welded plate is shown schematically in Fig. 1·21. X rays are potentially dangerous, and adequate safeguards must be employed to protect operating personnel.

A radiograph is a shadow picture of a material more or less transparent to radiation. The X rays darken the film so that regions of lower density which readily permit penetration appear dark on the negative as compared with regions of higher density which absorb

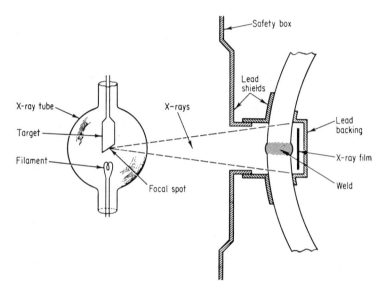

Fig. 1·21   Schematic representation of the use of X rays for examination of a welded plate.   (From "Basic Metallurgy," vol. II, American Society for Metals, Metals Park, Ohio, 1954)

more of the radiation. Thus a hole or crack appears as a darker area, whereas copper inclusions in aluminum alloy appear as lighter areas (see Fig. 1·22).

The radiography of metals has been used primarily for the inspection of castings and welded products.

1·36 Magnetic-particle inspection (Magnaflux). This is a method of detecting the presence of cracks, laps, tears, seams, inclusions, and similar discontinuities in ferromagnetic materials such as iron and steel. The method will detect surface discontinuities too fine to be seen by the naked eye and will also detect discontinuities which lie slightly below the surface. It is not applicable to nonmagnetic materials.

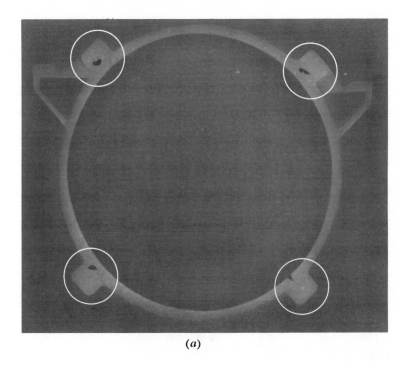

(a)

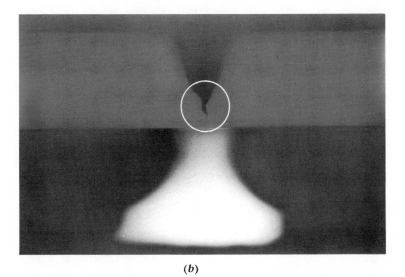

(b)

Fig. 1·22   (a) Radiograph of a stainless-steel casting.   Dark spots are shrinkage voids.   (b) Radiograph of a steel casting showing a hot tear at the root of the notch.

The piece to be inspected is magnetized and is then covered with fine magnetic particles (iron powder), or the magnetization and application of the particles may be done at the same time. The magnetic particles may be held in suspension in a liquid that is flushed over the piece, or the piece may be immersed in the suspension (wet method). The Magnaglo method developed by the Magnaflux Corporation is a variation of the Magnaflux test. The suspension flowed over the magnetized workpiece contains fluorescent magnetic particles. The workpiece is then viewed under black light. In some applications, the particles, in the form of a fine powder, are dusted over the surface of the workpiece (dry method). The presence of a discontinuity is shown by the formation and adherence of a particle pattern on the surface of the workpiece over the discontinuity. This pattern is called an *indication* and assumes the approximate shape of the surface projection of the discontinuity.

Where the discontinuity is open to the surface, the magnetic field leaks out to the surface and forms small north and south poles that attract the magnetic particles (see Fig. 1·23). When fine discontinuities are under the surface, some part of the field may still be deflected to the surface, but the leakage is less and fewer particles are attracted, so that the indication obtained is much weaker. If the discontinuity is far below the surface, no leakage of the field will be obtained and consequently no indication. Proper use of magnetizing methods is necessary to ensure that the magnetic field set up will be perpendicular to the discontinuity and give the clearest indication (see Fig. 1·24).

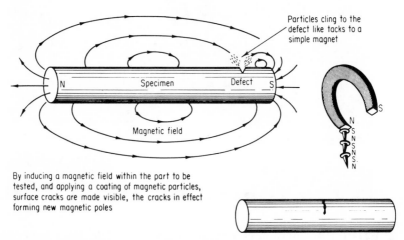

Fig. 1·23 **Principle of the Magnaflux test.** (*Magnaflux Corporation, Chicago, Ill.*)

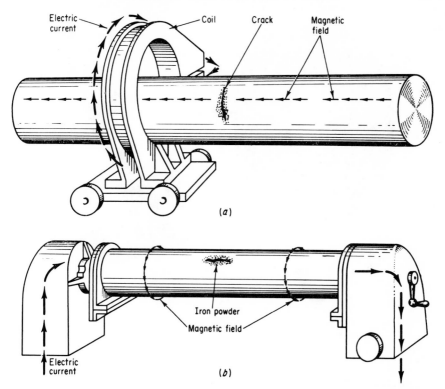

Fig. 1·24 Illustrating two kinds of magnetization. (*a*) **Longitudinal magnetization;** (*b*) **circular magnetization.** (*Magnaflux Corporation, Chicago, Ill.*)

The sensitivity of magnetic-particle inspection is affected by many factors, including strength of the indicating suspension, time in contact with the suspension, time allowed for indications to form, time subject to magnetizing current, and strength of the magnetizing current. Some examples of cracks detectable by Magnaflux or Magnaglo are shown in Fig. 1·25.

All machine parts that have been magnetized for inspection must be put through a demagnetizing operation. If these parts are placed in service without demagnetizing, they will attract filings, grindings, chips, and other steel particles which may cause scoring of bearings and other engine parts. Detection of parts which have not been demagnetized is usually accomplished by keeping a compass on the assembly bench.

1·37 Fluorescent-penetrant inspection (Zyglo). This is a sensitive nondestructive method of detecting minute discontinuities

Fig. 1·25 Typical defects revealed by Magnaflux and Magnaglo.
(a) Grinding cracks; (b) fatigue crack in an aircraft crankshaft;
(c) casting crack in lawn-mower casting; (d) cracks in critical jet-
engine blades. (*Magnaflux Corporation, Chicago, Ill.*)

such as cracks, shrinkage, and porosity that are open to the surface in parts that are nonmagnetic. Parts to be tested are usually briefly immersed in a liquid fluorescent penetrant which enters the discontinuities. The parts are then allowed to drain, and the excess penetrant is removed from the surface by washing with water or a solvent, depending upon the type of penetrant used. After washing, the parts are treated with a dry powder or a suspension of powder in a liquid. This powder or developer aids in drawing the penetrant from the defect and holding it on the surface adjacent to the defect. The parts are then inspected under ultraviolet light or black light. The indications, which are minute amounts of penetrant seeping back out from the discontinuities, appear brilliant under intense black light. Lines indicate cracks, and dots indicate porosity.

Industrial applications of fluorescent-penetrant inspection are many. It is applied in locating cracks and shrinkage in castings, cracks in fabrication and regrinding of carbide tools, cracks and pits in welded structures, cracks in steam- and gas-turbine blading, and cracks in ceramic insulators for spark plugs and electronic applications.

1·38 Ultrasonic inspection. This is a nondestructive method of testing or inspection which utilizes waves of frequency above the audible range; hence the term *ultrasonic*. The frequencies most commonly used range from 1 to 5 million cps. These high-frequency waves are reflected from surfaces and defects much the same way as light is reflected from a mirror. The reflected waves are then made visible by suitable instrumentation.

In an ultrasonic machine, called a *reflectoscope*, a high-frequency current, generated by a suitable electric circuit, is applied to a searching unit. This searching unit contains a crystal, usually quartz, such that the electric vibrations cause the crystal to expand and contract, thereby producing a compressional sound wave of the same frequency. This conversion of electrical energy to mechanical energy is known as the *piezoelectric effect*. As the sound wave enters the material being tested, part of it is reflected back to the crystal where it is converted back to an electrical impulse. This impulse is amplified and rendered visible as an indication or pip on the screen of the oscilloscope. When the sound wave reaches the other side of the material, it is reflected back and shows as another pip on the screen farther to the right of the first pip. If there is a flaw between the front and back surfaces of the material, it will show as a third pip on the screen between the two indications for the front and back surfaces. Since the indications on the oscilloscope screen measure the elapsed time between reflection of the pulse from the front and back surfaces, the distance between indications is a measure of the thickness of the material. The location

Fig. 1·26 Ultrasonic inspection of a steel bar. (*Bethlehem Steel Company*)

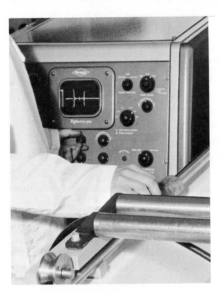

Fig. 1·27 Ultrasonic inspection by immersion in a water tank. (*Fansteel Metallurgical Corp.*)

of a defect may therefore be accurately determined from the indication on the screen.

In general, smooth surfaces are more suitable for the higher-frequency testing pulse and thereby permit detection of smaller defects. Proper transmission of the ultrasonic wave has a great influence on the reliability of the test results. For large parts, a film of oil ensures proper contact between the crystal searching unit and the test piece (Fig. 1·26). Smaller parts may be placed in a tank of water, oil, or glycerin. The crystal searching unit transmits sound waves through the medium and into the material being examined (Fig. 1·27). Close examination of the oscilloscope screen in this picture shows the presence of three pips. The left pip indicates the front of the piece, the right pip the back of the piece, and the smaller center pip is an indication of a flaw.

Ultrasonic inspection is used to detect and locate such defects as shrinkage cavities, internal bursts or cracks, porosity, and large non-metallic inclusions. Wall thickness can be measured in closed vessels or in cases where such measurement cannot otherwise be made.

QUESTIONS

1·1   How are thermocouples calibrated?

1·2   What factors may lead to errors in a thermoelectric circuit?

1·3   Aside from being able to measure high temperatures, what is another advantage of the optical pyrometer?

1·4   Assuming that a copper-constantan thermocouple is put into a liquid metal above the melting point of copper, will the thermocouple measure the temperature of the liquid metal?

1·5   Assume that the thermocouple wires are reversed when connected to the potentiometer; how may this be detected?

1·6   How is "true stress" calculated?

1·7   Differentiate between resilience and toughness.

1·8   Which property in a tension test is an indication of the stiffness of a material?

1·9   Which properties in a tension test indicate the ductility of a material?

1·10   How will the speed of testing affect the yield strength and ultimate strength?

1·11   On a stress-strain graph, for a load beyond the yield strength that is suddenly removed, show the elastic strain and the plastic strain.

1·12   Why is the yield strength usually determined rather than the elastic limit?

1·13   What is the difference between the proportional limit and the elastic limit?

1·14   Why are impact specimens notched?

1·15   Discuss the effect of the type of notch and velocity of the hammer on the results of the impact test.

1·16   What limits the range of hardness in the Brinell machine?

1.17   What are the units for the Brinell hardness number?

1.18   Why is it possible to obtain the approximate tensile strength of steel by 500 BHN?

1.19   Is there a unit associated with the Rockwell hardness number?   Explain.

1·20   Why is a correction factor necessary for Rockwell readings on a specimen less than 1 in. in diameter?

1·21   Is the correction factor in Question 1·20 to be added or subtracted from the observed readings?   Explain.

1·22   What is the minimum thickness of the specimen if a reading is to be taken in the range of Rockwell C 60?   (Refer to "Metals Handbook," 1948 edition.)

1·23   If the specimen in Question 1·22 is to be checked with the Brinell test, what should its minimum thickness be?

1·24   If the specimen in Question 1·22 is to be checked on the Rockwell 15 N scale, what should its minimum thickness be?

1·25   How may one determine whether the specimen was too thin to be checked with a particular Rockwell scale?

1·26   List three factors that contribute to the inaccuracy of a scleroscope reading.

1·27   What factors may be varied in taking a radiograph with X rays?

1·28   In a radiograph, what will be the difference in appearance of gas cavities, cracks, and impurities?

1·29   What are the limitations of magnetic-particle inspection?

1·30   What are the limitations of fluorescent-penetrant inspection?

REFERENCES

American Society for Metals: "Metals Handbook," 1948 edition, Metals Park, Ohio.

————: "Temperature Measurement," Metals Park, Ohio, 1956.

Churchill, H. D.: "Physical Testing of Metals and Interpretation of Test Results," American Society for Metals, Metals Park, Ohio, 1936.

Coxon, W. F.: "Temperature Measurement and Control," The Macmillan Company, New York, 1960.

Davis, H. E., G. E. Troxell, and C. T. Wiskocil: "The Testing and Inspection of Engineering Materials," 2d ed., McGraw-Hill Book Company, Inc., New York, 1955.

Dike, P. H.: "Thermoelectric Thermometry," Leeds & Northrup Company, Philadelphia, Pa., 1954.

Doane, F. B.: "Principles of Magnaflux Inspection," Magnaflux Corporation, Chicago, Ill., 1940.

Eastman Kodak Company: "Manual of Radiography," Rochester, N.Y., 1939.

Enos, G. M.: "Visual Examination of Steel," American Society for Metals, Metals Park, Ohio, 1940.

Kehl, G. L.: "Principles of Metallographic Laboratory Practice," 3d ed., McGraw-Hill Book Company, Inc., New York, 1949.

Lysaght, V. E.: "Indentation Hardness Testing," Reinhold Publishing Corporation, New York, 1949.

Vilella, J. R.: "Metallographic Technique for Steel," American Society for Metals, Metals Park, Ohio, 1938.

Williams, S. R.: "Hardness and Hardness Measurement," American Society for Metals, Metals Park, Ohio, 1942.

Chapter 2

METAL STRUCTURE AND CRYSTALLIZATION

2·1 Introduction. All matter is considered to be composed of unit substances known as *chemical elements*. These are the smallest units that are distinguishable on the basis of their chemical activity and physical properties. The elements are composed of atoms which have a distinct structure characteristic of each element.

2·2 Atomic structure. The free atom is composed of electrons, protons, and neutrons. Almost the entire mass of the atom is concentrated in the nucleus, which contains the protons (positive charges) and neutrons (electrically neutral particles). The mass of a proton is 1.673×10^{-24} g and a neutron is 1.675×10^{-24} g, while the mass of an electron is 9.11×10^{-28} g. The diameter of the nucleus is of the order of 10^{-12} cm and is very small compared with atomic diameter, which is of the order of 10^{-8} cm. Therefore, the atom consists of a minute positively charged nucleus surrounded by a sufficient number of electrons (negative charges) to keep the atom as a whole neutral. Since the electron and proton have equal but opposite electrical charge, the neutral atom must contain an equal number of electrons and protons.

The electrons, spinning on their own axes as they rotate around the nucleus, are arranged in definite shells. The maximum number of electrons that can fit in each shell is $2n^2$, where n is the shell number. Therefore, the maximum number of electrons that will fit in the first shell is two, the second eight, the third eighteen, the fourth thirty-two, etc. Each shell is further subdivided into energy states or levels. According to the Pauli exclusion principle, no more than two electrons can fit on any one energy level and if two are to fit they must be of opposite spin. The number of energy levels increases with distance from the nucleus, and electrons tend to occupy the lowest energy

Table 2·1 Atomic number, atomic weight, and chemical symbols of the elements*

Element	Symbol	At. No.	At. wt.	Element	Symbol	At. No.	At. wt.
Actinium	Ac	89	227	Mercury	Hg	80	200.61
Aluminum	Al	13	26.98	Molybdenum	Mo	42	95.95
Americium	Am	95	243	Neodymium	Nd	60	144.27
Antimony	Sb	51	121.76	Neon	Ne	10	20.183
Argon	A	18	39.944	Neptunium	Np	93	237
Arsenic	As	33	74.91	Nickel	Ni	28	58.69
Astatine	At	85	211	Niobium	Nb	41	92.91
Barium	Ba	56	137.36	(Columbium)	(Cb)		
Berkelium	Bk	97	247	Nitrogen	N	7	14.008
Beryllium	Be	4	9.013	Osmium	Os	76	190.2
Bismuth	Bi	83	209.00	Oxygen	O	8	16.000
Boron	B	5	10.82	Palladium	Pd	46	196.7
Bromine	Br	35	79.916	Phosphorus	P	15	30.975
Cadmium	Cd	48	112.41	Platinum	Pt	78	195.23
Calcium	Ca	20	40.08	Plutonium	Pu	94	242
Californium	Cf	98	251	Polonium	Po	84	210
Carbon	C	6	12.011	Potassium	K	19	39.100
Cerium	Ce	58	140.13	Praseodymium	Pr	59	140.92
Cesium	Cs	55	132.91	Promethium	Pm	61	145
Chlorine	Cl	17	35.457	Protactinium	Pa	91	231
Chromium	Cr	24	54.01	Radium	Ra	88	226.05
Cobalt	Co	27	58.94	Radon	Rn	86	222
Copper	Cu	29	63.54	Rhenium	Re	75	186.31
Curium	Cm	96	247	Rhodium	Rh	45	102.91
Dysprosium	Dy	66	162.46	Rubidium	Rb	37	85.48
Einsteinium	E	99	245	Ruthenium	Ru	44	101.1
Erbium	Er	68	167.2	Samarium	Sm	62	150.43
Europium	Eu	63	152.0	Scandium	Sc	21	44.96
Fermium	Fm	100	253	Selenium	Se	34	78.96
Fluorine	F	9	19.00	Silicon	Si	14	28.09
Francium	Fr	87	233	Silver	Ag	47	107.880
Gadolinium	Gd	64	156.9	Sodium	Na	11	22.991
Gallium	Ga	31	69.72	Strontium	Sr	38	87.63
Germanium	Ge	32	72.60	Sulfur	S	16	32.066
Gold	Au	79	197.0	Tantalum	Ta	73	180.95
Hafnium	Hf	72	178.6	Technetium	Te	43	98
Helium	He	2	4.003	Tellurium	Te	52	127.61
Holmium	Ho	67	164.94	Terbium	Tb	65	158.93
Hydrogen	H	1	1.008	Thallium	Tl	81	204.39
Indium	In	49	114.76	Thorium	Th	90	232.05
Iodine	I	53	126.91	Thulium	Tm	69	168.94
Iridium	Ir	77	192.2	Tin	Sn	50	118.70
Iron	Fe	26	55.85	Titanium	Ti	22	47.90
Krypton	Kr	36	83.80	Tungsten	W	74	183.92
Lanthanum	La	57	138.92	Uranium	U	92	238.07
Lawrencium	Lw	103	257	Vanadium	V	23	50.95
Lead	Pb	82	207.21	Xenon	Xe	54	131.3
Lithium	Li	3	6.940	Ytterbium	Yb	70	173.04
Lutecium	Lu	71	174.99	Yttrium	Y	39	88.92
Magnesium	Mg	12	24.32	Zinc	Zn	30	65.38
Manganese	Mn	25	54.94	Zirconium	Zr	40	91.22
Mendelevium	Mv	101	256				

* From "Metals Handbook," 1961 edition, American Society for Metals, Metals Park, Ohio.

NOTE: Element with atomic number 102 and atomic weight 254 has not yet been named.

levels. Therefore, the inner shells tend to fill up first, but this is not always true for some of the heavier elements. It is possible for the highest energy level of an inner shell to have more energy than the lowest energy level of the next shell.

It is not possible to determine the exact orbit of an electron, but rather its position is determined by the probability that it will be found in a given region of the atom. This probability is represented mathematically by a certain wave function, and the solution of the wave equation leads to four quantities known as the *quantum numbers* n, l, m_l, and m_s. Of these, n is the principal quantum number related to the total energy of the electron in a particular state and may have values $n = 1, 2, 3$, etc. The second quantum number l is a measure of the angular momentum of the electron and may have values from 0 to $(n - 1)$. The letters s, p, d, f, g, and h have been introduced to signify $l = 0, 1, 2, 3, 4, 5$. The quantum number m_l, related to the magnetic moment of the electron, may have values from $+l$ to $-l$ including zero; and the fourth quantum number m_s, related to the spin of the electron on its own axis, may have the value $\pm\frac{1}{2}$. The state of an electron is completely specified by the four quantum numbers, and no two electrons in an atom may have the same four quantum numbers.

The approximate electron configuration of an atom may be indicated by a number representing the principal shell number n followed by the letter representing the subshell (value of l) and finally the number of electrons in the subshell as a superscript. For example, the element lithium, which contains three electrons, would be represented as $(1s)^2 (2s)^1$; the element oxygen, containing eight electrons, as $(1s)^2 (2s)^2 (2p)^4$.

The atomic weight of an element is the weight of the particular atom relative to the atomic weight of oxygen, which is taken to be 16.000. On this scale, the atomic weight of hydrogen is 1.008. The atomic number of an element is equal to the number of electrons or the number of protons. The atomic number and atomic weight of the elements are given in Table 2·1.

2·3 Periodic table. The periodic table, published by Mendeleev in 1869, placed the known elements in definite groups according to a similarity in physical and chemical properties. The elements are generally in order of increasing atomic weight. There were naturally many blank spaces in the first table, but it predicted the existence of unknown elements and gave some idea of their probable properties. The periodic table is reproduced in modified form in Table 2·2. The horizontal rows are known as *periods* and the vertical columns as *groups*. Some understanding of the arrangement of elements may now be obtained.

Table 2·2   The periodic table of the elements*

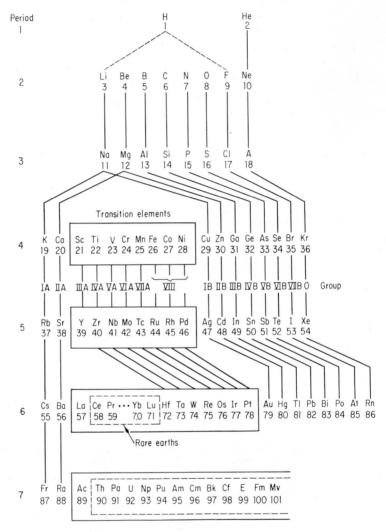

* From W. Hume-Rothery, "Atomic Theory for Students of Metallurgy," The Institute of Metals, London, 1955.

Since the first principal shell can contain a maximum of two electrons, the first period contains only two elements, hydrogen $(1s)^1$ and helium $(1s)^2$. In the next element, lithium, the third electron enters the second principal shell, $(1s)^2 (2s)^1$. Both hydrogen and lithium have similar electron configurations and are listed in the same group. The electrons in the unfilled shells are known as *valence electrons* and are largely responsible for the chemical behavior of the element.   In going from lithium to neon, the second shell is filled to its maximum of eight electrons.   In this process, the (2s) subshell is filled first with beryllium; then from boron to neon the electrons fill the (2p) subshell to a maximum of six.   The outer group of eight electrons, when the *s* and *p* subshells are filled (or two in the case of helium), is a very stable group, and whenever this occurs the element shows very little chemical activity.   Helium, neon, and the rest of the elements in the same group are known as *inert gases*.

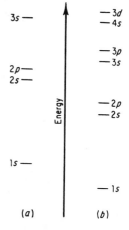

Fig. 2·1   Relative electronic energies in two free atoms.   (*a*) Magnesium; (*b*) iron.   (*From A. G. Guy, "Elements of Physical Metallurgy," 2d ed., Addison-Wesley Publishing Company, Inc., Reading, Mass., 1959*)

On passing to sodium, atomic number 11, the last electron has to enter the third principal shell, and sodium is therefore a univalent element similar to hydrogen and lithium.   From sodium to argon the process is analogous to that occurring between lithium and neon, and the third principal shell is built up to a group of eight electrons.   According to the $2n^2$ rule, the third shell can contain a maximum of 18 electrons; but by filling the (3s) and (3p) subshells a very stable grouping is obtained, and argon is therefore an inert gas.

The next electron enters the fourth shell to give potassium (similar to sodium) and then calcium (similar to magnesium).   On passing from scandium to copper the electrons do not enter the fourth shell but instead enter the third shell as shown in Table 2·3.   This results in an expansion of the third shell from a group of 8 electrons to the maximum of 18.   These elements are known as the *transition elements* and are all of variable valence, which implies that at this stage of the periodic table, the energies of the electrons in the (3d) state are slightly higher than in the (4s) state.   This is represented schematically in Fig. 2·1.   The filling of the (4p) subshell proceeds in

Table 2·3   Electron configuration of the elements in the first four periods*

Atomic number and element	Principal shell and subshells			
	$n = 1$	2	3	4
	$l = s$	$s\ p$	$s\ p\ d$	$s\ p\ d\ f$
1 H	1			
2 He	2			
3 Li	2	1		
4 Be	2	2		
5 B	2	2 1		
6 C	2	2 2		
7 N	2	2 3		
8 O	2	2 4		
9 F	2	2 5		
10 Ne	2	2 6		
11 Na	2	2 6	1	
12 Mg	2	2 6	2	
13 Al	2	2 6	2 1	
14 Si	2	2 6	2 2	
15 P	2	2 6	2 3	
16 S	2	2 6	2 4	
17 Cl	2	2 6	2 5	
18 A	2	2 6	2 6	
19 K	2	2 6	2 6	1
20 Ca	2	2 6	2 6	2
21 Sc†	2	2 6	2 6 1	2
22 Ti†	2	2 6	2 6 2	2
23 V†	2	2 6	2 6 3	2
24 Cr†	2	2 6	2 6 5	1
25 Mn†	2	2 6	2 6 5	2
26 Fe†	2	2 6	2 6 6	2
27 Co†	2	2 6	2 6 7	2
28 Ni†	2	2 6	2 6 8	2
29 Cu	2	2 6	2 6 10	1
30 Zn	2	2 6	2 6 10	2
31 Ga	2	2 6	2 6 10	2 1
32 Ge	2	2 6	2 6 10	2 2
33 As	2	2 6	2 6 10	2 3
34 Se	2	2 6	2 6 10	2 4
35 Br	2	2 6	2 6 10	2 5
36 Kr	2	2 6	2 6 10	2 6

* From W. Hume-Rothery, "Atomic Theory for Students of Metallurgy," The Institute of Metals, London, 1955.
† Transition elements.

a normal manner, reaching a stable grouping of eight electrons in the fourth shell with krypton, atomic number 36, an inert gas. The electron configuration of the elements in the first four periods is given in Table 2·3.

Transition processes also occur in the later periods, and a similar process gives rise to the rare-earth metals, atomic numbers 58 to 71.

The periodic table is constantly referred to in the development of new alloys for specific purposes. Since elements in the same group have similar electron configurations, they often may adequately replace each other in alloys. Tungsten is added to tool steels to improve their softening resistance at elevated temperatures, and molybdenum or chromium is sometimes used as a substitute. Sulfur is used to improve the machinability of steel; selenium and tellurium are added to stainless steels for the same purpose.

2·4 Isotope. It is possible for the nucleus of an element to have more or less than the normal number of neutrons. This will change the atomic weight but will not change the atomic number. Deuterium, an isotope of hydrogen, has one proton and one neutron, which results in twice the atomic weight of the normal hydrogen atom, yet the chemical behavior is not changed. Deuterium is the prime constituent of heavy water.

2·5 Classification of elements. The chemical elements may be very roughly classified into three groups, metals, metalloids, and nonmetals. Elements considered to be metals are distinguished by several characteristic properties: (1) in the solid state they exist in the form of crystals; (2) they have relatively high thermal and electrical conductivity; (3) they have the ability to be deformed plastically; (4) they have relatively high reflectivity of light (metallic luster). The metals are on the left side of the periodic table and constitute about three-fourths of the elements.

Metalloids resemble metals in some respects and nonmetals in others. Generally they have some conductivity but little or no plasticity. Examples of metalloids are carbon, boron, and silicon.

The remaining elements are known as *nonmetals*. This includes the inert gases, the elements in Group VIIB, and N, O, P, and S.

2·6 Atom binding. It is characteristic of the solid state that all true solids exhibit a crystal structure which is a definite geometric arrangement of atoms or molecules. Some materials, such as glass or tar, that are rigid at room temperature do not have a regular arrangement of molecules but rather the random distribution that is typical of the liquid state. These materials are not true solids but rather supercooled liquids.

The question now arises as to what holds the atoms or molecules of a solid together.   There are four possible types of bonds:

1. Ionic bond
2. Covalent or homopolar bond
3. Metallic bond
4. Van der Waals forces

2·7   Ionic bond.   As was pointed out earlier, the electron structure of atoms is relatively stable when the outer shells contain eight electrons (or two in the case of the first shell).   An element like sodium

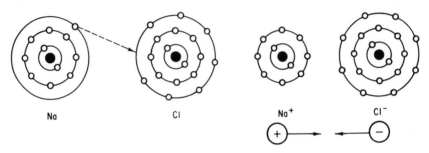

Na   Cl   Na⁺   Cl⁻

Fig. 2·2   Electron transfer in NaCl formation.   (*From L. H. Van Vlack, "Elements of Materials Science," Addison-Wesley Publishing Company, Inc., Reading, Mass., 1959*)

with one excess electron will readily give it up so that it has a completely filled outer shell.   It will then have more protons than electrons and become a positive ion (charged atom) with a $+1$ charge.   An atom of chlorine, on the other hand, with seven electrons in its outer shell would like to accept one electron.   When it does, it will have one more electron than protons and become a negative ion with a -1 charge.   When sodium and chlorine atoms are placed together, there is a transfer of electrons from the sodium to the chlorine atoms, resulting in a strong electrostatic attraction between the positive sodium ions and the negative chlorine ions (Fig. 2·2).   This explains the strong attraction between paired ions typical of the gas or liquid state. In the solid state, however, each sodium ion is surrounded by six negative chlorine ions, and vice versa, so that the attraction is equal in all directions.

2·8   Covalent bond.   Atoms of some elements may attain a stable electronic configuration by sharing one or more electrons with adjacent atoms (Fig. 2·3).   This results in a strong bond due to the attraction of the shared electrons by the positive nuclei.   In the structure of diamond, each carbon atom surrounds itself by four neighbors, with each of which it shares two electrons.

2·9   Metallic bond.   The lack of oppositely charged ions in the metallic structure and the lack of sufficient valence electrons to form a true covalent bond necessitate the sharing of valence electrons by more than two atoms.   Each of the atoms of the metal contributes its valence electrons to the formation of a negative electron "cloud."

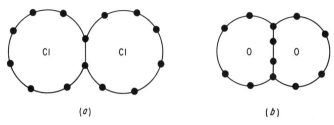

(a)   (b)

Fig. 2·3   Covalent bond in diatomic molecules.

These electrons are not associated with a particular ion but are free to move among the positive metallic ions in definite energy levels. The metallic ions are held together by virtue of their mutual attraction for the negative electron cloud.   This is illustrated schematically in Fig. 2·4.   The metallic bond may be thought of as an extension of the covalent bond to a large number of atoms.

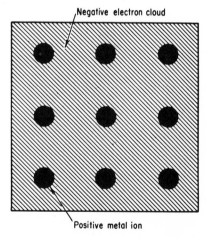

Fig. 2·4   Schematic illustration of the metallic bond.

2·10   Van der Waals forces.   This type of bond arises in neutral atoms such as the inert gases.   When the atoms are brought close together there is a separation of the centers of positive and negative charges and a weak attractive force results.   It is of importance only at low temperatures when the weak attractive force can overcome the thermal agitation of the atoms.

Table 2·4 Atomic diameter of the elements in Groups IA and IIA of the periodic table*

Element	Atomic number	Atomic diameter, angstroms†
Group IA		
Lithium	3	3.03
Sodium	11	3.71
Potassium	19	4.62
Rubidium	37	4.87
Cesium	55	5.24
Group IIA		
Beryllium	4	2.22
Magnesium	12	3.19
Calcium	20	3.93
Strontium	38	4.30
Barium	56	4.34

* From "Metals Handbook," 1948 edition, American Society for Metals, Metals Park, Ohio.

† One angstrom $= 10^{-8}$ cm.

Table 2·5 Atomic diameter and valence of the elements in Group A of the fourth period*

Element	Valence	Atomic diameter, angstroms
Potassium	1	4.62
Calcium	2	3.93
Scandium	3	3.20
Titanium	4	2.91
Vanadium	5	2.63
Chromium	Variable	2.49
Manganese	Variable	2.37
Iron	Variable	2.48
Cobalt	Variable	2.50
Nickel	Variable	2.49

* From "Metals Handbook," 1948 edition, American Society for Metals, Metals Park, Ohio.

METAL STRUCTURE

2·11 Atomic diameter. When atoms of a metal approach each other, two opposing forces influence the internal energy, an attractive force between the electrons and both positive nuclei, and a repulsive force between the positive nuclei and also between the electrons. The first force tends to decrease the internal energy and the second force tends to increase it. At some distance these two forces will just balance each other and the total internal energy E_0 will be a minimum, corresponding to an equilibrium condition (Fig. 2·5). The equilibrium distance r_0 is different for each element and is determined by

Fig. 2·5 Internal energy in relation to distance between atoms.

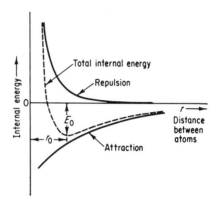

measuring the distance of closest approach of atoms in the solid state. If the atoms are visualized as spheres just touching at equilibrium, then the distance between centers of the spheres may be taken as the approximate atomic diameter. The atomic diameter increases as the number of occupied shells increases (Table 2·4) and decreases as the number of valence electrons increases (Table 2·5).

2·12 Crystal structure. Since atoms tend to assume relatively fixed positions, this gives rise to the formation of crystals in the solid state. The atoms oscillate about fixed locations and are in dynamic equilibrium rather than statically fixed. The three-dimensional network of imaginary lines connecting the atoms is called the *space lattice*, while the smallest unit having the full symmetry of the crystal is called the *unit cell*. The specific unit cell for each metal is defined by its parameters (Fig. 2·6), which are the edges of the unit cell a, b, c and the angles α (between b and c), β (between a and c), and γ (between a and b).

There are only 14 possible types of space lattices, and they fall into seven crystal systems listed in Table 2·6.

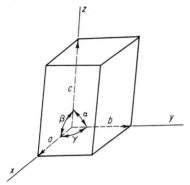

Fig. 2·6   Space lattice illustrating lattice parameters.

Fortunately, most of the important metals crystallize in either the cubic or hexagonal systems and only three types of space lattices are commonly encountered: the b.c.c. (body-centered cubic), the f.c.c. (face-centered cubic), and the c.p.h. (close-packed hexagonal).   Unit

Table 2·6   The crystal systems*

In this table $\neq$ means "not necessarily equal to"

1. Triclinic	Three unequal axes, no two of which are perpendicular $a \neq b \neq c \quad \alpha \neq \beta \neq \gamma \neq 90°$
2. Monoclinic	Three unequal axes, one of which is perpendicular to the other two $a \neq b \neq c \quad \alpha = \gamma = 90° \neq \beta$
3. Orthorhombic	Three unequal axes, all perpendicular $a \neq b \neq c \quad \alpha = \beta = \gamma = 90°$
4. Rhombohedral (trigonal)	Three equal axes, not at right angles $a = b = c \quad \alpha = \beta = \gamma \neq 90°$
5. Hexagonal	Three equal coplanar axes at 120° and a fourth unequal axis perpendicular to their plane $a = b \neq c \quad \alpha = \beta = 90° \quad \gamma = 120°$
6. Tetragonal	Three perpendicular axes, only two equal $a = b \neq c \quad \alpha = \beta = \gamma = 90°$
7. Cubic	Three equal axes, mutually perpendicular $a = b = c \quad \alpha = \beta = \gamma = 90°$

* From C. S. Barrett, "Structure of Metals," McGraw-Hill Book Company, Inc., New York, 1952.

cells of these are shown schematically in Figs. 2·7 to 2·9. In each case the atom is represented as a point (left) and more accurately as a sphere (right).

2·13 Body-centered cubic. If the atoms are represented as spheres, the center atom touches each corner atom but these do not touch each other. Since each corner atom is shared by eight adjoining cubes and the atom in the center cannot be shared by any other cube, the unit cell of the b.c.c. structure contains:

$$8 \text{ atoms at the corners} \times \tfrac{1}{8} = 1 \text{ atom}$$
$$1 \text{ center atom} = \underline{1 \text{ atom}}$$
$$\text{Total} = 2 \text{ atoms}$$

Examples of metals that crystallize in the b.c.c. structure are chromium, tungsten, alpha (α) iron, delta (δ) iron, molybdenum, vanadium, and sodium.

2·14 Face-centered cubic. In addition to an atom at each corner of the cube, there is one in the center of each face, but none in the center of the cube. Each face atom touches its nearest corner atom. Since each corner atom is shared by eight adjoining cubes and each face atom is shared by only one adjacent cube, the unit cell contains:

$$8 \text{ atoms at the corners} \times \tfrac{1}{8} = 1 \text{ atom}$$
$$6 \text{ face-centered atoms} \times \tfrac{1}{2} = \underline{3 \text{ atoms}}$$
$$\text{Total} = 4 \text{ atoms}$$

Examples of metals that crystallize in the f.c.c. lattice are aluminum, nickel, copper, gold, silver, lead, platinum, and gamma (γ) iron.

2·15 Close-packed hexagonal. The usual picture of the close-packed hexagonal lattice shows two basal planes in the form of regular hexagons with an atom at each corner of the hexagon and one atom at the center. In addition, there are three atoms in the form of a triangle midway between the two basal planes. If the basal plane is divided into six equilateral triangles, the additional three atoms are nestled in the center of alternate equilateral triangles (Fig. 2·9).

The parallel repetition of this hexagonal prism will not build up the entire lattice. The true unit cell of the hexagonal lattice is in fact only the portion shown by heavy lines in Fig. 2.9. The hexagonal prism, therefore, contains two whole unit cells and two halves.

It may not be readily apparent from the unit cell why the structure is called hexagonal. It remains to show that, if a number of these unit cells are packed together with axes parallel to one another, as in a space lattice, a hexagonal prism may be carved out of them.

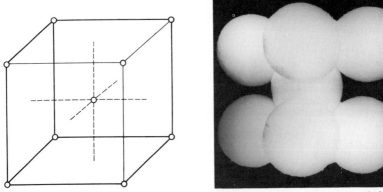

Fig. 2·7   Unit cell of the b.c.c. structure represented by points (left), and as spheres (right).

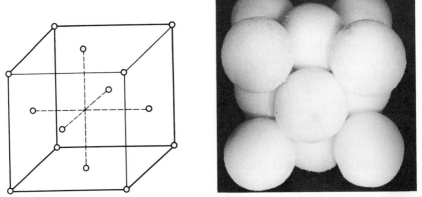

Fig. 2·8   Unit cell of the f.c.c. structure represented by points (left), and as spheres (right).

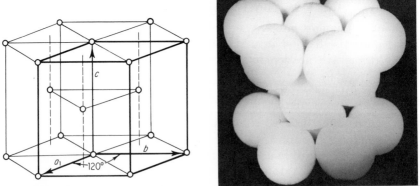

Fig. 2·9   The c.p.h. structure.   As points with the unit cell shown in heavy lines (left), and as spheres (right).

Figure 2·10 shows many unit cells with the open circles representing atoms in the plane of the paper and the filled circles representing atoms halfway above and below. The hexagonal lattice derived from the unit cells is shown by means of either the filled or the open circles. In each case, there are seven atoms representing the basal plane and three atoms in the form of a triangle in the center of alternate equilateral triangles.

Since each atom at the corner of the unit cell is shared by eight adjoining cells and one atom inside the cell cannot be shared, the c.p.h. unit cell contains two atoms. Examples of metals that crystallize in this type of structure are magnesium, beryllium, zinc, cadmium, and hafnium.

The unit cell of the cubic system may be specified by a single lattice parameter a, but the hexagonal cell requires the width of the hexagon a and the distance between basal planes c. These determine the axial ratio c/a, which is sometimes given. It may be shown mathematically that the axial ratio of a c.p.h. structure formed of spheres in contact is 1.633. In reality, metals of this structure have axial ratios that vary from 1.58 for beryllium to 1.88 for cadmium. Therefore, if the atoms are still considered to be in contact, they must be spheroidal in shape rather than spherical.

The types of crystal structure, lattice parameters, and other physical property data of the common metals are given in Table 2·7.

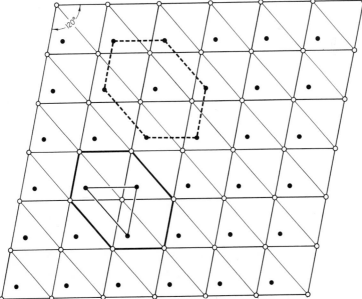

Fig. 2·10   Derivation of the hexagonal lattice from many unit cells.

Table 2·7 Physical property data of some common metals*

Metal	Symbol	Density at 68°F, lb per cu in.	Melting pt, °F	Boiling pt, °F	Crystal structure	Lattice parameter, angstroms†	Closest approach of atoms, angstroms†
Aluminum	Al	0.0975	1220.4	4442	f.c.c.	4.0491	2.862
Antimony	Sb	0.239	1166.9	2516	Rhombohedral	4.5065	2.904
Beryllium	Be	0.067	2332	5020	c.p.h.	$a = 2.2858$ $c = 3.5842$	2.221
Bismuth	Bi	0.354	520.3	2840	Rhombohedral	4.7457	3.111
Cadmium	Cd	0.313	609.6	1409	c.p.h.	$a = 2.9787$ $c = 5.617$	2.972
Carbon (graphite)	C	0.081	6740	8730	Hexagonal	$a = 2.4614$ $c = 6.7041$	1.42
Chromium	Cr	0.260	3407	4829	b.c.c.	2.884	2.498
Copper	Cu	0.324	1981.4	4703	f.c.c.	3.6153	2.556
Gold	Au	0.698	1945.4	5380	f.c.c.	4.078	2.882
Iron (α)	Fe	0.284	2797.7	5430	b.c.c.	2.8664	2.4824
Lead	Pb	0.4097	621.3	3137	f.c.c.	4.9489	3.499
Magnesium	Mg	0.0628	1202	2025	c.p.h.	$a = 3.2088$ $c = 5.2095$	3.196
Manganese	Mn	0.270	2273	3900	Cubic (complex)	8.912	2.24
Molybdenum	Mo	0.369	4730	10,040	b.c.c.	3.1468	2.725
Nickel	Ni	0.322	2647	4950	f.c.c.	3.5238	2.491
Platinum	Pt	0.775	3217	8185	f.c.c.	3.9310	2.775
Silicon	Si	0.084	2570	4860	Diamond cubic	5.428	2.351
Silver	Ag	0.379	1760.9	4010	f.c.c.	4.086	2.888
Tin	Sn	0.2637	449.4	4120	b.c. tetragonal	$a = 5.8314$ $c = 3.1815$	3.016
Titanium	Ti	0.164	3035	5900	c.p.h.	$a = 2.9503$ $c = 4.683$	2.91
Tungsten	W	0.697	6170	10,706	b.c.c.	3.1585	2.734
Vanadium	V	0.220	3450	6150	b.c.c.	3.039	2.632
Zinc	Zn	0.258	787	1663	c.p.h.	$a = 2.6649$ $c = 4.9470$	2.6648

* "Metals Handbook," 1961 edition, American Society for Metals, Metals Park, Ohio.
† One angstrom = 10^{-8} cm.

2·16 Polymorphism and allotropy. Polymorphism is the property of a material to exist in more than one type of space lattice in the solid state. If the change in structure is reversible, then the polymorphic change is known as *allotropy*. At least fifteen metals show this property, and the best-known example is iron. When iron crystallizes at 2800°F it is b.c.c. (δ Fe), at 2554°F the structure changes to f.c.c. (γ Fe), and at 1670°F it again becomes b.c.c. (α Fe).

2·17 Crystallographic planes. The layers of atoms or the planes along which atoms are arranged are known as *atomic* or *crystallographic planes*. The relation of a set of planes to the axes of the unit cell is designated by *Miller indices*. One corner of the unit cell is assumed to be the origin of the space coordinates, and any set of planes is identified by the reciprocals of its intersections with these coordinates. The unit of the coordinates is the lattice parameter of the crystal. If a plane is parallel to an axis, it intersects it at infinity.

In Fig. 2·11, or the cubic system, the crosshatched plane $BCHG$ intersects the Y axis at one unit from the origin and is parallel to the X and Z axes or intersects them at infinity. Therefore,

	X	Y	Z
Intersection	∞	1	∞
Reciprocal	$\dfrac{1}{\infty}$	$\dfrac{1}{1}$	$\dfrac{1}{\infty}$
Miller indices	0	1	0

The illustrated plane has Miller indices of (010). If a plane cuts any axis on the negative side of the origin, the index will be negative and is indicated by placing a minus sign above the index, as $(h\bar{k}l)$. For example, the Miller indices of the plane $ADEF$ which goes through the origin (point A) cannot be determined without changing the location of the origin. Any point in the cube may be selected as the origin. For convenience, take point B. The plane $ADEF$ is parallel to the X axis (BC) and the Z axis (BG) but intersects the Y axis at -1. The plane has Miller indices of ($0\bar{1}0$).

As another illustration, the Miller indices of the plane BDJ (Fig. 2·11) may be determined as follows:

	X	Y	Z
Intersection	1	1	$\tfrac{1}{2}$
Reciprocal	$\dfrac{1}{1}$	$\dfrac{1}{1}$	$\dfrac{1}{\frac{1}{2}}$
Miller indices	1	1	2

If the Miller indices of a plane result in fractions, these fractions must be cleared. For example, consider a plane that intersects the X axis at 1, the Y axis at 3, and the Z axis at 1. Taking reciprocals gives indices of 1, 1/3, and 1. Multiplying through by 3 to clear fractions results in Miller indices of (313) for the plane.

All parallel planes have the same indices. Parentheses (*hkl*) around Miller indices signify a specific plane or set of parallel planes. Braces signify a family of planes of the same "form" (which are equivalent

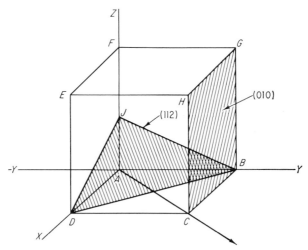

Fig. 2·11   Determination of Miller indices.   The (010) plane and the (112) plane.

in the crystal), such as the cube faces of a cubic crystal: $\{100\}$ = $(100) + (010) + (001) + (\bar{1}00) + (0\bar{1}0) + (00\bar{1})$.

Reciprocals are not used to determine the indices of a direction. In order to arrive at a point on a given direction, consider that starting at the origin it is necessary to move a distance u times the unit distance a along the X axis, v times the unit distance b along the Y axis, and w times the unit distance c along the Z axis. If u, v, and w are the smallest integers to accomplish the desired motion, they are the indices of the direction and are enclosed in square brackets [*uvw*]. A group of similar directions are enclosed in angular brackets ⟨*uvw*⟩. For example, in Fig. 2·11, to determine the direction AC, starting at the origin (point A), it is necessary to move one unit along the X axis to point D and one unit in the direction of the Y axis to reach point C. The direction AC would have indices of [110]. In a cubic crystal, a direction has the same indices as the plane to which it is perpendicular.

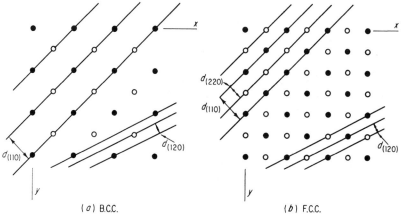

(*a*) B.C.C.   (*b*) F.C.C.

Fig. 2·12   Projection of the lattice on a plane perpendicular to the Z axis to illustrate interplanar spacing.   Filled circles are in the plane of the paper.

An approximate idea of the packing of atoms on a particular plane may be obtained by visualizing a single unit cell of the b.c.c. and f.c.c. structure.   Considering the atoms as the lattice points, the number of atoms on a particular plane would be:

Plane	b.c.c.	f.c.c.
(100)	4	5
(110)	5	6
(111)	3	6
(120)	2	3
(221)	1	1

An infinite number of planes may be taken through the crystal structure, but most are just geometrical constructions and have no

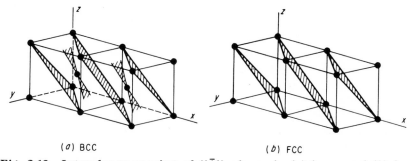

(*a*) BCC   (*b*) FCC

Fig. 2·13   Interplanar spacing of ($1\bar{1}1$) planes in (*a*) b.c.c. and (*b*) f.c.c. (*By permission from L. H. Van Vlack, "Elements of Materials Science," Addison-Wesley Publishing Company, Inc., Reading, Mass., 1959)

practical importance.   Remembering that each complete set of parallel planes must account for all the atoms, the most important planes are the ones of high atomic population and largest interplanar distance. In the b.c.c. structure these are the {110} planes, and in the f.c.c. structure these are the {111} planes (see Figs. 2·12 and 2·13).

CRYSTALLIZATION

2·18   The states of matter.   Three states of matter are distinguishable: gas, liquid, and solid.   In the gaseous state the metal atoms occupy a great deal of space because of their rapid motion. Their motion is entirely random, and as they travel they collide with each other and the walls of the container.   The combination of all the collisions with the wall is the pressure of the gas on the wall. The atoms move independently and are usually widely separated so that the attractive forces between atoms is negligible.   The arrangement of atoms in a gas is one of complete disorder.

At some lower temperature, the kinetic energy of the atoms has decreased so that the attractive forces became large enough to bring most of the atoms together in a liquid.   Not all the atoms are in the liquid.   Atoms remain in the vapor above the liquid, and there is a continual interchange of atoms between the vapor and liquid across the liquid surface.   In a confined vessel, at a definite temperature, the interchange of atoms will reach equilibrium and there will be a constant value of vapor pressure of the gas above the liquid.   If the vapor is free to escape, equilibrium will not be reached and more atoms will leave the liquid surface than are captured by it, resulting in evaporation.   Evidence of attractive forces between atoms in a liquid may be demonstrated by the application of pressure.   A gas may be easily compressed into a smaller volume, but it takes a high pressure to compress a liquid.   There is, however, still enough free space in the liquid to allow the atoms to move about irregularly.

As the temperature is decreased, the motions are less vigorous and the attractive forces pull the atoms closer together until the liquid solidifies.   Most materials contract upon solidification, indicating a closer packing of atoms in the solid state.   The atoms in the solid are not stationary but are vibrating around fixed points, giving rise to the orderly arrangement of crystal structures discussed previously.

2·19   Mechanism of crystallization.   Crystallization is the transition from the liquid to the solid state and occurs in two stages:

1. Nuclei formation
2. Crystal growth

Although the atoms in the liquid state do not have any definite arrangement it is possible that some atoms at any given instant are in positions exactly corresponding to the space lattice they assume when
solidified (Fig. 2·14).   These chance aggregates or groups are not permanent but continually break up and reform at other points.   How
long they last is determined by the temperature and size of the group.
The higher the temperature, the greater the kinetic energy of the

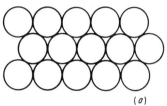

(a)

Fig. 2·14 Schematic diagram of
structures of (a) crystal and (b)
liquid. Area ABCDE in liquid is
identical in arrangement as in
crystal. (*From Chalmers, "Physical Metallurgy," John Wiley &
Sons, Inc., New York*, 1959)

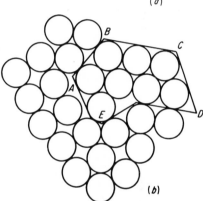

(b)

atoms and the shorter the life of the group.   Small groups are very
unstable since they are formed of only a small number of atoms and
the loss of only one atom may destroy the group.   When the temperature of the liquid is decreased, the atom movement decreases, length-
ening the life of the group, and more groups will be present at the
same time.

Atoms in a material have both kinetic and potential energy.
Kinetic energy is related to the speed at which the atoms move and is
strictly a function of temperature.   The higher the temperature, the
more active are the atoms and the greater is their kinetic energy.
Potential energy, on the other hand, is related to the distance between
atoms.   The greater the average distance between atoms, the greater
is their potential energy.

Now consider a pure metal at its freezing point where both the
liquid and solid states are at the same temperature.   The kinetic

energy of the atoms in the liquid and the solid must be the same but there is a significant difference in potential energy. The atoms in the solid are much closer together, so that solidification occurs with a release of energy. This difference in potential energy between the liquid and solid states is known as the *latent heat of fusion*. However, energy is required to establish a surface between the solid and liquid. In pure materials, at the freezing point, insufficient energy is released by the heat of fusion to create a stable boundary, and some under-cooling is always necessary to form stable nuclei. Subsequent

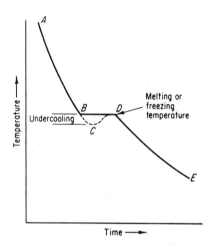

Fig. 2·15 Cooling curve for a pure metal. *ABDE* ideal, *ABCDE* actual.

release of the heat of fusion will raise the temperature to the freezing point (Fig. 2·15). The amount of undercooling required may be reduced by the presence of solid impurities which reduce the amount of surface energy required.

When the temperature of the liquid metal has dropped sufficiently below its freezing point, stable aggregates or nuclei appear spontane-ously at various points in the liquid. These nuclei, which have now solidified, act as centers for further crystallization. As cooling con-tinues, more atoms tend to freeze, and they may attach themselves to already existing nuclei or form new nuclei of their own. Each nucleus grows by the attraction of atoms from the liquid into its space lattice. Crystal growth continues in three dimensions, the atoms at-taching themselves in certain preferred directions, usually along the axes of the crystal. This gives rise to a characteristic treelike struc-ture which is called a *dendrite* (Fig. 2·16). Since each nucleus is formed by chance, the crystal axes are pointed at random and the dendrites growing from them will grow in different directions in each crystal. Finally, as the amount of liquid decreases, the gaps between the arms of the dendrite will be filled and the growth of the dendrite will be mutually obstructed by that of its neighbors.   This leads to a very irregular external shape.   The crystals found in all commercial metals are commonly called *grains* because of this variation in external shape. The area along which crystals meet, known as the *grain boundary*, is a region of mismatch (Fig. 2·17).   This leads to a noncrystalline (amorphous) structure at the grain boundary with the atoms irregularly spaced.   Since the last liquid to solidify is generally along the grain

Fig. 2·16   Magnesium dendrites growing from liquid.

boundaries, there tends to be a higher concentration of impurity atoms in that area.   Figure 2·18 shows schematically the process of crystallization from nuclei to the final grains.

2·20   Crystal imperfections.   It is interesting to realize the amount of activity that is occurring on the surface of a crystal during growth.   A very slow growth rate, such as 1 mm per day, requires the deposition of about one hundred layers of atoms per second on the surface.   All these atoms must be laid down in exactly the right sort of order for the crystal to be perfect.   It is therefore not surprising that few crystals are perfect and that imperfections exist on an atomic scale.

The most important crystal imperfections are vacancies, interstitials, and dislocations.   Vacancies are simply empty atom sites (Fig. 2·19). It may be shown by thermodynamic reasoning that lattice vacancies are a stable feature of metals at all temperatures above absolute zero.

By successive jumps of atoms it is possible for a vacancy to move in the lattice structure and therefore play an important role in diffusion.

It is possible, particularly in lattice structures that are not close-packed, that atoms may fall into interstitial positions (Fig. 2·19). Both vacancies and interstitials produce severe local distortion and interrupt the regularity of the space lattice. Vacancies probably allow the surrounding atoms to approach slightly closer than normally while

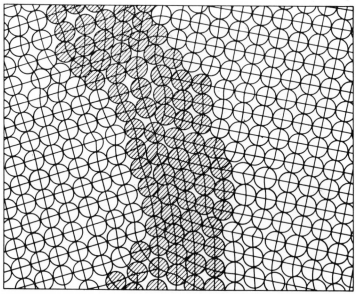

Fig. 2·17   Schematic representation of a grain boundary between two crystals. The crosshatched atoms are those which constitute the boundary material. (*By permission from L. F. Mondolfo and O. Zmeskal, "Engineering Metallurgy," McGraw-Hill Book Company, Inc., New York,* 1955)

interstitials push the surrounding atoms farther apart. Vacancies are not only present as a result of solidification but can be produced by raising the temperature or by irradiation with fast-moving nuclear particles. Interstitial atoms may be produced by the severe local distortion during plastic deformation as well as by irradiation.

A dislocation may be defined as a disturbed region between two substantially perfect parts of a crystal. Two simple kinds of dislocation are illustrated schematically in Fig. 2·20. The edge dislocation consists of an extra half plane of atoms in the crystal. The screw dislocation is so named because of the spiral surface formed by the atomic planes around the screw-dislocation line. The dislocation` line produces compressive stress below the dislocation and tensile

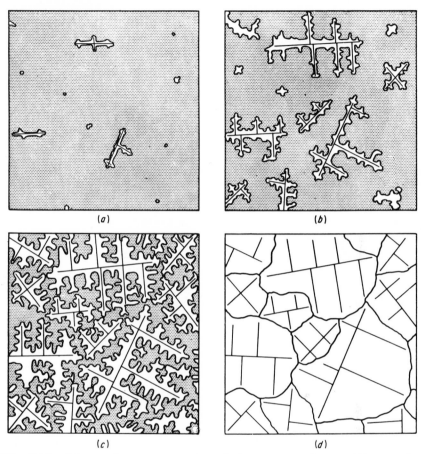

Fig. 2·18   Schematic representation of the process of crystallization by nucleation and dendritic growth. (*By permission from L. F. Mondolfo and O. Zmeskal, "Engineering Metallurgy," McGraw-Hill Book Company, Inc., New York*, 1955)

Fig. 2·19   Vacancy and interstitial crystal defects.

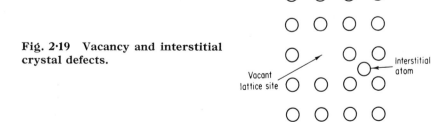

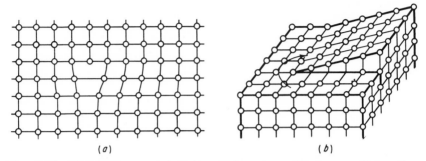

Fig. 2·20 Dislocations. (*a*) Edge dislocation; (*b*) screw dislocation. (*By permission from L. F. Mondolfo and O. Zmeskal, "Engineering Metallurgy," McGraw-Hill Book Company, Inc., New York, 1955*)

stresses above it and a disturbed region in the lattice structure.   Where the mismatch between neighboring grains is not too great, the grain boundary may be represented by an array of parallel edge dislocations (Fig. 2·21).   The creation, multiplication, and interaction between dislocations is very useful in explaining many of the properties of metals.

The student should refer to the references at the end of this chapter for a more complete description of the types and theory of dislocations.

2·21   Macrodefects in castings.   The preceding section discussed defects on an atomic scale that arise from solidification.   Other defects that may result from solidification are large enough to be visible to the naked eye.   These are known as *macrodefects*.   The most common macrodefects are shrinkage cavities and porosity.

Liquid metals, with few exceptions, undergo a contraction in volume due to solidification.   This decrease in volume may be as much as 6 per cent.   In a properly designed mold, with provision for liquid supply to the portion that solidifies last, the contraction in volume presents no serious problem.   If, however, the entire exterior of the casting should solidify first, the decrease in volume of the interior during solidification will result in a large *shrinkage cavity* at the midsection, as shown in Fig. 2·22.   In the solidification of steel ingots, the shrinkage cavity, called *pipe*, is usually concentrated in the top

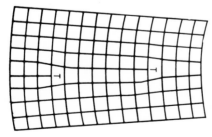

Fig. 2·21 A small angle boundary composed of edge dislocations, indicated at the T symbols. (*By permission from C. S. Barrett, "Structure of Metals," 2d ed., McGraw-Hill Book Company, Inc., New York, 1952*)

central portion of the ingot. This portion is cut off and discarded before working.

The ideal solidification would be that in which the metal first freezes at the bottom of the mold and continues upward to a riser at the top; however, heat is dissipated more rapidly from the top of the mold. To minimize the formation of shrinkage cavities, abrupt changes in thickness and combinations of heavy and light sections should be avoided. If the casting does have heavy sections, they should be

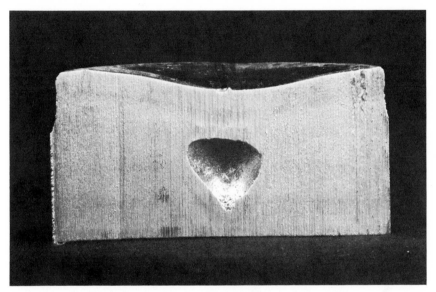

Fig. 2·22 Shrinkage cavity in a columbium-alloy billet. (*Fansteel Metallurgical Corporation*)

designed with risers at the top to supply liquid metal during solidification. Heavy sections should be cast uppermost in the mold, and chills may be used in the sand adjacent to the slow-cooling parts.

Porosity or *blowholes* occur whenever gases are trapped in the casting. They are usually more numerous and smaller than shrinkage cavities and may be distinguished by their rounded form (Fig. 2·23). Air may be entrapped in the casting by the sudden rush of metal during pouring. Since gases are generally more soluble in liquid metal than the solid, dissolved gases may be liberated during solidification. Gases may also be produced by reaction of the liquid metal with volatile substances, such as moisture, in the mold. Porosity may be greatly reduced by proper venting of the mold, and by not unduly compacting the sand.

Hot tears are cracks due to heavy shrinkage strains set up in the solid casting just after solidification.   A common cause is the failure of the sand mold to collapse and allow the casting to contract.   Hot tears may also result from the same nonuniform cooling conditions that give rise to shrinkage cavities.   Proper design of the casting will minimize the danger of hot tears.

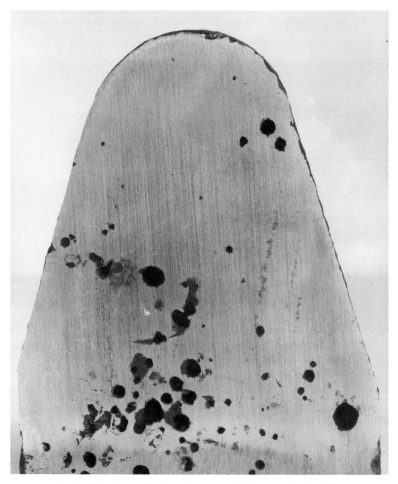

Fig. 2·23   Porosity in an iron casting, enlarged 3×.

2·22   Grain size.   The size of grains in a casting is determined by the relation between the rate of growth G and the rate of nucleation N.   If the number of nuclei formed is high, a fine-grained material will be produced, and if only a few nuclei are formed, a coarse-grained material will be produced.   The rate of cooling is the most important factor in determining the rate of nucleation and therefore the grain size. Rapid cooling (chill cast) will result in a large number of nuclei formed and fine grain size, whereas in slow cooling (sand cast or hot mold) only a few nuclei are formed and they will have a chance to grow, depleting the liquid before more nuclei can form.

Other factors that increase the rate of nucleation, thus promoting the formation of fine grain, are:

1. Insoluble impurities such as aluminum and titanium that form insoluble oxides in steel.

2. Stirring the melt during solidification tends to break up the crystals before they have a chance to grow very large.

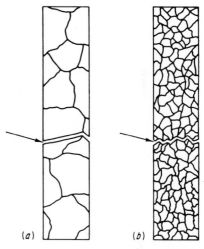

Fig. 2·24 (a) Brittleness of coarse-grained metal under shock; (b) frequent change of direction of force in rupture of fine-grained metal. (By permission from Doan and Mahla, "Principles of Physical Metallurgy," McGraw-Hill Book Company, Inc., New York, 1941)

(a)   (b)

The rate of growth relative to the rate of nucleation is greatest at or just under the freezing point. If the liquid is kept accurately at the freezing temperature and the surface is touched by a tiny crystal (seed), the crystal will grow downward into the liquid. If it is withdrawn slowly, a single crystal can be produced.

In general, fine-grained materials exhibit better toughness or resistance to shock (Fig. 2·24). They are harder and stronger than coarse-grained material.

In industrial casting processes, where a hot liquid is in contact with an originally cool mold, a temperature gradient (difference in temperature) will exist in the liquid. The outside is at a lower temperature than the center and therefore starts to solidify first. Thus many nuclei are formed at the mold wall and begin to grow in all directions. They soon run into the side of the mold and each other, so that the only unrestricted direction for growth is toward the center. The resulting grains are elongated columnar ones, perpendicular to the surface of the mold. This is illustrated in Fig. 2·25 of high-purity lead, as cast. Next to the mold wall, where the cooling rate is fast, the grains

Fig. 2·25 High-purity lead, as cast. Magnification 2×. (*National Lead Company, Research Laboratory*)

are small, while toward the center, where the cooling rate is much slower, the grains are larger and elongated.

If the mold has sharp edges, a plane of weakness will develop from this corner because both gaseous and solid impurities tend to concentrate along this plane. Such castings may cause internal rupture during rolling or forging operations. To avoid this plane, it is good casting design to provide the mold with rounded corners.

QUESTIONS

2·1 Differentiate between atomic number and atomic weight.

2·2 What is meant by an "isotope"?

2·3 Explain the arrangement of the elements in the periodic table.

2·4 What may be said about all the elements in the same group of the periodic table?

2·5 Why are some elements known as "transition elements"?

2·6 Using the system explained in Sec. 2·2, write the electron configuration of the elements in the fourth period.

2·7   Define a "solid." Glass is not considered a true solid. Why?

2·8   How does the metallic bond differ from the ionic and covalent bonds?

2·9   Describe an experiment to show that the atoms of a solid are in motion.

2·10   Explain the existence of attractive and repulsive forces between atoms.

2·11   What is "atomic diameter" and how may its value be approximated?

2·12   How does the atomic diameter change within one group of the periodic table? Why?

2·13   How does the atomic diameter change within a period of the periodic table? Why?

2·14   Give three examples of allotropic metals. For each example, give the temperatures and the changes in crystal structure.

2·15   What are the Miller indices of a plane that intersects the X axis at 2 and the Y axis at $\frac{1}{2}$ and is parallel to the Z axis? The structure is cubic.

2·16   What are the Miller indices of a plane in the cubic structure that goes through $Y = \frac{1}{2}$, $Z = 1$, and is parallel to the X axis? Draw the cubic structure and crosshatch this plane.

2·17   What are the Miller indices of a plane in the cubic structure that intersects the X axis at $\frac{1}{2}$, the Y axis at 1, and is perpendicular to the XY plane?

2·18   When a gas liquefies, energy is released as the heat of vaporization. What is this energy due to?

2·19   Is there any difference in the kinetic energy of the atoms in the liquid and the gas at the boiling point? Explain.

2·20   Differentiate between a crystal, a dendrite, and a grain.

2·21   Why is the grain boundary irregular?

2·22   List three factors that tend to promote fine grain in a casting.

2·23   Why is it important to avoid sharp corners in castings?

2·24   Describe a method of obtaining a uniform grain size in a casting which has a thick and thin section.

2·25   In the cubic system, the interplanar spacing d_{hkl} measured at right angles to the planes is given by the following formula:

$$d_{hkl} = \frac{a}{\sqrt{h^2 + k^2 + l^2}}$$

where (hkl) are the Miller indices and a is the lattice parameter. Calculate the interplanar spacing for the (110), (111), (120), (221), and (123) planes of copper. Which of the above planes has the greatest interplanar spacing?

2·26   In the cubic system, the angle ϕ between the plane $(h_1k_1l_1)$ and the plane $(h_2k_2l_2)$ may be found by the following formula:

$$\cos \phi = \frac{h_1h_2 + k_1k_2 + l_1l_2}{\sqrt{(h_1^2 + k_1^2 + l_1^2)(h_2^2 + k_2^2 + l_2^2)}}$$

Calculate the angle between the (100) plane and the (110) plane; the (100) plane and the (111) plane; the (110) plane and the (111) plane.

REFERENCES

American Society for Metals: "Atom Movements," Metals Park, Ohio, 1951.

Barrett, C. S.: "Structures of Metals," 2d ed., McGraw-Hill Book Company, Inc., New York, 1952.

Cottrell, A. H.: "Dislocations and Plastic Flow in Crystals," Oxford University Press, Fair Lawn, N.J., 1956.

Guy, A. G.: "Elements of Physical Metallurgy," 2d ed., Addison-Wesley Publishing Company, Inc., Reading, Mass., 1959.

Hume-Rothery, W.: "Atomic Theory for Students of Metallurgy," The Institute of Metals, London, 1955.

——— and G. V. Raynor: "The Structure of Metals and Alloys," The Institute of Metals, London, 1954.

Mason, C. W.: "Introductory Physical Metallurgy," American Society for Metals, Metals Park, Ohio, 1947.

Mondolfo, L. F., and O. Zmeskal: "Engineering Metallurgy," McGraw-Hill Book Company, Inc., New York, 1955.

Rogers, B. A.: "The Nature of Metals," American Society for Metals, Metals Park, Ohio, 1951.

Chapter 3

PLASTIC DEFORMATION

3·1 Introduction. When a material is stressed below its elastic limit, the resulting deformation or strain is temporary. Removal of the stress results in a gradual return of the object to its original dimensions. When a material is stressed beyond its elastic limit, plastic or permanent deformation takes place, and it will not return to its original shape by the application of force alone. The ability of a metal to undergo plastic deformation is probably its most outstanding characteristic in comparison with other materials. All shaping operations such as stamping, pressing, spinning, rolling, forging, drawing, and extruding involve plastic deformation of metals. Various machining operations such as milling, turning, sawing, and punching also involve plastic deformation. The behavior of a metal under plastic deformation and the mechanism by which it occurs are of essential interest in perfecting the working operation.

Much information regarding the mechanism of plastic deformation may be obtained by studying the behavior of a single crystal under stress, and later applying this knowledge to a polycrystalline material.

Plastic deformation may take place by slip, twinning, or a combination of both methods.

3·2 Deformation by slip. If a single crystal of a metal is stressed in tension beyond its elastic limit, it elongates slightly, a step appears on the surface indicating relative displacement of one part of the crystal with respect to the rest, and the elongation stops. Increasing the load will cause movement on another parallel plane, resulting in another step. Each successive elongation requires a higher stress and results in the appearance of another step, which is actually the intersection of a slip plane with the surface of the crystal. Progressive increase in the load eventually causes the material to fracture.

It was pointed out in the preceding chapter that parallel planes of high atomic density and corresponding large interplanar spacing exist in the crystal structure. Any movement in the crystal takes place either along these planes or parallel to them.

Investigation of the orientation of the slip plane with respect to the applied stress indicates that slip takes place as a result of simple shearing stress. Resolution of the axial tensile load F in Fig. 3·1

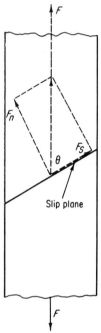

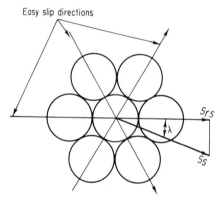

Fig. 3·1   Components of force on a slip plane.

Fig. 3·2   Resolution of shear stress into a slip direction.

gives two loads. One is a shear load ($F_s = F \cos \theta$) along the slip plane and the other a normal tensile load ($F_n = F \sin \theta$) perpendicular to the plane. The area of the slip plane is $A/\sin \theta$, where A is the cross-sectional area perpendicular to F. The resulting stresses are

$$\text{Shear stress } S_s = \frac{F \cos \theta}{A/\sin \theta} = \frac{F}{A} \cos \theta \sin \theta = \frac{F}{2A} \sin 2\theta \quad (3\cdot1)$$

$$\text{Normal stress } S_n = \frac{F \sin \theta}{A/\sin \theta} = \frac{F}{A} \sin^2 \theta \quad (3\cdot2)$$

From Eq. (3·1), it is evident that the shear stress on a slip plane will be maximum when $\theta = 45°$.

A more important factor in determining slip movement is the direction of shear on the slip plane. Movement will occur with the least amount of energy in the close-packed directions on the slip plane. The shear stress S_s on the slip plane has to be resolved into a slip direction to determine the resolved shear stress S_{rs}. This is illustrated in Fig. 3·2. The resolved shear stress is

$$S_{rs} = \frac{F}{2A} \sin 2\theta \cos \lambda \tag{3·3}$$

Investigation has shown that differently oriented crystals of a given metal will begin to slip when different axial stresses are applied but

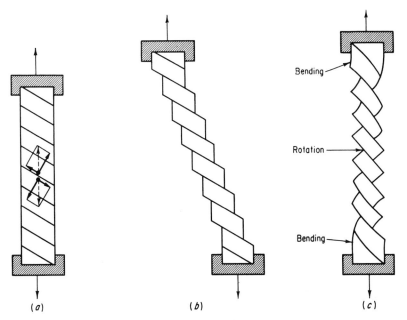

Fig. 3·3 Schematic representation of slip in tension. (a) Before straining; (b) with ends not constrained; (c) ends constrained. (From B. D. Cullity, "Elements of X-ray Diffraction," Addison-Wesley Publishing Company, Inc., Reading, Mass., 1956)

that the critical resolved shear stress is always the same.

If the slip planes are either parallel or perpendicular to the direction of applied stress, slip cannot occur and either the material deforms by twinning or it fractures. As deformation proceeds and the tensile load remains axial, both the plane of slip and the direction of slip tend to rotate into the axis of tension (Fig. 3·3).

3·3 Mechanism of slip. Portions of the crystal on either side of a specific slip plane move in opposite directions and come to rest with the atoms in nearly equilibrium positions so that there is very

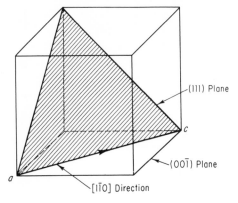

(111) Plane

(00$\bar{1}$) Plane

[1$\bar{1}$0] Direction

Fig. 3·4   Slip plane and slip direction in an f.c.c. lattice.

little change in the lattice orientation.   Thus the external shape of the crystal is changed without destroying it.   Sensitive X-ray methods show that some bending or twisting of the lattice planes has occurred and that the atoms are not in exactly normal positions after deformation.   Slip is illustrated schematically in Figs. 3·4 and 3·5 in an f.c.c. (face-centered cubic) lattice.

The (111) plane (Fig. 3·4), which is the plane of densest atomic population, intersects the (00$\bar{1}$) plane in the line ac.   When the (00$\bar{1}$) plane is assumed to be the plane of the paper and many unit cells are taken together (Fig. 3·5), slip is seen as a movement along the (111) planes in the close-packed [1$\bar{1}$0] direction, a distance of one lattice dimension or multiple of that dimension.   The series of steps formed will generally appear under the microscope as a group of approximately parallel lines (Figs. 3·6 and 3·7).   In Fig. 3·6, a single

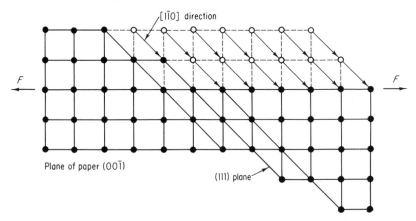

[1$\bar{1}$0] direction

F

F

Plane of paper (00$\bar{1}$)

(111) plane

Fig. 3·5   Schematic diagram of slip in an f.c.c. crystal.   (*By permission from Doan and Mahla, "Principles of Physical Metallurgy," McGraw-Hill Book Company, Inc., New York,* 1941)

Fig. 3·6 Single crystal of brass strained in tension. 200 ×. (*By permission from R. M. Brick and A. Phillips, "Structure and Properties of Alloys," 2d ed., McGraw-Hill Book Company, Inc., New York,* 1949)

Fig. 3·7 Slip lines in copper. Specimen polished, etched, and then strained. 100 ×.

vertical line was scribed on the surface before straining. After straining, the slip lines appear as parallel lines or steps at an angle of approximately 45°. The vertical line is no longer straight, and each step amounts to a movement of about 700 to 800 atoms.

One may assume, at first, that the motion in slip consists of a simultaneous movement of planes of atoms across each other. This requires that the shearing force must have the same value over all points of the slip plane, but the vibrations of the atoms and the difficulties of applying a uniformly distributed force make this condition unattainable. A more reasonable assumption is that the atoms slip consecutively, starting at one place or at a few places in the slip plane and then moving outward over the rest of the plane, somewhat analogous to the motion of an earthworm (Fig. 3·8). Examination

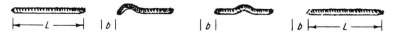

Fig. 3·8 Motion of an earthworm a distance b **analogous to the motion of a dislocation.**

of Fig. 3·9 shows that, by application of the shear force, an extra plane of atoms (called a *dislocation*) has been formed below the slip plane. This dislocation moves across the slip plane and leaves a step when it comes out at the surface of the crystal. Each time the dislocation moves across the slip plane, the crystal moves one atom spacing. Since the atoms do not end up in exactly normal positions after the passage of the dislocation, subsequent movement of the dislocation across the same slip plane encounters greater resistance. Eventually, this resistance or distortion of the slip plane becomes great enough to lock the dislocation in the crystal structure and the movement stops. Further deformation will require movement on another slip plane. Although the distortion is greatest on the active slip plane, its effect is felt throughout the lattice structure and the applied load must be increased to cause movement on another slip plane.

The stress required to initiate slip in a perfect crystal, that is, the stress required to move one atom over another, may be calculated for a given metal. This result, however, is 1,000 to 10,000 times larger than the experimentally observed critical resolved shear stress for slip in single crystals. The much lower observed critical resolved shear stress is not surprising since it was pointed out in Sec. 2·20 that dislocations already exist in the crystal structure as a result of solidification. It is therefore not necessary to create a dislocation, but simply to start an existing one moving on the slip plane. This

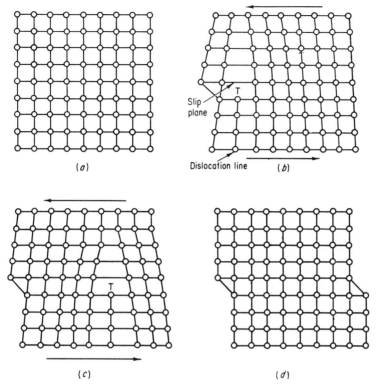

Slip plane

Dislocation line

(a)   (b)   (c)   (d)

Fig. 3·9   Generation and movement of an edge dislocation to produce plastic deformation.

theory suggests that one method of attaining high strength in metals would be to manufacture more nearly perfect crystals without imperfections. The strength of metal "whiskers," which are nearly perfect crystals, has approached the theoretical strength and lends support to the dislocation theory.

3·4   Slip in different lattice structures. The combination of a slip plane and a slip direction is known as a *slip system*. The slip direction is always the one of densest atomic packing in the slip plane and is the most important factor in the slip system.

In f.c.c. materials, there are four sets of (111) planes and three close-packed ⟨110⟩ directions (Fig. 3·2) in each plane, amounting to the highest degree of atomic concentration and symmetry encountered in any lattice. Therefore, there are sufficient slip systems so that there are always a plane and direction properly oriented to permit plastic deformation, and metals with this type of lattice structure (silver, gold, lead, copper, aluminum) are easily deformed.

Since b.c.c. (body-centered cubic) metals have fewer atoms per unit cell, they do not have a well-defined slip system but deform by movement along various planes, such as {110} and {112}, depending upon the relations of applied stress and the close-packed directions. This condition does not allow a high degree of plasticity, and metals of this lattice type [tungsten, molybdenum, alpha (α) iron] have medium ductility.

The c.p.h. (close-packed hexagonal) metals (cadmium, magnesium, zinc) have only one plane of high atomic population, the (001) plane (or basal plane), and three close-packed directions in that plane (Fig. 3·10). This structure does not have so many slip systems as the f.c.c.

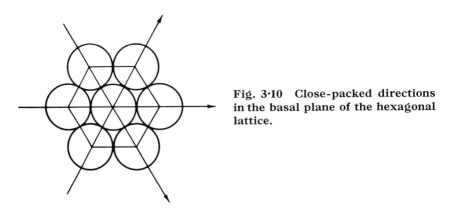

Fig. 3·10   Close-packed directions in the basal plane of the hexagonal lattice.

lattice, but deformation by twinning helps to bring more slip systems into proper position, thereby approaching the plasticity of the f.c.c. structure and surpassing that of the b.c.c. metals.

3·5 Deformation by twinning. In certain materials, particularly c.p.h. metals, twinning is a major means of deformation. This may accomplish an extensive change in shape or may bring potential slip planes into a more favorable position for slip. Twinning is a movement of planes of atoms in the lattice parallel to a specific (twinning) plane so that the lattice is divided into two symmetrical parts which are differently oriented. The amount of movement of each plane of atoms in the twinned region is proportional to its distance from the twinning plane so that a mirror image is formed across the twin plane. Twinning is illustrated schematically in an f.c.c. lattice in Figs. 3·11 and 3·12.

In Fig. 3·11, the (111) twinning plane intersects the {110} plane along the line AB, which is the twin direction. The mechanism of twinning is shown in Fig. 3·12. The plane of the paper is the {110} plane, and many unit cells are taken together. Each (111) plane in

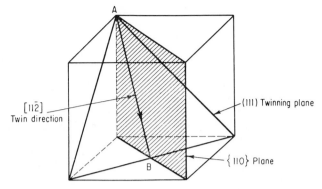

Fig. 3·11 Diagram of a twin plane and twin direction in an f.c.c. lattice.

the twin region moves in shear in the $[11\bar{2}]$ direction. The first one, CD, moves one-third of an interatomic distance; the second one, EF, moves two-thirds of an interatomic distance; and the third one, GH, moves an entire spacing. The twinned region is a mirror image of the untwinned region of the crystal. The atoms end up in inter-atomic spaces, and therefore the orientation of the atoms has been changed. Since the twinned section involves a large number of atoms,

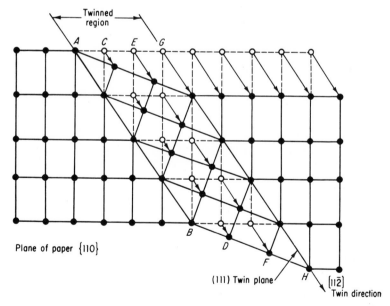

Fig. 3·12 Schematic diagram of twinning in an f.c.c. lattice. (*By permission from G. E. Doan, "Principles of Physical Metallurgy," 3d ed., McGraw-Hill Book Company, Inc., New York, 1953*)

it generally appears microscopically as a broad line or band (Fig. 3·13).

The twinning plane and direction are not necessarily the same as those for slip. In f.c.c. metals the twin plane is the (111) plane and

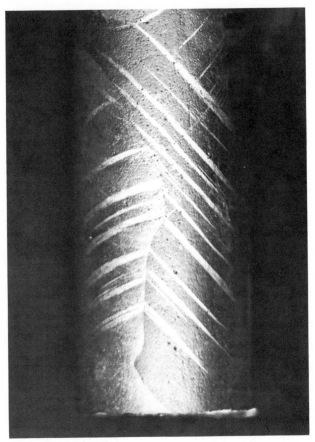

Fig. 3·13   Twin bands in zinc.   2×.

the twin direction is the [11$\bar{2}$] direction; in b.c.c. it is the (112) plane and the [111] direction.

Two kinds of twins are of interest to the metallurgist:

1. Deformation or mechanical twins, most prevalent in c.p.h. metals (magnesium, zinc, etc.) and b.c.c. metals (tungsten, α iron, etc.).

2. Annealing twins, most prevalent in f.c.c. metals (aluminum, copper, brass, etc.). These metals have been previously worked and then reheated. The twins are formed because of a change in the normal growth mechanism.

3·6 Slip vs. twinning. Slip and twinning differ in:

1. Amount of movement: in slip, atoms move a whole number of interatomic spacings while in twinning the atoms move fractional amounts depending on their distance from the twinning plane.

2. Microscopic appearance: slip appears as thin lines while twinning appears as broad lines or bands.

3. Lattice orientation: in slip there is very little change in lattice orientation and the steps are visible only on the surface of the crystal. If the steps are removed by polishing, there will be no evidence that slip had taken place. In twinning, however, since there is a different lattice orientation in the twinned region, removal of the steps by surface polishing will not destroy the evidence of twinning. Proper etching solutions, sensitive to the differences in orientation, will reveal the twinned region.

3·7 Slip, twinning, and fracture. The amount of deformation that can occur before fracture is determined by the relative values of the stresses required for slip, twinning, and cleavage. There is a critical resolved shear stress for slip which is increased by alloying, decreasing temperature, and prior deformation. There is a critical resolved shear stress for twinning which is also increased by prior deformation. There is also a critical normal stress for cleavage on a particular plane which is not sensitive to prior deformation and temperature. When a stress is applied to a crystal, which process takes place depends upon which critical stress is exceeded first. If the critical resolved shear stress for slip or twinning is reached first, the crystal will slip or twin and show some ductility. If, however, the critical normal stress is reached first, the crystal will cleave along the plane concerned with little or no plastic deformation.

3·8 Polycrystalline material. The preceding discussion described plastic deformation in single crystals. Commercial material, however, is always made up of polycrystalline grains, whose crystal axes are oriented at random. When a polycrystalline material is subjected to stress, slip starts first in those grains in which the slip system is most favorably situated with respect to the applied stress. Since contact at the grain boundaries must be maintained, it may be necessary for more than one slip system to operate. The rotation into the axis of tension brings other grains, originally less favorably oriented, into a position where they can now deform. As deformation and rotation proceed, the individual grains tend to elongate in the direction of flow. After a certain amount of deformation, most grains will have a particular crystal plane in the direction of deformation. The material now shows *preferred orientation*, which will result in somewhat different properties, depending upon the direction of measurement.

If the deformation is severe, the grains may be fragmented or broken. Not all the work done in deformation is dissipated in heat; part of it is stored in the crystal as an increase in internal energy. Since the crystal axes of adjacent grains are randomly oriented, the slip planes and twinning planes must change direction in going from grain to grain (Figs. 3·7 and 3·13). This means that more work is done at the grain boundaries and more internal energy will exist at those points.

Fig. 3·14 Polycrystalline brass, polished, etched, and then deformed slightly in a vise. 100×. (*By permission from R. M. Brick and A. Phillips, "Structure and Properties of Alloys," 2d ed., McGraw-Hill Book Company, Inc., New York*, 1949)

Figure 3·14 shows the microstructure of polycrystalline brass after being deformed slightly in a vise. Notice that the thin, parallel slip lines change direction at the grain boundaries. The grain in the lower portion of the picture is interesting in that it illustrates both slip and twinning in the same grain. The slip lines, running vertically and to the right, become horizontal when they cross the twinning band and then resume their original direction on the other side. Since the slip lines have the same direction on either side of the twinning band, this indicates that the deformation is occurring in the same grain.

When a crystal deforms, there is some distortion of the lattice structure. This distortion is greatest on the slip planes and grain boundaries and increases with increasing deformation. This is manifested by an increase in resistance to further deformation. The material is undergoing *strain hardening* or *work hardening*. One of the remarkable features of plastic deformation is that the stress required to initiate slip is lower than that required to continue deformation on subsequent planes. Aside from distortion of the lattice structure, the pile-up of dislocations against obstacles (such as grain boundaries and foreign atoms) and the locking of dislocations on intersecting slip planes increase the resistance to further deformation.

It is important to remember that whenever there is distortion of the lattice structure, whether it is a result of plastic deformation, heat treatment, or alloying, there will be an increase in the strength and hardness of the material.

3·9 Effect of cold working on properties. All the properties of a metal that are dependent on the lattice structure are affected by plastic deformation or cold working. Tensile strength, yield strength,

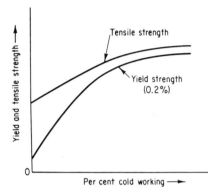

Fig. 3·15 Effect of cold working on tensile and yield strength of copper.

and hardness are increased while ductility, as represented by per cent elongation, is decreased (Table 3·1). Although both strength and hardness increase, the rate of change is not the same. Hardness generally increases most rapidly in the first 10 per cent reduction,

Table 3·1 Effect of plastic deformation on the tensile properties of 70:30 brass*

Reduction by cold rolling, per cent	Tensile strength, psi	Elongation, % in 2 in.	Hardness, Rockwell X†
0	43,000	70	12
10	48,000	52	62
20	53,000	35	83
30	60,000	20	89
40	70,900	12	94
50	80,000	8	97
60	90,000	6	100

* From R. M. Brick and A. Phillips, "Structure and Properties of Alloys," 1st ed., McGraw-Hill Book Company, Inc., New York, 1942.
† Rockwell X = $\frac{1}{16}$-in. ball penetrator, 75 kg load.

whereas the tensile strength increases more or less linearly. The yield strength increases more rapidly than the tensile strength, so that, as the amount of plastic deformation is increased, the gap between the yield and tensile strengths decreases (Fig. 3·15). This is important in certain forming operations where appreciable deformation is required.

In drawing, for example, the load must be above the yield point to obtain appreciable deformation but below the tensile strength to avoid failure.   If the gap is narrow, very close control of the load is required.

Ductility follows a path opposite to that of hardness, a large decrease in the first 10 per cent reduction and then a decrease at a slower rate.

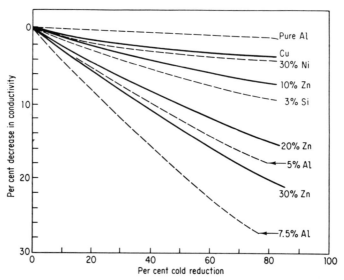

Fig. 3·16   Effect of cold working on the electrical conductivity of pure aluminum; pure copper; Cu + 30 per cent Ni; Cu + 3 per cent Si; Cu + 5 per cent and 7.5 per cent Al; Cu + 10 per cent, 20 per cent, and 30 per cent Zn. (By permission from R. M. Brick and A. Phillips, "Structure and Properties of Alloys," 2d ed., McGraw-Hill Book Company, Inc., New York, 1949)

Distortion of the lattice structure hinders the passage of electrons and decreases electrical conductivity.   This effect is slight in pure metals but is appreciable in alloys (Fig. 3·16).

The increase in internal energy, particularly at the grain boundaries, makes the material more susceptible to intergranular corrosion, thereby reducing its corrosion resistance.

QUESTIONS

3·1   Describe an experiment to determine the increase in internal energy of a crystal as a result of deformation.

3·2   The movement in slip is sometimes described as analogous to simple gliding.   Why is this a poor analogy?

3·3   Is it possible to have both slip and twinning occur in the same grain? Explain.

3·4 How may one distinguish between slip and twinning if the width of the twin band is of the same order as a slip line?

3·5 What is the effect of the rate of deformation on the mechanical properties?

3·6 How would a difference in grain size affect the change in mechanical properties due to deformation?

3·7 Which properties would be affected by preferred orientation and why?

3·8 In Fig. 3·16, why does the addition of 30 per cent nickel to copper have less effect on electrical conductivity than the addition of 5 per cent aluminum to copper?

3·9 Using Eqs. (3·1) and (3·2), plot a curve showing the variation of the shear stress and the normal stress as θ varies from 0 to 90°. Assume F is constant.

3·10 The critical resolved shear stress for slip in copper is 142 psi. Using Eq. (3·3) and assuming λ to remain constant at 10°, plot a curve showing the change in the axial load F with change in θ.

REFERENCES

Barrett, C. S.: "Structure of Metals," 2d ed., McGraw-Hill Book Company, Inc., New York, 1952.

Boas, W.: "An Introduction to the Physics of Metals and Alloys," John Wiley & Sons, Inc., New York, 1947.

Brick, R. M., and A. Phillips: "Structure and Properties of Alloys," 2d ed., McGraw-Hill Book Company, Inc., New York, 1949.

Cottrell, A. H.: "Dislocations and Plastic Flow in Crystals," Oxford University Press, Fair Lawn, N.J., 1956.

Guy, A. G.: "Elements of Physical Metallurgy," 2d ed., Addison-Wesley Publishing Company, Inc., Reading, Mass., 1959.

Mondolfo, L. F., and O. Zmeskal: "Engineering Metallurgy," McGraw-Hill Book Company, Inc., New York, 1955.

Rogers, B. A.: "The Nature of Metals," American Society for Metals, Metals Park, Ohio, 1951.

Van Vlack, L. H.: "Elements of Materials Science," Addison-Wesley Publishing Company, Inc., Reading, Mass., 1959.

Chapter 4

ANNEALING AND HOT WORKING

FULL ANNEALING

Full annealing is the process by which the distorted cold-worked lattice structure is changed back to one which is strain-free through the application of heat. This process is carried out entirely in the solid state and is usually followed by slow cooling in the furnace from the desired temperature. The annealing process may be divided into three stages: recovery, recrystallization, and grain growth.

4·1 Recovery. This is primarily a low-temperature effect and consists mainly of the release of internal stresses. When the load which has caused plastic deformation in a polycrystalline material is released, all the elastic deformation does not disappear. This is due to the different orientation of the crystals which will not allow some of them to move back when the load is released. As the temperature is increased, there is some springback of these elastically displaced atoms which relieves most of the internal stress. In some cases there may be a slight amount of plastic flow, which may result in a slight increase in hardness and strength. Electrical conductivity is increased but there is no visible change in the microstructure. Commercially, this low-temperature treatment in the recovery range is known as *stress-relief annealing*.

4·2 Recrystallization. As the upper temperature of the recovery range is reached, minute new crystals appear in the microstructure. These new crystals have the same composition and lattice structure as the original undeformed grains and are not elongated but are approximately uniform in dimensions (equiaxed). The new crystals generally appear at the most drastically deformed portions of the grain, usually the grain boundaries and slip planes. The cluster of atoms from which the new grains are formed is called a nucleus. Recrystallization takes place by a combination of nucleation of strain-free grains and the growth of these nuclei to absorb the entire cold-worked material.

Exactly how recrystallization takes place is not yet. clearly understood; however, some idea of the process may be obtained by examining it in terms of the energy of the lattice. In the discussion of plastic deformation, it was emphasized that the slip planes and grain boundaries were localized points of high internal energy as a result of the pile-up of dislocations. Because of the nature of strain hardening, it is not possible for the dislocation or the atoms to move back to

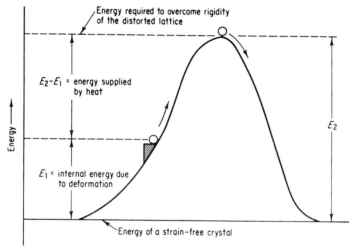

Fig. 4.1 Schematic representation of recrystallization.

form a strain-free lattice from the distorted lattice. A simplified analogy is shown in Fig. 4·1. Consider that some atoms, at the grain boundaries or slip planes, have been pushed up an energy hill to a value of E_1 above the internal energy of atoms in the undeformed lattice. The energy required to overcome the rigidity of the distorted lattice is equal to E_2. The atoms cannot reach the energy of the strain-free crystal by the same path they went up the hill; instead, they must get over the top from which they are able to roll down easily. This difference in energy, $E_2 - E_1$, is supplied by heat. When the temperature is reached at which these localized areas have an energy content equal to E_2, they give up part of their energy as *heat of recrystallization* and form nuclei of new strain-free grains. Part of this heat of recrystallization is absorbed by surrounding atoms so that they have sufficient energy to overcome the rigidity of the distorted lattice and be attracted into the lattice structure of the strain-free grains, initiating grain growth. The number and energy content of these high-energy points depend to a large extent on the amount of prior deformation, the number increasing with increasing deformation.

4·3 Recrystallization temperature.   The term *recrystallization temperature* does not refer to a definite temperature below which recrystallization will not occur but refers to the approximate temperature at which a highly cold-worked material completely recrystallizes in 1 hr.   The recrystallization temperature of several metals and alloys is listed in Table 4·1.

Table 4·1   Approximate recrystallization temperatures for several metals and alloys*

Material	Recrystallization Temp, °F
Copper (99.999%)	250
Copper, 5% zinc	600
Copper, 5% aluminum	550
Copper, 2% beryllium	700
Aluminum (99.999%)	175
Aluminum (99.0% +)	550
Aluminum alloys	600
Nickel (99.99%)	700
Monel metal	1100
Iron (electrolytic)	750
Low-carbon steel	1000
Magnesium (99.99%)	150
Magnesium alloys	450
Zinc	50
Tin	25
Lead	25

* By permission from A. G. Guy, "Elements of Physical Metallurgy," 2d ed., Addison-Wesley Publishing Company, Inc., Reading, Mass., 1959.

The greater the amount of prior deformation, the lower the temperature for the start of recrystallization (Fig. 4·2), since there will be greater distortion and more internal energy left.

Increasing the annealing time decreases the recrystallization temperature.   The recrystallization process is far more sensitive to changes in temperature than to variations in time at constant temperature. The influence of time and temperature on the tensile strength of highly cold-worked copper is shown in Fig. 4·3.   Recrystallization is indicated by the sharp drop in tensile strength.   A tensile strength of 40,000 psi may be obtained by heating for 12 hr at 300°F, 6 hr at 320°F, 2 hr at 340°F, 1 hr at 370°F, or ½ hr at 390°F.

A certain minimum amount of cold working (usually 2 to 8 per cent) is necessary for recrystallization.   In Fig. 4·4, it is seen that a deformation of approximately 7 per cent is required before any change in grain size occurs.   This is known as the *critical deformation*.   At degrees of deformation smaller than this, the number of recrystallization nuclei becomes very small.

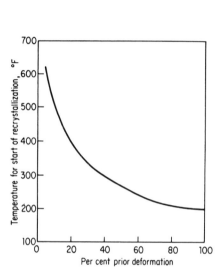

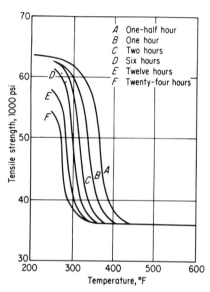

Fig. 4·2   Effect of prior deformation on the temperature for the start of recrystallization of copper.

Fig. 4·3   Effect of time and temperature on annealing. (*From "Metals Handbook," 1948 edition, American Society for Metals, Metals Park, Ohio*)

4·4   Grain growth.

Large grains have lower free energy than small grains.   This is associated with the reduction of the amount of grain boundary.   Therefore, under ideal conditions, the lowest energy state for a metal would be as a single crystal.   This is the driving force for grain growth.   Opposing this force is the rigidity of the lattice.   As the temperature increases, the rigidity of the lattice decreases and the rate of grain growth is more rapid.   At any given temperature there is a maximum grain size at which these two effects are in equilibrium (Fig. 4·5).

It is therefore theoretically possible to grow very large grains by holding a specimen for a long time high in the grain-growth region. The very large grains shown in Fig. 4·6 were obtained by this method. The specimen was held at a temperature just under the melting point of this alloy.   Notice that some melting has occurred in the upper right corner because of temperature fluctuation in the furnace.

4·5   Grain size.   Since annealing involves nucleation and grain growth, factors that favor rapid nucleation and slow growth will result in fine-grained material and those which favor slow nucleation and rapid growth will result in coarse-grained material.   The factors that govern the final recrystallized grain size are:

Degree of Prior Deformation.   This is the most important factor. Increasing the amount of prior deformation favors nucleation and

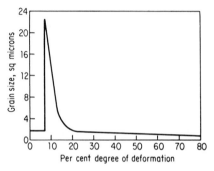

Fig. 4·4   Effect of cold working on grain size developed in a low-carbon steel annealed at 1740°F.   (From "Metals Handbook," 1948 edition, American Society for Metals, Metals Park, Ohio)

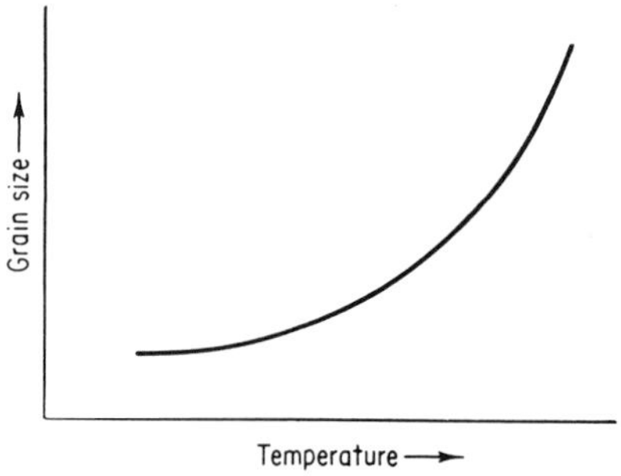

Fig. 4·5   Effect of temperature on recrystallized grain size.

decreases the final grain size (see Fig. 4·4).   It is interesting to note that, at the critical deformation, the grains will grow to a very large size upon annealing.   The formation of large grains during recrystallization with the minimum deformation is due to the very few recrystallization nuclei that are formed during the time available for recrystallization.   If the deformation is carefully controlled at the critical amount, subsequent annealing will result in very large grains or single crystals. This is the basis for the strain-anneal method of producing single crystals.

Time at Temperature.   Increasing the time at any temperature favors grain growth and increases the final grain size.   The progress of recrystallization of cold-worked brass is shown in the group of photomicrographs of Fig. 4·7.   The first one (*a*) shows the alloy after the rolling operation in which the reduction was 33 per cent.   There are numerous slip lines and several dark twinning bands.   The remaining samples were reheated at 1075°F in a lead bath for increasing periods of time. The second one (b) shows new grains beginning to form along the slip lines and at the grain boundaries, which are points of high internal energy. After 8 min at 1075°F (photomicrograph c), recrystallization is just about complete, there being no evidence of the old distorted structure. Beyond this point, increasing the time at 1075°F (photomicrographs d to g) merely serves to increase the grain size. Notice the presence of annealing twin bands, which are found in wrought and annealed brasses. They arise during annealing by a change in the normal growth mechanism due to previous straining.

Annealing Temperature. The lower the temperature above the recrystallization temperature, the finer the final grain size (see Fig. 4·5).

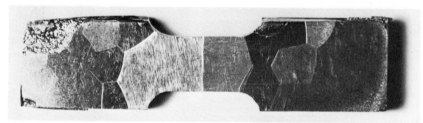

Fig. 4·6 Large grains in a titanium-vanadium alloy formed by holding for a long time high in the grain-growth region. Magnification 2×.

Heating Time. The shorter the time heating to the annealing temperature, the finer the final grain size. Slow heating will form few nuclei, favoring grain growth and resulting in coarse grain.

Insoluble Impurities. The greater the amount and the finer the distribution of insoluble impurities the finer the final grain size. They not only increase nucleation but act as barriers to the growth of grains.

The amount of strain hardening introduced by a given amount of elongation increases as the grain size decreases. If both coarse- and fine-grained material are given the same amount of strain hardening, their annealing behavior will be very similar.

The rate of cooling from the annealing temperature has a negligible effect on final grain size. This factor will be of interest only if the material has been heated far in the grain-growth range and slow-cooled. During slow cooling the material may have enough energy to continue grain growth, and some coarsening may result.

4·6 Effect on properties. Since full annealing restores the material to a strain-free lattice structure, it is essentially a softening process. Property changes produced by plastic deformation are removed, and the material returns very nearly to its original properties.

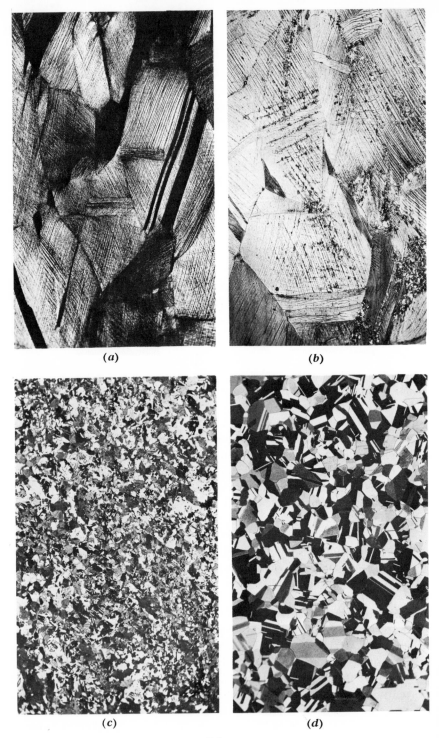

(a)

(b)

(c)

(d)

(e)

(f)

Fig. 4·7 Series of photomicrographs illustrating the progress of recrystallization at 1075°F of cold-worked brass. Magnification 40×. (*J. E. Burke, General Electric Company*)

(g)

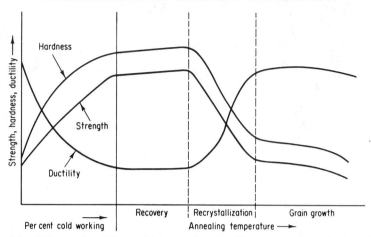

Fig. 4·8 Effect of cold working and annealing on strength, hardness, and ductility.

Therefore, during annealing, the hardness and strength decrease, whereas the ductility increases. The change in properties is shown schematically in Fig. 4·8 and for 70-30 brass in Table 4·2.

Table 4·2   Annealing of 70-30 brass after 50 per cent cold reduction with time constant at 30 min*

Annealing temp, °F	Hardness, Rockwell X†	Tensile strength, psi	Elongation, % in 2 in.
None (cold work)	97	80,000	8
300	98	81,000	8
392	100	82,000	8
482	101	82,000	8
572	98	76,000	12
662	80	60,000	28
842	58	46,000	51
1112	34	44,000	66
1292	14	42,000	70

* From R. M. Brick and A. Phillips, "Structure and Properties of Alloys," 2d ed., McGraw-Hill Book Company, Inc., New York, 1949.

† Rockwell X = $\frac{1}{16}$-in. ball penetrator, 75 kg load.

HOT WORKING

Hot working is usually described as working a material above its recrystallization temperature. The above definition, however, does not take into account the rate of working.

4·7 Dividing line between hot and cold working. When a material is plastically deformed it tends to become harder but the rate of work hardening decreases as the temperature is increased. When a material is plastically deformed at an elevated temperature, two opposing effects take place at the same time, a hardening effect due to plastic deformation and a softening effect due to recrystallization. For a given rate of working, there must be some temperature at which these two effects will just balance. If the material is worked above this temperature, it is known as *hot working* and below this temperature as *cold working*. The hardening of copper under slow

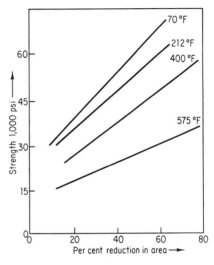

Fig. 4·9 Effect of the amount of cold working on the strength of copper determined by tension tests at various temperatures.

deformation in a tension test at various temperatures is shown in Fig. 4·9. At about 750°F, the rate of softening will equal the rate of hardening and the material can be continuously deformed without an increase in load. If the rate of deformation is increased considerably, such as in hammer forging, the temperature will have to be increased to about 1475°F before the two rates will be equal. The effect of working temperature on hardness with varying rate of working is shown schematically in Fig. 4·10.

The terms *hot* and *cold* as applied to working do not have the same significance that they ordinarily have. For example, lead and tin, whose recrystallization temperature is below room temperature, may be hot-worked at room temperature; but steel, with a high recrystallization temperature, may be cold-worked at 1000°F.

4·8 Hot working vs. cold working. Most of the metal shapes are produced from cast ingots. To manufacture sheet, plate, rod, wire, etc., from this ingot, the most economical method is by hot working. However, in the case of steel, the hot-worked material reacts with oxygen as it cools down to room temperature and forms a

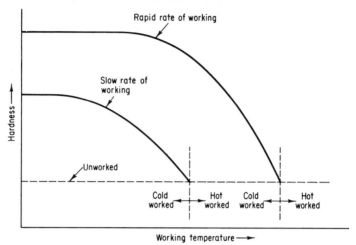

Fig. 4·10   Schematic illustration of the effect of working temperature on hardness with varying rate of working.

characteristic dark oxide coating called *scale*.   Occasionally, this scale may give difficulty during machining or forming operations.

It is not possible to manufacture hot-worked material to exact size because of dimensional changes that take place during cooling.   Cold-worked material, on the other hand, may be held to close tolerances.

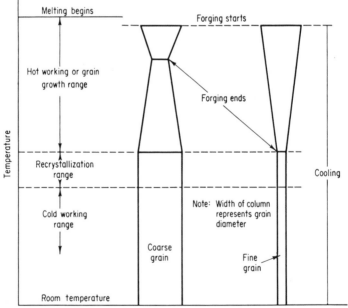

Fig. 4·11   Effect of finishing temperature in forging on grain size.

It is free of surface scale but requires more power for deformation and is therefore more expensive to produce.   The initial reductions are carried out with the material at an elevated temperature, and the final reductions are done cold to take advantage of both processes.

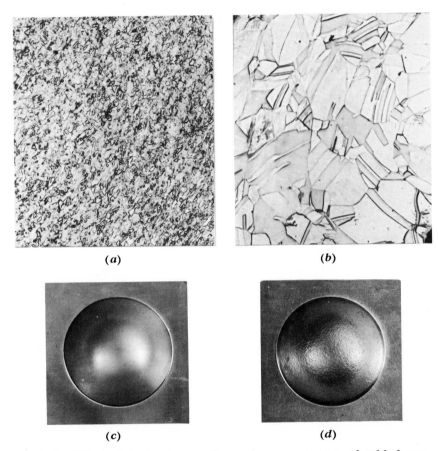

(a)   (b)

(c)   (d)

Fig. 4·12   Effect of grain size on the surface appearance of cold-drawn 70-30 brass sheet. (H. L. Burghoff, Chase Brass and Copper Company)

The finishing temperature in hot working will determine the grain size that is available for further cold working.   Higher temperatures are used initially to promote uniformity in the material, and the resulting large grains allow more economical reduction during the early working operation.   As the material cools and working continues, the grain size will decrease, becoming very fine just above the recrystallization temperature.   This is illustrated schematically in Fig. 4·11.

Proper control of annealing temperature will approximate the final grain size required for subsequent cold working. Although coarse-grained material has better ductility, the nonuniformity of deformation from grain to grain creates a problem in surface appearance. Figure 4·12 shows the "orange-peel" surface on coarse-grained material that is subjected to severe deformation. The choice of grain size is therefore a compromise determined by the particular cold-forming operation (Table 4·3).

Table 4·3   Recommended grain sizes in brass for cold-forming operations*

Grain Size, mm	Type of Cold-forming Operation
0.015	Slight forming operations
0.025	Shallow drawing
0.035	For best average surface combined with drawing
0.050	Deep drawing
0.100	Heavy drawing on thick sheet

* From "Metals Handbook," 1948 edition, table II, p. 879, American Society for Metals, Metals Park, Ohio.

QUESTIONS

4·1   Explain the importance of heating in the recovery range for some industrial applications.

4·2   Give two methods of lowering the recrystallization temperature of a given metal.

4·3   Assume that a tapered piece of copper has been stressed in tension beyond its yield point and then annealed. Explain how the grain size will change along the taper.

4·4   Suppose a bullet hole is made in a plate of aluminum. How will the grain size vary if the plate is annealed?

4·5   How is grain size measured?

4·6   Why does the recrystallization temperature vary with different metals?

4·7   Why does the addition of alloying elements change the recrystallization temperature?

4·8   Cite an industrial application which requires periodic annealing between cold-working operations.

4·9   Many heat-treating processes, including annealing, involve nucleation and growth. The relation between the rate of the process and the temperature may be expressed, in general, as

$$\text{Rate} = Ae^{-B/T}$$

where A and B are constants, and T is the absolute temperature in degrees Kelvin. For 50 per cent recrystallization of copper, $A = 10^{12}\,\text{min}^{-1}$ and $B = 15,000$. The time for 50 per cent recrystallization may be taken as the reciprocal of the rate. Calculate the time for 50 per cent recrystallization at 100, 150, 200, 250, and 275°F.

4·10   Plot the results obtained in Question 4·9 on semilog paper with time on the log scale and temperature as the ordinate. This plot should be a straight line.

4·11 Extrapolate the line obtained in Question 4·10 and determine the temperature at which copper will be 50 per cent recrystallized after 15 years.

REFERENCES

American Society for Metals: "Metals Handbook," 1948 edition, Metals Park, Ohio.

Brick, R. M., and A. Phillips: "Structure and Properties of Alloys," 2d ed., McGraw-Hill Book Company, Inc., New York, 1949.

Guy, A. G.: "Elements of Physical Metallurgy," Addison-Wesley Publishing Company, Inc., Reading, Mass., 1959.

Kehl, G. L.: "Principles of Metallographic Laboratory Practice," 3d ed., McGraw-Hill Book Company, Inc., New York, 1949.

Mason, C. W.: "Introductory Physical Metallurgy," American Society for Metals, Metals Park, Ohio, 1947.

Rogers, B. A.: "The Nature of Metals," American Society for Metals, Metals Park, Ohio, 1951.

Chapter 5

CONSTITUTION OF ALLOYS

5·1 Introduction. An alloy is a substance that has metallic properties and is composed of two or more chemical elements, of which at least one is a metal.

An alloy system contains all the alloys that can be formed by several elements combined in all possible proportions. If the system is made up of two elements, it is called a *binary alloy system;* three elements, a *ternary alloy system;* etc. Taking only 45 of the most common metals, any combination of two gives 890 binary systems. Combinations of three give over 10,000 ternary systems. However, in each system, a large number of different alloys are possible. If the composition is varied by 1 per cent, each binary system will yield 100 different alloys. Since commercial alloys often contain many elements, it is apparent that the number of possible alloys is almost infinite.

Alloys may be classified according to their structure, and complete alloy systems may be classified according to the type of their equilibrium diagram. The basic types of equilibrium diagrams will be studied in Chap. 6.

5·2 Classification of alloys. Alloys may be homogeneous (uniform) or mixtures. If the alloy is homogeneous it will consist of a single phase, and if it is a mixture it will be a combination of several phases. A phase is anything which is homogeneous and physically distinct. The uniformity of an alloy phase is not determined on an atomic scale, such as the composition of each unit lattice cell, but rather on a much larger scale. Any structure which is visible as physically distinct microscopically may be considered a phase. For most pure elements the term *phase* is synonymous with *state.* There is, therefore, for pure elements, a gaseous, liquid, and solid phase. Some metals are allotropic in the solid state and will have different solid phases. When the metal undergoes a change in crystal structure, it undergoes a phase change since each type of crystal structure is physically distinct.

In the solid state there are three possible phases: (1) pure metal, (2) intermediate alloy phase or compound, and (3) solid solution.

If an alloy is homogeneous (composed of a single phase) in the solid state, it can be only a solid solution or a compound. If the alloy is a mixture, it is then composed of any combination of the phases possible in the solid state. It may be a mixture of two pure metals,

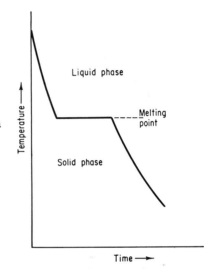

Fig. 5·1   Ideal cooling curve for a pure metal.

or two solid solutions, or two compounds, or a pure metal and a solid solution, and so on. The mixture may also vary in degree of fineness.

5·3   Pure metal. The characteristics of a pure metal have been discussed in detail in an earlier chapter. However, one property is worth repeating. Under equilibrium conditions, all metals exhibit a definite melting or freezing point. The term *under equilibrium conditions* implies conditions of extremely slow heating and cooling. In other words, if any change is to occur, sufficient time must be allowed for it to take place. If a cooling curve is plotted for a pure metal, it will show a horizontal line at the melting or freezing point (Fig. 5·1).

5·4   Intermediate alloy phase or compound. Because the reason for referring to this type of solid phase as an *intermediate alloy phase* will be more apparent during the study of equilibrium diagrams, it will be simpler at this point to call it a *compound*.

It is now necessary to obtain some understanding of compounds in general. Most ordinary chemical compounds are combinations of positive and negative valence elements. The various kinds of atoms are combined in a definite proportion, which is expressed by a chemical formula. Some typical examples are water, H_2O (two atoms of hydrogen combined with one atom of oxygen), and table salt, NaCl (one atom of sodium combined with one atom of chlorine). The atoms that are combined to form the molecule, which is the smallest unit that has the properties of the compound, are held together in a definite bond. Various types of atomic bonding have been discussed in Chap. 2. The bond is generally strong and the atoms are not easily separated. Most students are familiar with the classical high school chemistry demonstration of the electrolysis of water. By passing an electric current through water it is possible to separate the hydrogen and oxygen atoms.

When a compound is formed, the elements lose their individual identity and characteristic properties to a large extent. A good example is table salt (NaCl). Sodium (Na) is a very active metal that oxidizes rapidly and is usually stored under kerosene. Chlorine (Cl) is a poisonous gas. Yet one atom of each combines to give the harmless and important compound, table salt. Water (H_2O) is composed of elements that are normally gases at room temperature, yet the compound is a liquid at room temperature. What exists then is not the individual elements but rather the combination or compound. The compound will have its own characteristic physical, mechanical, and chemical properties.

Most compounds, like pure metals, also exhibit a definite melting point within narrow limits of temperature. Therefore, the cooling curve for a compound is similar to that for a pure metal (see Fig. 5·1). It is then referred to as a *congruent melting phase.* In reference to equilibrium diagrams, the intermediate alloy phases are phases whose chemical compositions are intermediate between the two pure metals and generally have crystal structures different from those of the pure metals.

The three most common intermediate alloy phases are:

Intermetallic Compounds or Valency Compounds. These are generally formed between chemically dissimilar metals and are combined by following the rules of chemical valence. Since they generally have strong bonding (ionic or covalent), their properties are essentially nonmetallic. They usually show poor ductility and poor electrical conductivity and may have a complex crystal structure. Examples of valency compounds are $CaSe$, Mg_2Pb, Mg_2Sn, and Cu_2Se.

Interstitial Compounds. These are compounds formed between the transition metals such as scandium (Sc), titanium (Ti), tantalum (Ta), tungsten (W), and iron (Fe), and by hydrogen, oxygen, carbon, boron, and nitrogen. The word *interstitial* means between the spaces, and the latter five elements have relatively small atoms that fit into the spaces of the lattice structure of the metal.   These same five elements also form interstitial solid solutions, which will be described shortly. The interstitial compounds are metallic, have a narrow range of composition, high melting points, and are extremely hard.   Examples are TiC, TaC, Fe_2N, Fe_3C, W_2C, CrN, and TiH.   Many of these compounds are useful in hardening steel and in cemented-carbide tools.

Electron Compounds.   A study of the equilibrium diagrams of the alloys of copper, gold, silver, iron, and nickel with the metals cadmium, magnesium, tin, zinc, and aluminum shows striking similarities.   A

Table 5·1   Examples of electron compounds

Electron-atom ratio 3:2 (b.c.c. structure)	Electron-atom ratio 21:13 (complex cubic)	Electron-atom ratio 7:4 (c.p.h. structure)
AgCd	Ag_5Cd_8	$AgCd_3$
AgZn	Cu_9Al_4	Ag_5Al_3
Cu_3Al	$Cu_{31}Sn_8$	$AuZn_3$
AuMg	Au_5Zn_8	Cu_3Si
FeAl	Fe_5Zn_{21}	$FeZn_7$
Cu_5Sn	Ni_5Zn_{21}	Ag_3Sn

number of intermediate phases are formed in these systems with similar lattice structures.   Hume-Rothery first pointed out that these intermediate phases are found to exist at or near compositions in each system that have a definite ratio of valence electrons to atoms and are therefore called *electron compounds*.   Some examples are given in Table 5·1.   For example, in the compound AgZn, the atom of silver has one valence electron while that of zinc has two valence electrons so that the two atoms of the compound will have three valence electrons, or an electron-to-atom ratio of 3:2.   In the compound Cu_9Al_4, each atom of copper has one valence electron and each atom of aluminum three valence electrons, so that the 13 atoms that make up the compound have 21 valence electrons, or an electron-to-atom ratio of 21:13.   For the purpose of calculation, the atoms of iron and nickel are assumed to have zero valence.

Many electron compounds have properties resembling those of solid solutions, including a wide range of composition, high ductility, and low hardness.

5·5   Solid solutions.   Any solution is composed of two parts: a solute and a solvent.   The solute is the minor part of the solution or the material which is dissolved, while the solvent constitutes the major portion of the solution. It is possible to have solutions involving gases, liquids, or solids as either the solute or the solvent. The most common solutions involve water as the solvent, such as sugar or salt dissolved in water.

The amount of solute that may be dissolved by the solvent is generally a function of temperature (with pressure constant) and usually increases with increasing temperature.

There are three possible conditions for a solution: unsaturated, saturated, and supersaturated. If the solvent is dissolving less of the solute than it could dissolve at a given temperature and pressure, it is said to be *unsaturated*. If it is dissolving the limiting amount of solute, it is *saturated*. If it is dissolving more of the solute than it should, under equilibrium conditions, the solution is *supersaturated*. This latter condition may be accomplished by doing work on the solution, such as stirring, or preventing equilibrium conditions by rapidly cooling the solution. The supersaturated condition is an unstable one, and given enough time or a little energy, the solution tends to become stable or saturated by rejecting or precipitating the excess solute.

A solid solution is simply a solution in the solid state and consists of two kinds of atoms combined in one type of space lattice. There is usually a considerable difference in the solubility of the solute in the liquid and solid states of the solution. The solute is generally more soluble in the liquid state than in the solid state. Moreover, when solidification of the solution starts, the temperature may be higher or lower than the freezing point of the pure solvent. Most solid solutions solidify over a range of temperature (see Fig. 5·2). There are two types of solid solutions, substitutional and interstitial.

5·6   Substitutional solid solution. In this type of solution, the atoms of the solute substitute for atoms of the solvent in the lattice structure of the solvent. For example, silver atoms may substitute for gold atoms without losing the f.c.c. (face-centered cubic) structure of gold, and gold atoms may substitute for silver atoms in the f.c.c. lattice structure of silver. All alloys in the silver-gold system consist of an f.c.c. lattice with silver and gold atoms distributed at random through the lattice structure. This entire system consists of a continuous series of solid solutions.

Several factors are now known, largely through the work of Hume-Rothery, that control ranges of solubility in alloy systems.

Crystal-structure Factor. Complete solid solubility of two elements is never attained unless the elements have the same type of crystal lattice structure.

Relative-size Factor. The size factor is favorable for solid-solution formation when the difference in atomic radii is less than about 15 per cent. If the relative size factor is greater than 8 per cent but less than 15 per cent, the alloy system usually shows a minimum. If the relative-size factor is greater than 15 per cent, solid-solution formation is very limited. For example, silver and lead are both f.c.c. and the relative-size factor is about 20 per cent. The solubility of lead in solid silver is about 1.5 per cent and the solubility of silver in solid lead is about 0.1 per cent. Antimony and bismuth are completely soluble in each other in all proportions. They have the same type of crystal structure (rhombohedral) and differ in atomic radii

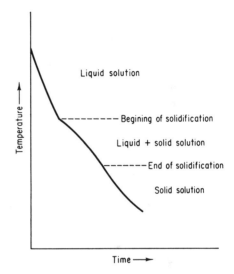

Fig. 5·2 **Typical cooling curve for a solid solution.**

by about 7 per cent. However, the solubility of antimony in f.c.c. aluminum is less than 0.1 per cent, although the relative-size factor is only about 2 per cent.

Chemical-affinity Factor. The greater the chemical affinity of two metals, the more restricted is their solid solubility and the greater is the tendency toward compound formation. Generally, the farther apart the elements are in the periodic table, the greater is their chemical affinity.

Relative-valence Factor. A metal of lower valence tends to dissolve more of a metal of higher valence than vice versa. Gold (valence 1) dissolves about 5 per cent of magnesium (valence 2), but magnesium dissolves less than 0.1 per cent gold.

The lattice structure of a solid solution is basically that of the solvent with slight changes in lattice parameter. An expansion results if the solute atom is larger than the solvent atom and a contraction if the solute atom is smaller.

5·7   Interstitial solid solutions. These are formed when atoms of small atomic radii fit into the spaces or interstices of the lattice structure of the larger solvent atoms. Since the spaces of the lattice structure are restricted in size, only atoms with atomic radii less than 1 angstrom are likely to form interstitial solid solutions. These are hydrogen (0.46), boron (0.97), carbon (0.77), nitrogen (0.71), and oxygen (0.60).

This type of solution differs from interstitial compounds in that the amount of smaller atoms required to form the compound is always

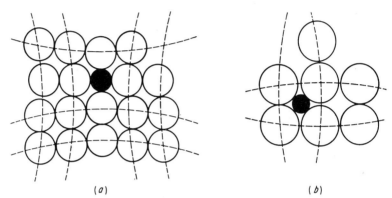

(a)   (b)

Fig. 5·3   Schematic representation of both types of solid solutions. (a) Substitutional; (b) interstitial.

greater than the amount that may be dissolved interstitially. When a small amount of solute is added to the solvent and the difference in atomic radii is great enough, an interstitial solid solution is formed. In this condition, the solute atoms have considerable mobility and may move in the interstitial spaces of the lattice structure. More solute atoms may be dissolved interstitially until the solution becomes saturated at that temperature. Increasing the amount of solute atoms beyond this limit severely restricts the mobility of these atoms in a particular area and the interstitial compound of fixed composition starts to form. The interstitial compound, showing a narrow range of composition, is expressed by a chemical formula, but the interstitial solution, being of variable composition, cannot be represented by a chemical formula.

The lattice structure always shows an expansion when this type of solution is formed. The best-known example is the interstitial solution of carbon in iron.

Both types of solid solutions are illustrated in Fig. 5·3. Distortion of the lattice structure will exist in the region of the solute atom. This distortion will interfere with the movement of dislocations on slip planes and will therefore increase the strength of the alloy. This is the primary basis for the strengthening of a metal by alloying.

In contrast to intermetallic and interstitial compounds, solid solutions in general are easier to separate, melt over a range in temperature, have properties that are influenced by those of the solvent and solute, and usually show a wide range of composition so that they are not expressed by a chemical formula.

Chapter 6

EQUILIBRIUM DIAGRAMS

6·1 Introduction. The phase changes that occur in metals and alloys have been studied for many years, and the best method of recording this information is by use of equilibrium diagrams, also known as *phase diagrams* or *constitutional diagrams*.

In order to specify completely the state of a system in equilibrium, it is necessary to specify three independent variables. These variables, which are externally controllable, are temperature, pressure, and composition. With pressure assumed to be constant at atmospheric value, the equilibrium diagram indicates the structural changes due to variation of temperature and composition. The diagram is essentially a graphical representation of an alloy system.

It is extremely important for the student to remember that the diagram is valid only under equilibrium conditions, that is, under extremely slow heating and cooling conditions. In actual practice, phase changes tend to occur at slightly higher or lower temperatures, depending upon the rate at which the alloy is heated or cooled. Rapid variation in temperature, which may prevent phase changes that would normally occur under equilibrium conditions, will distort and sometimes limit the application of these diagrams.

In order to understand and interpret more complex alloy systems, certain elementary-type diagrams will be studied which illustrate the basic principles involved. Only binary systems (combinations of only two metals) will be studied.

6·2 Coordinates of phase diagrams. Phase diagrams are usually plotted with temperature, in degrees centigrade or Fahrenheit, as the ordinate and the alloy composition in weight percentage as the abscissa. It is sometimes more convenient to express the alloy composition in atomic per cent. The conversion from weight percentage to atomic percentage may be made by the following formulas:

$$\text{Atomic per cent of } A = \frac{100X}{X + Y(M/N)} \qquad (6\cdot1)$$

$$\text{Atomic per cent of } B = \frac{100Y(M/N)}{X + Y(M/N)} \qquad (6\cdot2)$$

where M = atomic weight of metal A
$\quad\ \ N$ = atomic weight of metal B
$\quad\ \ X$ = weight percentage of metal A
$\quad\ \ Y$ = weight percentage of metal B

Regardless of the scale chosen for temperature or composition, there will be no difference in the form of the resulting phase diagram.

6·3 Experimental methods. The data for the construction of equilibrium diagrams are determined experimentally by a variety of methods, the most common being:

Thermal Analysis. This is by far the most widely used experimental method. As was shown in Chap. 5, when a plot is made of temperature vs. time, at constant composition, the resulting cooling curve will show a change in slope when a phase change occurs because of the evolution of heat by the phase change. This method seems to be best for determining the initial and final temperature of solidification. Phase changes occurring solely in the solid state generally involve only small heat changes, and other methods give more accurate results.

Metallographic Methods. This method consists in heating samples of an alloy to different temperatures, waiting for equilibrium to be established, and then quickly cooling to retain their high-temperature structure. The samples are then examined microscopically.

This method is difficult to apply to metals at high temperatures because the rapidly cooled samples do not always retain their high-temperature structure and considerable skill is then required to interpret the observed microstructure correctly. This method is best suited for verification of a diagram.

X-ray diffraction. Since this method measures lattice dimensions, it will indicate the appearance of a new phase either by the change in lattice dimension or by the appearance of a new crystal structure. This method is simple, precise, and very useful in determining the changes in solid solubility with temperature.

6·4 Type I—two metals completely soluble in the liquid and solid states. Since the two metals are completely soluble in the solid state, the only type of solid phase formed will be a substitutional solid solution. The two metals will generally have the same type of crystal structure and differ in atomic radii by less than 8 per cent.

The result of running a series of cooling curves for various combinations or alloys between metals A and B, varying in composition from 100 per cent A 0 per cent B to 0 per cent A 100 per cent B, is shown

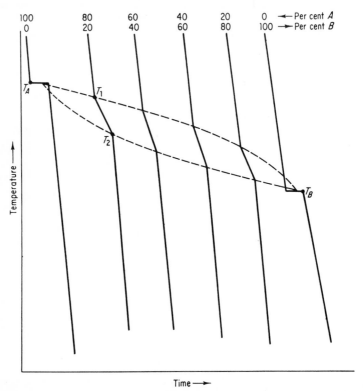

Fig. 6·1 Series of cooling curves for different alloys in a completely soluble system. The dotted lines indicate the form of the equilibrium diagram.

in Fig. 6·1. The cooling curves for the pure metals A and B show only a horizontal line because the beginning and end of solidification take place at a constant temperature. However, the cooling curves for the intermediate compositions show two breaks or changes in slope. The upper one indicates the beginning of solidification and the lower one the end of solidification. The sense or some idea of the form of the equilibrium diagram may be obtained by drawing one line connecting all points that show the beginning of solidification and another line connecting all the points that show the end of solidification.

It is now possible to determine the actual equilibrium diagram by plotting temperature vs. composition. The appropriate points are taken from the series of cooling curves and plotted on the new diagram. For example, in Fig. 6·2, since the left axis represents the pure metal A, T_A is plotted along this line. Similarly, T_B is plotted. Since all intermediate compositions are percentages of A and B, for simplicity the per cent sign will be omitted. A vertical line representing the alloy $80A$-$20B$ is drawn and T_1 and T_2 are plotted along this line. The same procedure is used for the other compositions.

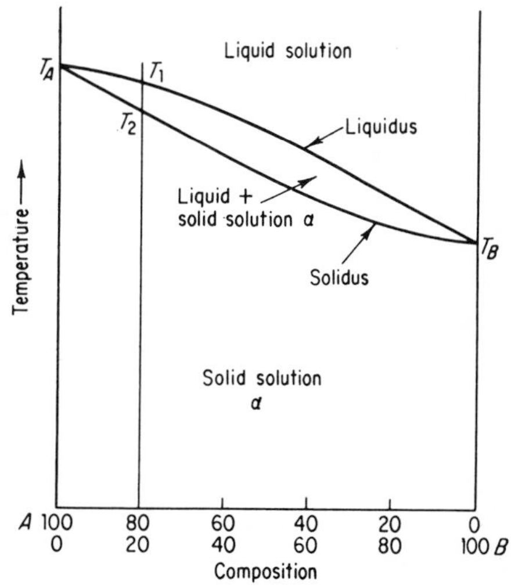

Fig. 6·2 Equilibrium diagram of two metals completely soluble in the liquid and solid states.

The upper line, obtained by connecting the points showing the beginning of solidification, is called the *liquidus* line; and the lower line, determined by connecting the points showing the end of solidification, is called the *solidus* line. The area above the liquidus line is a single-phase region, and any alloy in that region will consist of a homogeneous liquid solution. Similarly, the area below the solidus line is a single-phase region, and any alloy in this region will consist of a homogeneous solid solution. It is common practice, in the labeling of equilibrium diagrams, to represent solid solutions and sometimes intermediate alloys by Greek letters. In this case, let us label the solid solution alpha (α). Uppercase letters such as A and B will be used to represent the pure metals. Between the liquidus and solidus lines there exists a two-phase region. Any alloy in this region will consist of a mixture of a liquid solution and a solid solution.

Specification of temperature and composition of an alloy in a two-phase region indicates that the alloy consists of a mixture of two phases but does not give any information regarding this mixture.   It is sometimes desirable to know the actual chemical composition and the relative amounts of the two phases that are present.   In order to determine this information, it is necessary to apply two rules.

6·5   Rule I—chemical composition of phases.   To determine the actual chemical composition of the phases of an alloy, in equilibrium at any specified temperature in a two-phase region, draw a horizontal temperature line, called a *tie line*, to the boundaries of the field.

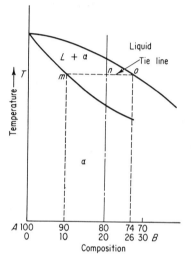

Fig. 6·3   Diagram showing the tie line *mo* drawn in the two-phase region at temperature *T*.

These points of intersection are dropped to the base line, and the composition is read directly.

In Fig. 6·3, consider the alloy composed of $80A$-$20B$ at the temperature T.   The alloy is in a two-phase region.   Applying Rule I, draw the tie line *mo* to the boundaries of the field.   Point *m*, the intersection of the tie line with the solidus line, when dropped to the base line, gives the composition of the phase that exists at that boundary.   In this case, the phase is a solid solution α of composition $90A$-$10B$. Similarly, point *o*, when dropped to the base line, will give the composition of the other phase constituting the mixture, in this case the liquid solution of composition $74A$-$26B$.

6·6   Rule II—relative amounts of each phase.   To determine the relative amounts of the two phases in equilibrium at any specified temperature in a two-phase region, draw a vertical line representing the alloy and a horizontal temperature line to the boundaries of the field.   The vertical line will divide the horizontal line into two parts whose lengths are inversely proportional to the amount of the phases present.   This is also known as the *lever rule*.   The point where the vertical line intersects the horizontal line may be considered as the fulcrum of a lever system. The relative lengths of the lever arms multiplied by the amounts of the phases present must balance.

In Fig. 6·3, the vertical line, representing the alloy 80A, divides the horizontal tie line into two parts, mn and no. If the entire length of the tie line mo is taken to represent 100 per cent, or the total weight

Fig. 6·4   The tie line mo **removed from Fig. 6·3 to illustrate application of the lever rule.**

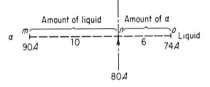

of the two phases present at temperature T, the lever rule may be expressed mathematically as

$$\text{Liquid (per cent)} = \frac{mn}{mo} \times 100$$

$$\alpha \text{ (per cent)} = \frac{no}{mo} \times 100$$

If the tie line is removed from the phase diagram and the numerical values are inserted, it will appear as shown in Fig. 6·4. Applying the above equations,

$$\text{Liquid (per cent)} = \frac{10}{16} \times 100 = 62.5 \text{ per cent}$$

$$\alpha \text{ (per cent)} = \frac{6}{16} \times 100 = 37.5 \text{ per cent}$$

To summarize both rules, the alloy of composition 80A-20B at the temperature T consists of a mixture of two phases. One is a liquid solution of composition 74A-26B constituting 62.5 per cent of all the material present and the other a solid solution of composition 90A-10B making up 37.5 per cent of all the material present.

6·7   Equilibrium cooling of a solid-solution alloy.   The very slow cooling, under equilibrium conditions, of a particular alloy 70A-30B will now be studied to observe the phase changes that occur. This alloy (Fig. 6·5) at temperature T_0 is a homogeneous single-phase liquid solution and remains so until temperature T_1 is reached.   Freezing or solidification now begins to take place by the formation of solid-solution crystals of composition α_1.   These first solid nuclei are very rich in the higher-melting-point metal A and are composed of 95A (Rule I).   Since the solid solution in forming takes material very

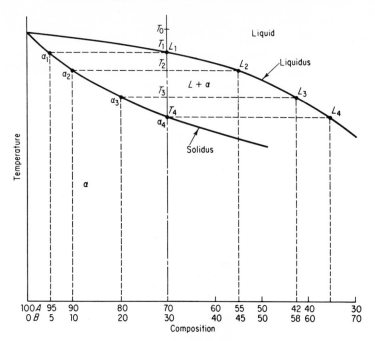

Fig. 6·5   The slow cooling of a 70A-30B alloy.

rich in A from the liquid, the liquid must get richer in B.   Therefore, when the lower temperature T_2 is reached, the liquid composition is at L_2.   The only solid solution in equilibrium with L_2 and therefore the only solid solution forming at T_2 is α_2.   Applying Rule I, α_2 is composed of 90A.   Hence, as the temperature is decreased, not only does the liquid composition become richer in B but also the solid solution.   At T_2, crystals of α_2 are formed surrounding the α_1 composition cores and also separate dendrites of α_z (Fig. 6·6).   In order for equilibrium to be established at T_2, the entire solid phase must be of composition α_2.   This requires diffusion of B atoms to the A-rich core not only from the solid just formed but also from the liquid.

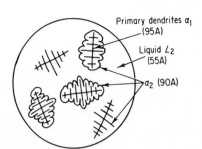

Fig. 6·6   Schematic picture of the alloy 70A at temperature T_2.

This is possible only if the cooling is extremely slow so that diffusion may keep pace with crystal growth.

At T_2, the relative amounts of the liquid and solid solution may be determined by applying Rule II:

$$\text{Liquid (per cent)} = \frac{\alpha_2 T_2}{\alpha_2 L_2} \times 100 = \frac{20}{35} \times 100 = 57 \text{ per cent}$$

$$\alpha_2 \text{ (per cent)} = \frac{T_2 L_2}{\alpha_2 L_2} \times 100 = \frac{15}{35} \times 100 = 43 \text{ per cent}$$

As the temperature falls, the solid solution continues to grow at the expense of the liquid. The composition of the solid solution follows the solidus line while the composition of liquid follows the liquidus line, and both phases are becoming richer in B. At T_3, the solid solution will make up approximately three-fourths of all the material present. The student should apply the lever rule at T_3 and determine the relative quantities of α_3 and L_3. Finally, the solidus line is reached at T_4 and the last liquid L_4, very rich in B, solidifies primarily at the grain boundaries. However, diffusion will take place and all the solid solution will be of uniform composition α_4, which is the overall composition of the alloy.

6·8 Nonequilibrium cooling—origin of coring. In actual practice it is extremely difficult to cool under equilibrium conditions. Since diffusion in the solid state takes place at a very slow rate, it is expected that with ordinary cooling rates there will be some difference in the conditions as indicated by the equilibrium diagram. Referring again to the alloy 70A (Fig. 6·7), solidification starts at T_1, forming a solid solution of composition α_1. At T_2 the liquid is at L_2 and the solid solution now forming is of composition α_2. Since diffusion is too slow to keep pace with crystal growth, not enough time will be allowed to achieve uniformity in the solid and the composition will be between α_1 and α_2, say α_2'. As the temperature drops, the average composition will depart still further from equilibrium conditions. At T_3 the average solid solution will be of composition α_3' instead of α_3. Under equilibrium cooling, solidification should be complete at T_4; however, since the average composition of the solid solution α_4' has not reached the composition of the alloy, some liquid must still remain. Applying the lever rule at T_4 gives

$$\alpha_4' \text{ (per cent)} = \frac{T_4 L_4}{\alpha_4' L_4} \times 100 \approx 75 \text{ per cent}$$

$$L_4 \text{ (per cent)} = \frac{\alpha_4' T_4}{\alpha_4' L_4} \times 100 \approx 25 \text{ per cent}$$

Solidification will therefore continue until T_5 is reached.   At this temperature the composition of the solid solution α_5' coincides with the alloy composition and solidification is complete.   The last liquid to solidify L_5 is richer in B than the last liquid to solidify under equilibrium conditions.   It is apparent from a study of Fig. 6·7 that the more rapidly the alloy is cooled the greater will be the composition range in the solidified alloy.   Since the rate of chemical attack varies

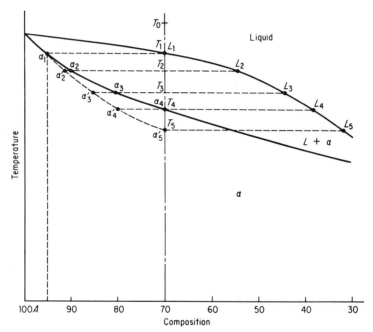

Fig. 6·7   Nonequilibrium cooling; the origin of coring.

with composition, proper etching will reveal the dendritic structure microscopically (Fig. 6·8).   The final solid consists of a "cored" structure with a higher-melting central portion surrounded by the lower-melting, last to solidify, shell.   The above condition is referred to as *coring* or *dendritic segregation*.

6·9   Homogenization.   From the above discussion of the origin of a cored structure, it is apparent that the last solid formed along the grain boundaries and in the interdendritic spaces is very rich in the lower-melting-point metal.   Depending upon the properties of this lower-melting-point metal, the grain boundaries may act as a plane of weakness.   Therefore, for some applications, a cored structure is objectionable.   The equalization of composition or homogenization of the cored structure will take place by diffusion in the solid state.

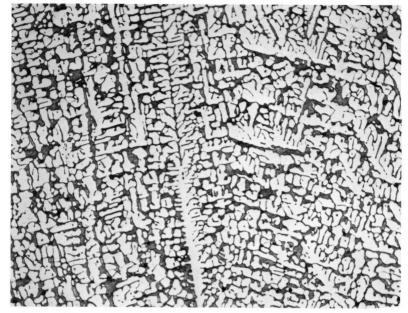

Fig. 6·8 Fine-cored dendrites in a copper-lead alloy; magnification 100×. (*Research Laboratories, National Lead Company*)

At room temperature, for most metals, the diffusion rate is very slow; but if the alloy is reheated to a temperature below the solidus line, diffusion will be more rapid and homogenization will occur in a relatively short time.

Figure 6·9 shows the actual equilibrium diagram for the copper-nickel system, and the alloy 85Cu-15Ni is shown as a dotted line. The effect of homogenization on the cored structure of an 85Cu-15Ni alloy is illustrated by the series of photomicrographs in Fig. 6·10.

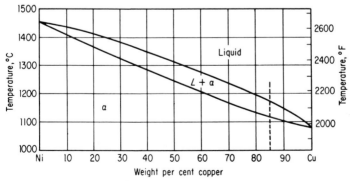

Fig. 6·9 Copper-nickel equilibrium diagram. (*From "Metals Handbook," 1948 edition, p. 1198, Metals Park, Ohio*)

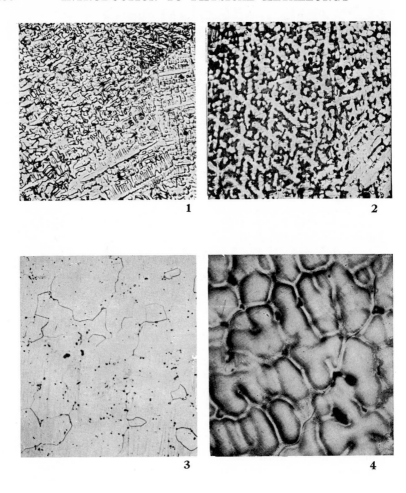

1   2

3   4

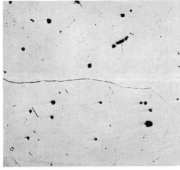

5

Fig. 6·10 Photomicrographs of an 85Cu-15Ni alloy. (1) Chill-cast, 50×; (2) chill-cast, reheated 3 hr at 1382°F, 50×; (3) chill-cast, reheated 9 hr at 1742°F, 50×; (4) cast in a hot mold, 50×; (5) cast in a hot mold, reheated 15 hr at 1742°F, 50×. (*By permission from R. M. Brick and A. Phillips, "Structure and Properties of Alloys," 2d ed., McGraw-Hill Book Company, Inc., New York, 1949*)

The first picture of this sequence shows the microstructure of the alloy as chill-cast. As the equilibrium diagram predicts, the first solid to be formed in the central axes of the dendrites is rich in nickel. Because of rapid cooling, there is a great difference in nickel content between the central axes of the dendrites and the interdendritic spaces. This difference is revealed by suitable etching. The next figure shows the same sample after heating at 1382°F for 3 hr. Counterdiffusion of nickel and copper atoms between the nickel-rich cores and the copper-rich fillings has reduced the composition differences somewhat. The microstructure of the same sample heated to 1742°F for 9 hr is shown in the third figure. The composition is completely equalized and the dendrites have disappeared. The grain boundaries are clearly evident. Black particles are copper oxide or nickel oxide inclusions. The fourth figure illustrates the same alloy slowly cooled by casting in a hot mold. The dendritic structure is coarser than that of the chill-cast alloy. The last figure shows this same sample heated 15 hr at 1742°F. The structure is now completely homogenized. Despite the smaller initial composition differences across the coarse dendrites as compared with the fine dendrites, it took a longer time for equalization because of the greater distance through which the copper and nickel atoms had to diffuse in the coarse structure. Extreme care must be exercised in this treatment not to cross the solidus line; otherwise liquation of the grain boundaries will occur, impairing the shape and physical properties of the casting (Fig. 6·11).

6·10 Properties of solid-solution alloys. In general, in an alloy system forming a continuous series of solid solutions, the strength and hardness will show a maximum although the two maxima do not necessarily come at the same composition. The ductility and electrical conductivity are decreased. The effect of composition on some physical and mechanical properties of alloys in the copper-nickel system is given in Table 6·1.

6·11 Variations of Type I. Every alloy in the Type I system covered has a melting point between the melting points of A and B. It is possible to have a system in which the liquidus and solidus lines go through a minimum or a maximum (Fig. 6·12a, b). The alloy composition x in Fig. 6·12a behaves just like a pure metal. There is no difference in the liquid and solid composition. It begins and ends solidification at a constant temperature with no change in composition, and its cooling curve will show a horizontal line. Such alloys are known as *congruent-melting alloys*. Because alloy x has the lowest melting point in the series, and the equilibrium diagram resembles the eutectic type to be discussed shortly, it is sometimes known as a *pseudoeutectic alloy*. Examples of alloy systems that show a

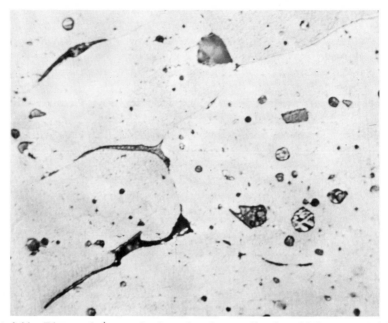

Fig. 6·11　Photomicrograph of an aluminum alloy in which some melting has occurred at the grain boundaries during heating. After cooling, these portions of the grain boundaries appear as dark broad lines, 1,000×. (*ALCOA Research Laboratories, Aluminum Company of America*)

Table 6·1　Properties of annealed copper-nickel alloys*

Composition, % nickel	Tensile strength, psi	Elongation, % in 2 in.	BHN, 10 mm, 500 kg	Lattice parameter, 10^{-8} cm	Electrical resistivity, microhms per cu cm
0	30,000	53	36	3.6073	1.7
10	35,000	47	51	3.5975	14
20	39,000	43	58	3.5871	27
30	44,000	40	67	3.5770	38
40	48,000	39	70	3.5679	46
50	50,000	41	73	3.5593	51
60	53,000	41	74	3.5510	50
70	53,000	42	73	3.5432	40
80	50,000	43	68	3.5350	30
90	48,000	45	61	3.5265	19
100	43,000	48	54	3.5170	6.8

* By permission from R. M. Brick and A. Phillips, "Structure and Properties of Alloys," 2d ed., McGraw-Hill Book Company, Inc., New York, 1949.

minimum are Cu-Au and Ni-Pd.   Those showing a maximum are rare, and there are no known metallic systems of this type.

6·12   Type II—two metals completely soluble in the liquid state and completely insoluble in the solid state.   Technically, no two metals are completely insoluble in each other.   However, in some cases the solubility is so restricted that they may be considered insoluble.

Raoult's law states that the freezing point of a pure substance will be lowered by the addition of a second substance provided the latter

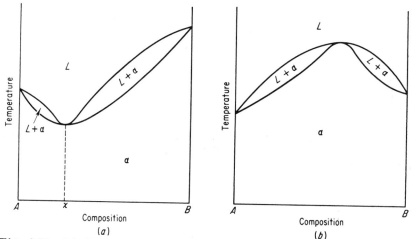

Fig. 6·12   (a) Solid-solution system showing a minimum.   (b) Solid-solution system showing a maximum.

is soluble in the pure substance when liquid and insoluble when solidified.   The amount of lowering of the freezing point is proportional to the molecular weight of the solute.

The cooling curves of the pure metals and various alloys are shown in Fig. 6·13.   If a small quantity of B is added to A, the freezing point of the alloy is lowered, and if the quantity of B is increased, the freezing point is lowered still further.   Therefore, since each metal lowers the freezing point of the other, the line connecting these freezing points must show a minimum as illustrated in Fig. 6·13.   Transferring the breaks on the cooling curves to a plot of temperature vs. composition results in the equilibrium diagram in Fig. 6·14.

The point at which the liquidus lines intersect, the minimum point E, is known as the *eutectic point*. T_E is called the *eutectic temperature* and $40A$-$60B$ the *eutectic composition*.   The solidus line is always a continuous line connecting the melting points of the pure metals so that the complete solidus line is $MFGN$.

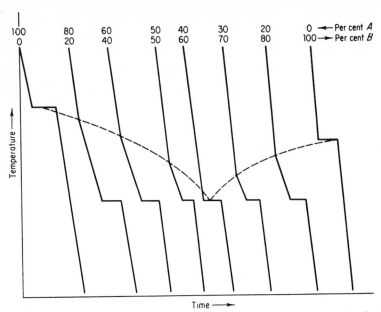

Fig. 6·13 Cooling curves for a series of alloys of two metals that are insoluble in the solid state. The dotted line indicates the form of the liquidus line.

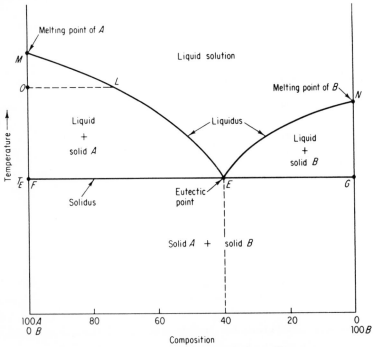

Fig. 6·14 Eutectic-type equilibrium diagram.

In the labeling of equilibrium diagrams, it is important to label the single-phase areas first. Every two-phase area must be bounded along a horizontal line by single phases. Therefore, in Fig. 6·14, to determine the phases that exist in the two-phase area MFE, the horizontal tie line OL is drawn. This line intersects the liquidus at L, which means that the liquid is one of the phases existing in that area, and intersects the left axis at point O. The left axis represents a single phase, the pure metal A which below its melting point is solid. Therefore, the two phases existing in area MFE are liquid and solid A. The above ideas may be applied to any equilibrium diagram and will be very useful to the student for the labeling of more complex diagrams.

Since the two metals are assumed to be completely insoluble in the solid state, it should be apparent that when freezing starts the only solid that can form is a pure metal. Also, every alloy when completely solidified must be a mixture of the two pure metals. It is common practice to consider alloys to the left of the eutectic composition as *hypoeutectic alloys* and those to the right as *hypereutectic alloys*. The way in which solidification takes place is of interest and will now be studied by following the slow cooling of several alloys.

Alloy 1 in Fig. 6·15 is the eutectic composition $40A$-$60B$. As it is cooled from temperature T_0, it remains a uniform liquid solution until point E, the eutectic-temperature line, is reached. Since this is the intersection of the liquidus and solidus lines, the liquid must now start to solidify, and the temperature cannot drop until the alloy is completely solid. The liquid will solidify into a mixture of two phases. These phases are always the ones that appear at either end of the horizontal eutectic-temperature line, in this case point F, which is the pure metal A, and point G, the pure metal B. Let us assume that a small amount of pure metal A is solidified. This leaves the remaining liquid richer in B; the liquid composition has shifted slightly to the right. To restore the liquid composition to its equilibrium value, B will solidify. If slightly too much B is solidified, the liquid composition will have shifted to the left, requiring A to solidify to restore equilibrium. Therefore, at constant temperature, the liquid solidifies alternately pure A and pure B, resulting in an extremely fine mixture usually visible only under the microscope. This is known as the *eutectic mixture* (Fig. 6·16). The change of this liquid of composition E into two solids at constant temperature is known as the *eutectic reaction* and may be written as

$$\text{Liquid} \underset{\text{heating}}{\overset{\text{cooling}}{\rightleftharpoons}} \underbrace{\text{solid } A + \text{solid } B}_{\text{eutectic mixture}}$$

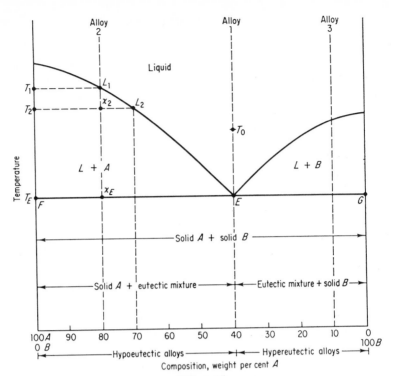

Fig. 6·15

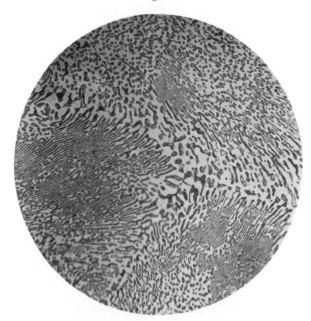

Fig. 6·16   Lead-bismuth eutectic mixture, 1,000×.   (*Research Laboratories, National Lead Company*)

Since solidification of the eutectic alloy occurs at constant temperature, its cooling curve would be the same as that for a pure metal or any congruent-melting alloy. The eutectic solidification, however, is incongruent since there is a difference in composition between the liquid and the individual solid phases.

Alloy 2, a hypoeutectic alloy composed of $80A\text{-}20B$, remains a uniform liquid solution until the liquidus line, temperature T_1, is reached. At this point the liquid L_1 is saturated in A, and as the temperature is dropped slightly, the excess A must solidify. The liquid, by depositing crystals of pure A, must become richer in B. Applying Rule

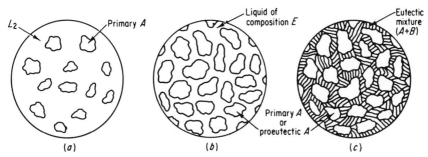

Fig. 6·17   Stages in the slow cooling of an $80A\text{-}20B$ alloy.

I at temperature T_2 shows the solid phase to be pure A and the liquid composition L_2 as $70A\text{-}30B$. The amount which has solidified up to this temperature would be found by applying Rule II:

$$A \text{ (per cent)} = \frac{x_2L_2}{T_2L_2} \times 100 = \frac{10}{30} \times 100 = 33 \text{ per cent}$$

$$L_2 \text{ (per cent)} = \frac{T_2x_2}{T_2L_2} \times 100 = \frac{20}{30} \times 100 = 67 \text{ per cent}$$

The microstructure would appear as in Fig. 6·17a. As solidification continues, the amount of pure A increases gradually by continued precipitation from the liquid. The liquid composition, becoming richer in B, is slowly traveling downward and to the right along the liquidus curve, while the amount of liquid is gradually decreasing. When the alloy reaches x_E, the eutectic line, the liquid is at point E. The conditions existing just a fraction of a degree above T_E are:

Phases	Liquid	Solid A
Composition	$40A\text{-}60B$	$100A$
Relative amount	$\dfrac{T_Ex_E}{T_EE} \times 100 = 33\%$	$\dfrac{x_EE}{T_EE} \times 100 = 67\%$

The microstructure would appear as in Fig. 6·17b. The remaining liquid (33 per cent), having reached the eutectic point, now solidifies into the fine intimate mixture of A and B as described under alloy 1. When solidified, the alloy will consist of 67 per cent of grains of primary A or proeutectic A (which formed between T_1 and T_E or before the eutectic reaction) and 33 per cent eutectic ($A + B$) mixture (Fig. 6·17c). Every alloy to the left of the eutectic point E, when solidified, will consist of grains of proeutectic A and the eutectic mixture. The only difference will be in the relative amounts. The closer the alloy composition is to the eutectic composition, the more eutectic mixture will be present in the solidified alloy.

Alloy 3, a hypereutectic alloy composed of 10A-90B, undergoes the same cooling process as alloy 2 except that when the liquidus line is reached the liquid deposits crystals of pure B instead of A. As the temperature is decreased, more and more B will solidify, leaving the liquid richer in A. The amount of liquid gradually decreases, and its composition gradually moves down and to the left along the liquidus line until point E is reached at the eutectic temperature. The remaining liquid now solidifies into the eutectic ($A + B$) mixture. After solidification, the alloy will consist of 75 per cent grains of primary B or proeutectic B and 25 per cent eutectic ($A + B$) mixture. The student should verify these figures and sketch the microstructure at room temperature. Every alloy to the right of the eutectic point, when solidified, will consist of grains of proeutectic B and the eutectic mixture. The only difference will be in the relative amounts. The relationship between alloy composition and microstructure may be shown by using the eutectic composition as an imaginary boundary line. The area below the solidus line and to the left of the eutectic composition is labeled solid $A +$ eutectic mixture, and that to the right, solid $B +$ eutectic mixture (Fig. 6·15). Figure 6·18 shows the relation between alloy composition and relative amounts.

From the previous discussion it is apparent that, regardless of alloy composition, the same reaction takes place whenever the eutectic-temperature line is reached, namely,

$$\text{Liquid} \underset{\text{heating}}{\overset{\text{cooling}}{\rightleftharpoons}} \underbrace{\text{solid } A + \text{solid } B}_{\text{eutectic mixture}}$$

The above reaction applies specifically to this diagram; however, the eutectic reaction may be written in general as

$$\text{Liquid} \underset{\text{heating}}{\overset{\text{cooling}}{\rightleftharpoons}} \underbrace{\text{solid} + \text{solid}}_{\text{eutectic mixture}}$$

the only requirement being that the eutectic mixture consist of two different solid phases.　This mixture may be two pure metals, two solid solutions, two intermediate phases, or any combination of the above.

The simplified aluminum-silicon equilibrium diagram is shown in Fig. 6·19, neglecting the slight solubility of silicon in aluminum.　The numbers at the bottom of this diagram refer to the photomicrographs in Fig. 6·20.　Beginning with alloy 1 at the left of Fig. 6·19, the microstructure of pure aluminum is shown in Fig. 6·20a.　Alloy 2

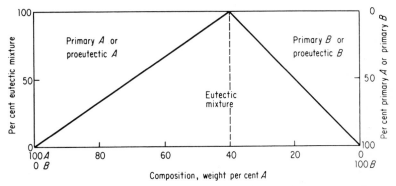

Fig. 6·18　Diagram showing the linear relationship between the parts of the microstructure and alloy composition for the eutectic system of Fig. 6·15.

(Fig. 6·20b), containing 8 per cent silicon, consists of dendrites of primary or proeutectic aluminum surrounded by the eutectic mixture of aluminum and silicon.　Notice the fine alternate light and dark structure of the eutectic.　Since the eutectic is formed from the last liquid to solidify, it fills the spaces between the arms of the dendrites. Alloy 3 (Fig. 6·20c) is the eutectic composition of 12 per cent silicon and consists entirely of the eutectic mixture.　As we move to the right, the microstructure will consist of primary silicon (black) and the eutectic mixture, the amount of primary silicon increasing with increasing silicon content as shown in Fig. 6·20d and e.　Finally, Fig. 6·20f shows the microstructure of pure silicon.　It is therefore possible to predict from an equilibrium diagram, with reasonable accuracy, the proportions of each phase which will exist in an alloy after slow cooling to room temperature.

6·13　Type III—two metals completely soluble in the liquid state but only partly soluble in the solid state.　This type is intermediate to the two previous types.　A solid solution is formed over only part of the composition range.

It is assumed that the experimental method of determination of an equilibrium diagram is familiar and that it is no longer necessary to refer to a series of cooling curves. The remaining types will be drawn and studied directly.

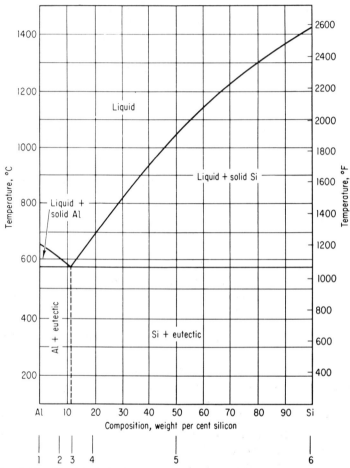

Fig. 6·19 Simplified aluminum-silicon equilibrium diagram.

The equilibrium diagram of this type is shown in Fig. 6·21. The melting points of the two pure metals are indicated at points T_A and T_B, respectively. The liquidus line is $T_A E T_B$ and the solidus line is $T_A F E G T_B$. The single-phase areas should be labeled first. Above the liquidus line, there is only a single-phase liquid solution. At the melting points, where the liquidus and solidus lines meet, the diagram resembles the cigar-shaped diagram of Type I (complete solid solubility), and since these metals are partly soluble in the solid state, a

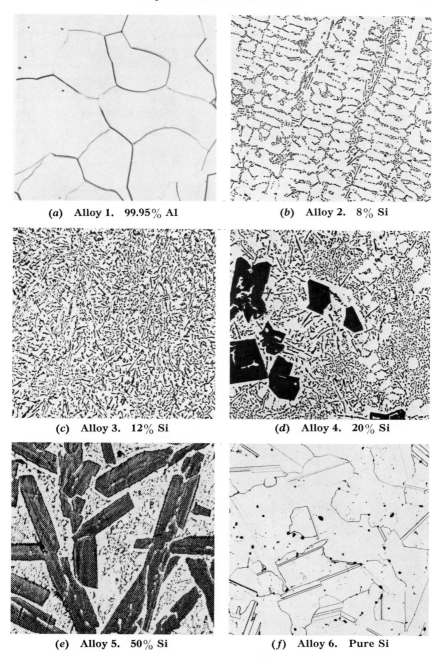

(a)   Alloy 1.   99.95% Al

(b)   Alloy 2.   8% Si

(c)   Alloy 3.   12% Si

(d)   Alloy 4.   20% Si

(e)   Alloy 5.   50% Si

(f)   Alloy 6.   Pure Si

Fig. 6·20   Photomicrographs of aluminum-silicon alloys as numbered at the bottom of Fig. 6·19.   (*Research Laboratories, Aluminum Company of America*)

solid solution must be formed.   Alloys in this system never solidify crystals of pure A or pure B but always a solid solution or mixture of solid solutions.   The single-phase α (alpha) and β (beta) solid-solution areas are now labeled.   Since these solid solutions are next to the axes, they are known as *terminal solid solutions*.   The remaining three two-phase areas may now be labeled as liquid $+$ α, liquid $+$ β, and $\alpha + \beta$.   At T_E, the α solid solution dissolves a maximum of 20 per

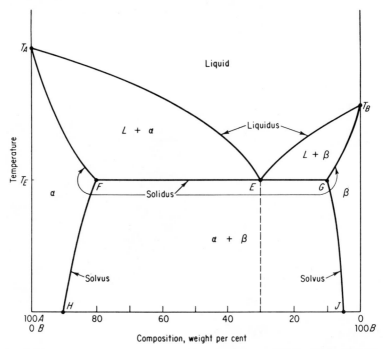

Fig. 6·21   Equilibrium diagram illustrating partial solid solubility.

cent B as shown by point F and the β solid solution a maximum of 10 per cent A as shown by point G.   With decreasing temperature, the maximum amount of solute that can be dissolved decreases, as indicated by lines FH and GJ.   These lines are called *solvus* lines and indicate the maximum solubility (saturated solution) of B in A (α solution) or A in B (β solution) as a function of temperature.   Point E, where the liquidus lines meet at a minimum, as in Type II, is known as the *eutectic point*.   The slow cooling of several alloys will now be studied.

Alloy 1 (Fig. 6·22), composed of $95A$-$5B$, when slow-cooled will follow a process exactly the same as any alloy in Type I.   When the liquidus line is crossed at T_1, it will begin to solidify by forming crystals of α solid solution extremely rich in A. This process continues, with the liquid getting richer in B and gradually moving down along the liquidus line. The α solid solution, also getting richer in B, is moving down along the solidus line. When the solidus line is finally crossed at T_4 and with diffusion keeping pace with crystal growth,

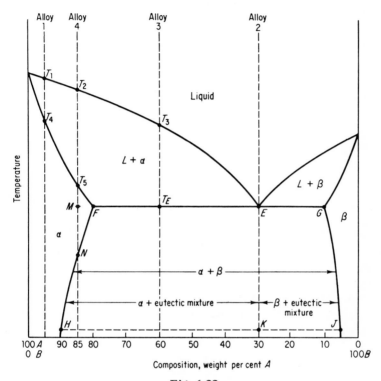

Fig. 6·22

the entire solid will be a homogeneous solid solution and will remain that way down to room temperature.

Alloy 2, 30A-70B, is the eutectic composition and remains liquid until the eutectic temperature is reached at point E. Since this is also the solidus line, the liquid now undergoes the eutectic reaction, forming a very fine mixture of two solids. The two solids that make up the eutectic mixtures are given by the extremities of the eutectic-temperature line, α of composition F and $β$ of composition G. The eutectic reaction may be written as

$$\text{Liquid} \underset{\text{heating}}{\overset{\text{cooling}}{\rightleftharpoons}} \underbrace{\alpha + \beta}_{\text{eutectic mixture}}$$

This reaction is the same as the one which occurred in the Type II diagram except for the substitution of solid solutions for pure metals. The relative amounts of α and β in the eutectic mixture may be determined by applying Rule II (lever rule):

$$\alpha \text{ (per cent)} = \frac{EG}{FG} \times 100 = \frac{20}{70} \times 100 = 28.6 \text{ per cent}$$

$$\beta \text{ (per cent)} = \frac{EF}{FG} \times 100 = \frac{50}{70} \times 100 = 71.4 \text{ per cent}$$

Because of the change in solubility of B in A, line FH, and of A in B, line GJ, there will be a slight change in the relative amounts of α and β as the alloy is cooled to room temperature. The relative amounts of α and β at room temperature are

$$\alpha \text{ (per cent)} = \frac{KJ}{HJ} \times 100 = \frac{25}{85} \times 100 = 29.4 \text{ per cent}$$

$$\beta \text{ (per cent)} = \frac{HK}{HJ} \times 100 = \frac{60}{85} \times 100 = 70.6 \text{ per cent}$$

Alloy 3, $60A$-$40B$, remains liquid until the liquidus line is reached at T_3. The liquid starts to solidify crystals of primary or proeutectic α solid solution very rich in A. As the temperature decreases the liquid becomes richer and richer in B, gradually moving down and to the right along the liquidus line until it reaches point E. Examining the conditions which exist just above the eutectic temperature T_E, there are two phases present:

Phases	Liquid	Primary α
Chemical composition	$30A$-$70B$	$80A$-$20B$
Relative amounts	40%	60%

The student should verify the above numbers by applying Rules I and II at the eutectic temperature. Since the remaining liquid (40 per cent) is at point E, the right temperature and composition to form the eutectic mixture, it now solidifies by forming alternately crystals of α and β of the composition appearing at the ends of the eutectic temperature line (points F and G). The temperature does not drop until solidification is complete, and when complete, the microstructure appears as shown in Fig. 6·23. Notice the similarity in microstructure between this alloy and Fig. 6·17c. As the alloy cools to room temperature because of the change in solubility indicated by the solvus line FH, some excess β is precipitated from the solution.

Alloy 4, $85A$-$15B$, follows the same process as described for alloy 1. Solidification starts at T_2 and is complete at T_5, the resultant solid being a homogeneous single phase, the α solid solution. At point M the solution is unsaturated. The solvus line FH, as explained previously, shows the decrease in solubility of B in A with decreasing temperature. As the alloy cools, the solvus line is reached at point N. The α solution is now saturated in B. Below this temperature, under conditions of slow cooling, the excess B must come out of solution. Since A is soluble in B, the precipitate does not come out as the pure metal B, but rather the β solid solution. At room temperature, the alloy will consist largely of α with a small amount of

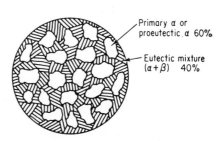

Fig. 6·23 Schematic picture of the microstructure, after solidification, of alloy 3 in Fig. 6·22.

Primary α or proeutectic α 60%

Eutectic mixture $(\alpha + \beta)$ 40%

excess β, primarily along the grain boundaries (Fig. 6·26a). The student should determine the amount of excess β by applying the lever rule at the line HJ.

If the β phase is relatively brittle, the alloy will not be very strong or ductile. The strength of an alloy to a large extent is determined by the phase that is continuous through the alloy. In this case, although the β solution constitutes only about 5 per cent of the alloy, it exists as a continuous network along the grain boundaries. Therefore, the alloy will tend to rupture along these boundaries. This alloy, however, may be made to undergo a significant change in strength and hardness after being properly heat-treated.

The lead-antimony equilibrium diagram and photomicrographs of various alloys in this system are shown in Fig. 6·24. Alloy 1 (Fig. 6·24b), containing 6.5 per cent antimony, illustrates a typical hypoeutectic structure of primary α dendrites (black) and the eutectic mixture filling the spaces between the dendrites. Alloy 2 (Fig. 6·24c), containing 11.5 per cent antimony, consists entirely of the eutectic mixture of α and β solid solutions. To the right of the eutectic composition, the alloys consist of primary β (white) surrounded by the eutectic mixture (Fig. 6·24d) and differ only in the relative amounts of the phases present. The amount of the eutectic mixture decreases as the alloy composition moves away from the eutectic composition.

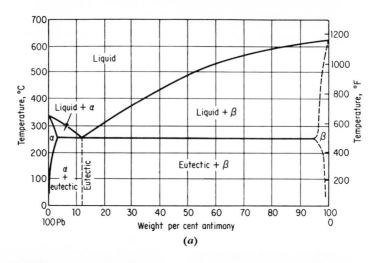

(a)

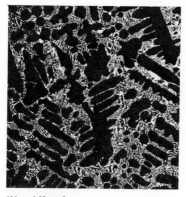

(b)   Alloy 1

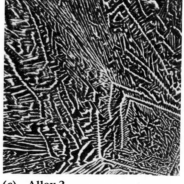

(c)   Alloy 2

(d)   Alloy 3

Fig. 6·24 (a) The lead-antimony equilibrium diagram. (b) 6.5 per cent antimony alloy, 75×. (c) Eutectic alloy, 11.5 per cent antimony, 250×. (d) 12.25 per cent antimony alloy, 250×. (American Smelting and Refining Company)

The lead-tin equilibrium diagram and photomicrographs of various alloys in this system are shown in Fig. 6·25. Alloy 1 (Fig. 6·25b), containing 70 per cent tin, is to the right of the eutectic composition. The microstructure consists of primary β dendrites (white) surrounded by the eutectic mixture. Alloy 2 (Fig. 6·25c) is the eutectic composition and consists entirely of a very fine mixture of α and β solid solutions. Alloys 3 and 4 (Fig. 6·25d and e), containing 60 and 50 per cent tin, respectively, consist of dendrites of the lead-rich primary α solid solution (black) surrounded by the eutectic mixture, the amount of α increasing as the alloy composition moves to the left. Notice the similarity of the photomicrographs shown in Figs. 6·20, 6·24, and 6·25.

6·14 Age hardening. There are only two principal methods to increase the strength and hardness of a given alloy: cold working or heat treatment. The most important heat-treating process for non-ferrous alloys is age hardening. In order to apply this heat treatment, the equilibrium diagram must show partial solubility and the slope of the solvus line must be such that there is greater solubility at a higher temperature than at a lower temperature. These conditions are satisfied by Fig. 6·22.

Two stages are generally required in heat treatment to produce age hardening: solution treatment and aging.

Solution Treatment. If alloy 4 (Fig. 6·22) is reheated to point M, all the excess β will be dissolved and the structure will be a homogeneous α solid solution. The alloy is then cooled rapidly (quenched) to room temperature. A supersaturated solution results with the excess β trapped in solution. The quench is usually carried out in a cold-water bath or by a water spray. Drastic quenching tends to set up stresses which often result in distortion, especially if the parts are intricately designed. In such instances, boiling water may be used as a quench medium to minimize distortion. If α is a ductile phase, the alloy will be ductile immediately after quenching. This allows warped or distorted parts to be straightened easily. The straightening operations should be carried out as soon as possible after quenching. The microstructure is shown schematically in Fig. 6·26b.

Aging Process. The alloy, as quenched, is a supersaturated solid solution and is in an unstable state. The excess solute will tend to come out of solution. Those alloys in which precipitation takes place at room temperature so that they obtain their full strength after 4 or 5 days at room temperature are known as *natural-aging* alloys. Those alloys which require reheating to elevated temperatures to develop their full strength are *artificially aging* alloys. However, these alloys also age a limited amount at room temperature, the rate and

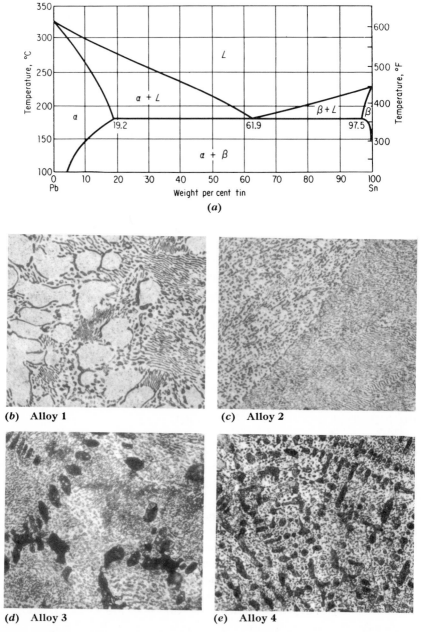

(b) Alloy 1

(c) Alloy 2

(d) Alloy 3

(e) Alloy 4

Fig. 6·25 (a) The lead-tin equilibrium diagram. (b) 70 per cent tin alloy. (c) Eutectic alloy. (d) 60 per cent tin alloy. (e) 50 per cent tin alloy. All photomicrographs at 200×. (*From H. Manko, "Solders and Soldering," McGraw-Hill Book Company, Inc., New York, 1964*)

extent of the strengthening depending upon the alloys. Refrigeration retards the rate of natural aging. At 32°F, the beginning of the aging process is delayed for several hours, while dry ice (−50 to −100°F) retards aging for an extended period. In the early theory of the aging process, it was thought that the excess phase comes out of solution as fine submicroscopic particles many of which fall on the

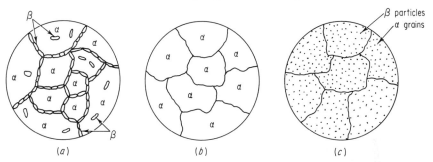

Fig. 6·26 (a) Microstructure of an 85A-15B alloy after slow cooling. (b) Microstructure after rapid cooling to room temperature. (c) Microstructure after aging.

slip planes (Fig. 6·26c). These particles were considered to have a keying action, thereby interfering with movement along planes of ready slip, thus increasing strength and hardness (Table 6·2).

Subsequent studies have led to a more complete understanding of the age-hardening process. The strengthening of a heat-treatable alloy

Table 6·2 Effect of aging on properties of aluminum alloy 2014
(3.5 to 4.5 per cent copper)

Alloy and condition	Ultimate strength, psi	Yield strength, psi	Elongation, % in 2 in.	BHN, 500 kg, 10 mm	Shear strength, psi
Annealed	27,000	14,000	18	45	18,000
Solution treated, naturally aged	62,000	42,000	20	105	38,000
Solution treated, artificially aged	70,000	60,000	13	135	42,000

by aging is not due merely to the presence of a precipitate. It is due to both the uniform distribution of a finely dispersed submicroscopic precipitate and the distortion of the lattice structure by these particles before they reach a visible size. There is usually an incubation period at first, followed by a rapid increase in hardness, tensile strength, and yield strength as distortion of the lattice increases.

Eventually precipitation predominates and softening occurs. After precipitation is complete and the solid solution has reached the equilibrium composition, the properties remain the same (Fig. 6·27). Electrical conductivity decreases at first because of lattice distortion; then it increases when precipitation takes place. The final conductivity of the alloy in equilibrium is always higher than that of the supersaturated solid-solution alloy.

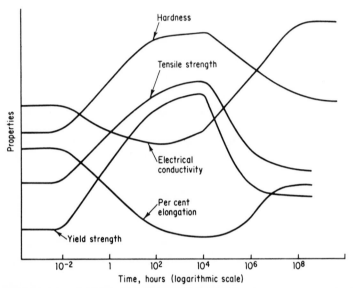

Fig. 6·27   Effect of aging time on properties. (*By permission from L. F. Mondolfo and O. Zmeskal, "Engineering Metallurgy," McGraw-Hill Book Company, Inc., New York, 1955*)

In "abnormal aging" an increase in strength may be obtained without actual precipitation. The dissolved particles move to certain positions in the lattice structure before precipitation, and this movement produces lattice distortion with an increase in strength and hardness without actual precipitation.

Aging does not have the same effect on the properties of all alloys. In some alloys the change in hardness and strength may be small; in others the changes may be large. This is not due to the amount dissolved in excess of the saturation limit, but to the effect of the precipitate on lattice distortion. For example, magnesium can dissolve 46 per cent lead at the eutectic temperature but only 2 per cent lead at room temperature. With proper heat treatment, precipitation takes place but no age hardening occurs. This is due to the absence of localized distortion during precipitation. On the other hand, if the precipitation involves extensive changes in the lattice, a large amount of distortion occurs with wide changes in properties. In this case, the greater the amount of metal dissolved in excess of the saturation limit, the greater the distortion produced and the greater will be the effect on hardness and strength. This is illustrated for an aluminum-copper alloy in Table 6·2 and for copper-beryllium alloys in Table 6·3.

Table 6·3 Effect of aging and composition on the mechanical properties of some copper-beryllium alloys

Alloy and condition	Tensile strength, psi	Elongation, % in 2 in.	Rockwell hardness
1.90–2.15% Be:			
Solution annealed	60,000–80,000	35–50	B 45–65
After aging	165,000–180,000	5–8	C 36–40
1.60–1.80% Be:			
Solution annealed	60,000–80,000	35–50	B 45–65
After aging	150,000–165,000	5–8	C 33–37

6·15 Properties in eutectic systems. The properties of any multiphase alloy depend upon the individual characteristics of the phases and how these phases are distributed in the microstructure. This statement is particularly true for eutectic-system alloys. Many physical properties, such as density, electrical conductivity, and coefficient of expansion, vary linearly across the range of two-phase equilibrium. Strength, hardness, and ductility properties are related to the size, number, distribution, and properties of the crystals of both phases. In many commercially important eutectic alloy systems, one phase is relatively weak and plastic while the other is relatively hard and brittle. As the eutectic composition is approached from the plastic-phase side, there will be a rapid increase in strength of the alloy. There will be a decrease in strength beyond the eutectic composition due to the decrease in amount of the small eutectic particles and the increase in size and amount of the primary or proeutectic brittle phase. Therefore, in this kind of system, the eutectic composition will generally show maximum strength.

As mentioned previously, the resulting properties of a mixture most nearly resemble those of the phase which is physically continuous, that is, the phase that forms the background or matrix in which particles of the other phase are dispersed. The eutectic mixture is always the phase which is continuous since it is the last liquid to solidify and surrounds the primary grains. It is generally true that the phase that makes up the greater proportion in the eutectic will be the continuous phase in the mixture. If this phase is plastic, the entire series of alloys will show some plasticity. If this phase is brittle, the entire series will be relatively brittle. In addition to the above factors, an increase in cooling rate during freezing may result in a finer eutectic mixture, a greater amount of eutectic mixture, and smaller primary grains, which in turn may influence the mechanical properties considerably.

6·16   Type IV—the congruent-melting intermediate phase.
When one phase changes into another phase isothermally (at constant temperature) and without any change in chemical composition it is

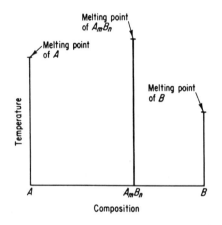

Fig. 6·28   Composition and melting point of pure A, pure B, and a compound A_mB_n.

said to be a *congruent phase change* or *congruent transformation*. All pure metals solidify congruently. If an intermediate phase melts congruently it may be treated as another component on the equilibrium diagram. If the intermediate phase exists over a range of composition, it is generally an electron compound and is labeled with a Greek letter. In recent years, some authors tend to use Greek letters for all intermediate phases. If the intermediate phase has a narrow range of composition, as do intermetallic compounds and interstitial compounds, it is then represented on the diagram as a vertical line and labeled with the chemical formula of the compound.

It is apparent from Fig. 6·28 that the A-B system may be separated into two independent parts, one to show all the alloys between A and the compound A_mB_n and the other to show those between A_mB_n and B. The portion of the diagram between A and A_mB_n may be any of the types studied in this chapter; similarly for the portion between A_mB_n and B. If the compound shows no solubility for either pure metal and the pure metals show some solubility for the compound, the equilibrium diagram will be as shown in Fig. 6·29. This diagram shows two different eutectic mixtures. The eutectic equations may be written as follows:

At T_1: $\qquad$ Liquid $\underset{\text{heating}}{\overset{\text{cooling}}{\rightleftarrows}} \alpha + A_m B_n$

At T_2: $\qquad$ Liquid $\underset{\text{heating}}{\overset{\text{cooling}}{\rightleftarrows}} A_m B_n + \beta$

The study of many actual systems that show the formation of

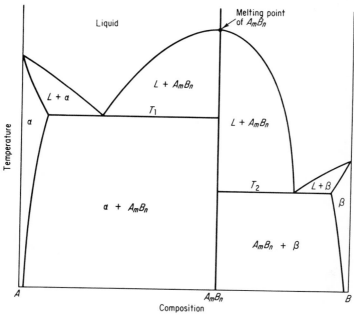

Fig. 6·29 **Equilibrium diagram illustrating an intermediate alloy which is an intermetallic compound.**

several congruent-melting intermediate phases may be simplified by the above approach.

6·17 Type V—the peritectic reaction. In the peritectic reaction a liquid and a solid react isothermally to form a new solid. The reaction is expressed in general as

$$\text{Liquid} + \text{solid} \underset{\text{heating}}{\overset{\text{cooling}}{\rightleftarrows}} \text{new solid}$$

The new solid formed is usually an intermediate phase (Fig. 6·30), but in some cases it may be a terminal solid solution (Fig. 6·31).

Consideration of Fig. 6·30 shows that the compound $A_m B_n$, 70A-30B, when heated to the peritectic temperature, point G, decomposes into two phases, liquid and solid A. Therefore, this is an example of an

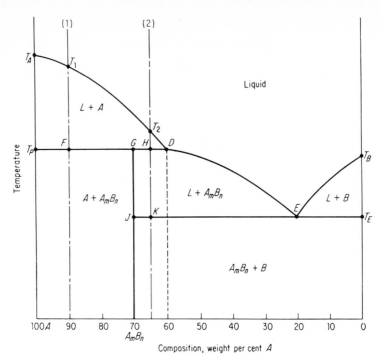

Fig. 6·30   Equilibrium diagram showing the formation of an incongruent-melting intermediate phase by a peritectic reaction.

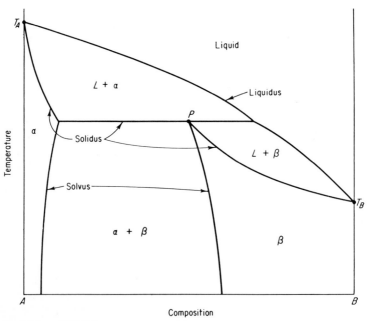

Fig. 6·31   Equilibrium diagram showing the formation of a terminal solid solution by a peritectic reaction.

incongruent-melting intermediate alloy. The student should realize that the peritectic reaction is just the reverse of the eutectic reaction where a single phase formed two new phases *on cooling*. The liquidus line is $T_A D E T_B$ and the solidus line is $T_A T_P G J T_E T_B$. The peritectic-reaction line is $T_P D$. Notice that only part of this line, the length $T_P G$, coincides with the solidus line. The slow cooling of several alloys will now be studied.

Alloy 1, 90A-10B, remains liquid until the liquidus line is reached at T_1. Solidification now takes place by forming crystals of the pure metal A. As the temperature falls, the liquid is decreasing in amount and its composition is moving down along the liquidus line. Let us examine the conditions that exist just above the peritectic temperature T_P:

Phases	Liquid	Solid A
Composition	60A-40B	100 A
Relative amount	$\dfrac{T_P F}{T_P D} \times 100 = 25\%$	$\dfrac{F D}{T_P D} \times 100 = 75\%$

The conditions that exist just below the peritectic temperature are:

Phases	$A_m B_n$	Solid A
Composition	70A-30B	100 A
Relative amount	$\dfrac{T_P F}{T_P G} \times 100 = 33\%$	$\dfrac{F G}{T_P G} \times 100 = 67\%$

A first glance at these two areas seems to indicate that the liquid has disappeared at the horizontal line and in its place is the compound $A_m B_n$. Consideration of the chemical compositions shows that this is not possible. The liquid contains 60A while $A_m B_n$ contains 70A. The liquid is not rich enough in A to form the compound by itself. The liquid must therefore react with just the right amount of solid A to bring its composition to that of the compound $A_m B_n$. The following reaction must have taken place at the peritectic temperature:

Composition: 60A 100A 70A

Equation: Liquid + solid $A \xrightarrow{\text{cooling}}$ solid $A_m B_n$

Relative amount: 25%   8%   33%

The reaction takes place all around the surface of each grain of solid A where the liquid touches it. When the correct composition is reached the layer solidifies into $A_m B_n$ material surrounding every grain of A. Further reaction is slow since it must wait for the diffusion of atoms through the peritectic wall of $A_m B_n$ in order to continue (see

Fig. 6·32). When diffusion is completed, all the liquid will have been consumed, and since only 8 per cent of pure A was required for the reaction, there will be 67 per cent of A left. The final microstructure will show grains of primary A surrounded by the compound A_mB_n. The story will be the same for any alloy to the left of point G. The only difference will be in the amount of excess A remaining after the peritectic reaction is complete. The closer the alloy composition is to the composition of the compound, the less primary A will remain.

Alloy 2, $65A$-$35B$, solidifies pure A when the liquidus line is crossed at T_2, and as solidification continues, the liquid becomes richer in B. When point H is reached, the liquid composition is $60A$-$40B$. Applying the lever rule for this alloy, there is $^{35}\!/_{40} \times 100$ or 87.5 per cent

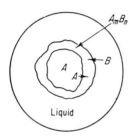

Fig. 6·32 Schematic picture of the peritectic reaction. Envelope of A_mB_n increases in thickness by diffusion of A atoms outward and B atoms inward through A_mB_n. (By permission from F. N. Rhines, "Phase Diagrams in Metallurgy," McGraw-Hill Book Company, Inc., New York, 1956)

liquid and 12.5 per cent solid A. Since the line GD is not part of the solidus line, some liquid must remain after the reaction takes place. It is therefore the solid A which must disappear in reacting with some of the liquid to form the compound A_mB_n. The same reaction takes place again:

Composition: $60A$ $100A$ $70A$

Reaction: $\text{Liquid} + \text{solid } A \xrightarrow{\text{cooling}} A_mB_n$

The amount of liquid entering into the above reaction may be determined by applying the lever rule below the reaction temperature.

$$\text{Liquid (per cent)} = \frac{GH}{DG} \times 100 = \frac{10}{20} \times 100 = 50 \text{ per cent}$$

Since there was 87.5 per cent liquid before the reaction and 50 per cent liquid after the reaction, it is apparent that 37.5 per cent of the liquid reacted with 12.5 per cent of solid A to give 50 per cent of the compound A_mB_n at the peritectic temperature. As cooling continues, the liquid now separates crystals of A_mB_n. The liquid becomes richer in B and its composition gradually moves down and to the right along the liquidus line until it reaches point E, the eutectic temperature. At this temperature, there is only $^{5}\!/_{50} \times 100$ or 10 per cent liquid left. Since the liquid has reached the eutectic point, it now solidifies into the eutectic mixture of $A_mB_n + B$. This alloy, at room temperature, will consist of 90 per cent primary or proeutectic A_mB_n surrounded by 10 per cent of the eutectic $(A_mB_n + B)$ mixture.

The student should study the slow cooling of alloys on either side of the peritectic point P in the equilibrium diagram that illustrates

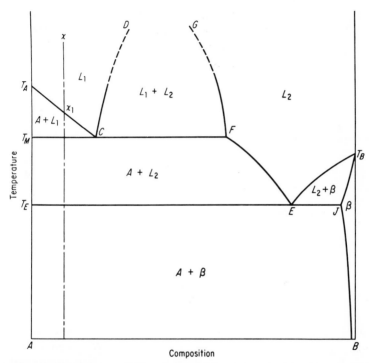

Fig. 6·33 Equilibrium diagram showing two metals partly soluble in the liquid state; the monotectic reaction.

the formation of a terminal solid solution by a peritectic reaction (Fig. 6·31).

6·18 Type VI—two liquids partly soluble in the liquid state. The monotectic reaction. In all the types discussed previously it was assumed that there was complete solubility in the liquid state. It is quite possible, however, that over a certain composition range two liquid solutions are formed that are not soluble in each other. Another term for solubility is *miscibility*. Liquids that are not soluble in each other, such as oil and water, are said to be *immiscible*.

The equilibrium diagram of this type is shown in Fig. 6·33. The liquidus line is T_ACFET_B and the solidus line is $T_AT_EJT_B$. Alloys having compositions between C and F at a temperature just above T_M will consist of two liquid solutions. The lines CD and FG show the composition of the liquid phases in equilibrium with each other at higher temperatures. In most cases, these lines are shown dotted because experimental difficulties usually prevent an accurate determination of their position. Since these lines tend to approach each other, it is possible that at higher temperatures the area will be closed and a single homogeneous liquid solution will be formed. This area is treated like any other two-phase area, and the same rules may be applied to determine the chemical composition of L_1 and L_2 and their relative amounts at any temperature.

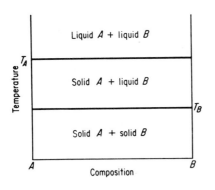

Fig. 6·34 Equilibrium diagram for two metals insoluble in the liquid and solid states.

A study of this diagram shows that L_1 (liquid solution rich in A) does not exist below the monotectic temperature T_M.

Let us follow the slow cooling of alloy x. It remains liquid L_1, until the liquidus line is reached at x_1. Solidification starts by forming crystals of pure A. The liquid becomes richer in B, gradually moving down and to the right along the liquidus line. When the monotectic temperature line T_M is reached, L_1 has the composition given by point C. Below the line, the two phases that exist are solid $A + L_2$. At first it may seem that L_1 has changed to L_2, but this is not possible because at T_M, L_2 has the composition given by point F. L_1 is too rich in A. Therefore, at T_M, L_1 undergoes a monotectic reaction in which pure A is solidified from L_1 until the remaining liquid reaches the composition of L_2. This reaction may be written in general form as

$$L_1 \underset{\text{heating}}{\overset{\text{cooling}}{\rightleftharpoons}} L_2 + \text{solid}$$

When the reaction is completed, there should be more solid A than existed before the reaction. As the temperature falls, solid A will be formed from L_2, and when the eutectic temperature is reached at T_E, L_2 will be at point E. The eutectic reaction now takes place:

$$L_2 \xrightleftharpoons[\text{heating}]{\text{cooling}} \underbrace{A + \beta}_{\text{eutectic mixture}}$$

The final microstructure will consist of grains of primary A surrounded by the eutectic $(A + \beta)$ mixture.

6·19 Type VII—two metals insoluble in the liquid and solid states. The equilibrium diagram is shown in Fig. 6·34. These metals do not form true alloys. This diagram is really the limiting case of the monotectic reaction. If points C and F in Fig. 6·33 are

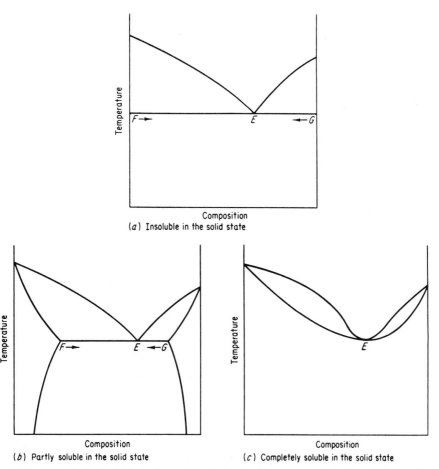

(a) Insoluble in the solid state

(b) Partly soluble in the solid state

(c) Completely soluble in the solid state

Fig. 6·35 Interrelation of equilibrium diagrams as the solubility in the solid state is varied.

moved in opposite directions, that is, toward greater liquid insolubility, eventually they will hit the axes to give the diagram shown in Fig. 6·34. If aluminum and lead are melted together, liquid aluminum will be on top because of its lower density and liquid lead will be on the bottom. When solidified they form a two-layer alloy, that is, two distinct layers with a sharp line of contact and almost no diffusion.

6·20   Interrelation of basic types.   The various types of equilibrium diagram that have been discussed may be combined in many ways to make up actual diagrams. It is important for the student to understand the interrelation between the basic types to make the study of complex diagrams much simpler. The first three types differ only by the solubility in the solid state. Starting with a completely insoluble system of Type II (Fig. 6·35a), if the points at either end of the eutectic line (F and G) are moved toward each other, that is, toward greater solubility in the solid state, this will result in a diagram of Type III, partly soluble in the solid state (Fig. 6·35b). If they are moved until they coincide with the eutectic composition at E a completely soluble system results (Fig. 6·35c). Types IV and V are determined by the intermediate phase. If this phase decomposes on heating (incongruent melting), the diagram will show a peritectic reaction. If the intermediate phase shows a true melting point (congruent melting), the diagram may show a eutectic reaction.

TRANSFORMATIONS IN THE SOLID STATE

There are several equilibrium changes and reactions which take place entirely in the solid state.

6·21   Allotropy.   During the discussion of metals and crystal structure in Chap. 2, it was pointed out that several metals may exist in more than one type of crystal structure depending upon temperature. Iron, tin, manganese, and cobalt are some examples of metals which exhibit this property known as *allotropy*. On an equilibrium diagram, this allotropic change is indicated by a point or points on the vertical line which represents the pure metal. This is illustrated in Fig. 6·36. In this diagram, the gamma solid-solution field is "looped." The pure metal A and alloys rich in A undergo two transformations. Many of the equilibrium diagrams involving iron such as Fe-Si, Fe-Mo, and Fe-Cr show this looped solid-solution field. Since the type of iron that exists in this temperature range is gamma iron, the field is usually called the *gamma loop*.

6·22   Order-disorder transformation.   Ordinarily in the formation of a substitutional type of solid solution the solute atoms do not occupy any specific position but are distributed at random in the

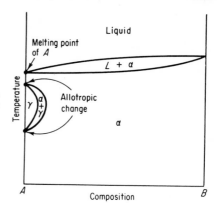

Fig. 6.36 Equilibrium diagram showing metal A undergoing two allotropic changes.

lattice structure of the solvent. The alloy is said to be in a "disordered" condition. Some of these random solid solutions, if cooled slowly, undergo a rearrangement of the atoms where the solute atoms move into definite positions in the lattice. This structure is now known as an *ordered solid solution* or *superlattice* (Fig. 6·37). Ordering is most common in metals that are completely soluble in the solid state, and usually the maximum amount of ordering occurs at a simple atomic ratio of the two elements. For this reason, the ordered phase is sometimes given a chemical formula such as AuCu and $AuCu_3$. On the equilibrium diagram, the ordered solutions are frequently designated as α', β', etc., and the area in which they are found is usually bounded by a dot-dash line. The actual equilibrium diagram for the Au-Cu system is shown in Fig. 6·38.

When the ordered phase has the same lattice structure as the disordered phase, the effect of ordering on mechanical properties is negligible. Hardening associated with the ordering process is most pronounced in those systems where the shape of the unit cell is

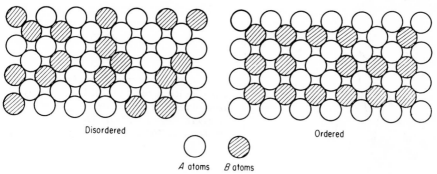

Fig. 6.37 Atomic arrangements in a disordered and ordered solid solution.

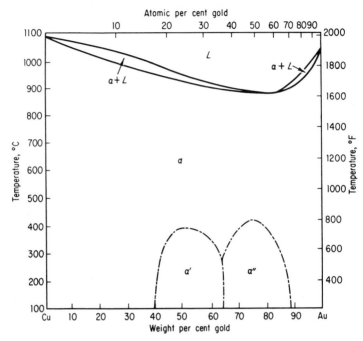

Fig. 6·38   The gold-copper equilibrium diagram. (*From "Metals Handbook," 1948 edition, p. 1171, American Society for Metals, Metals Park, Ohio*)

changed by ordering.   In either case, electrical resistivity is much lower in the ordered condition (Fig. 6·39).

6·23   The eutectoid reaction.   This is a common reaction in the solid state.   It is very similar to the eutectic reaction but does not involve the liquid.   In this case, a solid phase transforms on cooling

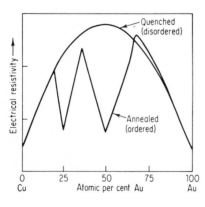

Fig. 6·39 Electrical resistivity vs. composition for the gold-copper system. (*By permission from C. S. Barrett, "Structure of Metals," 2d ed., McGraw-Hill Book Company, Inc., New York, 1952*)

into two new solid phases. The general equation may be written as

$$\text{Solid} \underset{\text{heating}}{\overset{\text{cooling}}{\rightleftharpoons}} \underbrace{\text{solid} + \text{solid}}_{\text{eutectoid mixture}}$$

The resultant eutectoid mixture is extremely fine, just like the eutectic mixture. Under the microscope both mixtures generally appear the

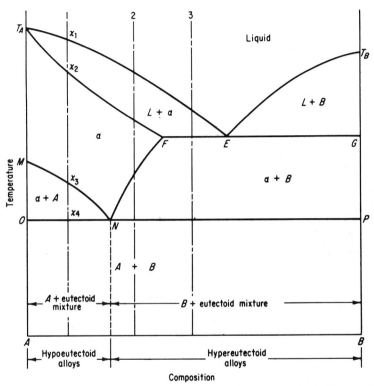

Fig. 6·40   Equilibrium diagram illustrating the eutectoid reaction.

same, and it is not possible to determine microscopically whether the mixture resulted from a eutectic reaction or a eutectoid reaction. An equilibrium diagram illustrating the eutectoid reaction is shown in Fig. 6·40.

The liquidus line is $T_A E T_B$ and the solidus line is $T_A F G T_B$. The eutectic mixture is composed of the phases that occur at both ends of the eutectic temperature line, namely, α solid solution (point F) and solid B (point G). Point M indicates an allotropic change for the pure metal A. The significance of the solvus line MN is that, as the alloy composition is increased in B, the temperature at which the allotropic change takes place is decreased, reaching a minimum at point N. The solvus line FN shows the decrease in solubility of B in A as the temperature is decreased. Point N is known as the *eutectoid point*. Its composition is the eutectoid composition, and the line OP is the eutectoid temperature line. Like the eutectic diagram, it is common practice to call all alloys to the left of the eutectoid

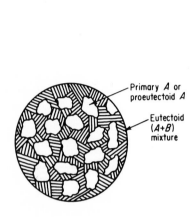

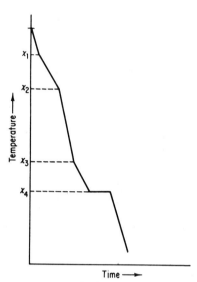

Fig. 6·41 Microstructure of a slow-cooled hypoeutectoid alloy.

Fig. 6·42 Cooling curve for alloy 1 of Fig. 6·40.

composition *hypoeutectoid alloys* and those to the right of point N *hypereutectoid alloys*.

When the hypoeutectoid alloy 1 is slow-cooled, α solid solution is formed when the liquidus line is crossed at x_1. More and more α is formed until the solidus line is crossed at x_2. It remains a uniform solid solution until the solvus line is crossed at x_3. The pure metal A must now start to undergo an allotropic change. Since there is no partial-solubility area below point M, this indicates that the new crystal structure of A cannot dissolve any B. The B atoms that are dissolved in the area that will undergo the allotropic change must first diffuse out of that area. With the area free of B atoms, the remaining atoms of A can now rearrange themselves into the new crystal structure. The excess B dissolves in the remaining α solution, which becomes richer in B as the temperature falls. The composition of the remaining α is gradually moving down and to the right along the solvus line MN. When the alloy reaches the eutectoid temperature x_4, the remaining α has reached the eutectoid point N. The eutectoid reaction now takes place by which the remaining α separates alternately crystals of the two pure metals A and B in an extremely fine mixture. The reaction may be written as

$$\alpha \underset{\text{heating}}{\overset{\text{cooling}}{\rightleftharpoons}} \underbrace{A + B}_{\text{eutectoid mixture}}$$

The microstructure at room temperature consists of primary A or proeutectoid A which was formed between x_3 and x_4, surrounded by

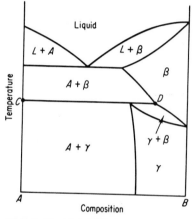

Fig. 6·43 Equilibrium diagram showing the formation of the terminal solid solution γ by a peritectoid reaction.

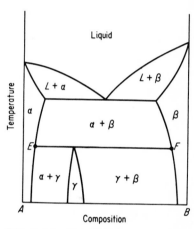

Fig. 6·44 Equilibrium diagram showing the formation of the electron compound γ by a peritectoid reaction.

the eutectoid $(A + B)$ mixture (Fig. 6·41). Compare this microstructure with Fig. 6·17c. The cooling curve for this hypoeutectoid alloy is shown in Fig. 6·42. The slow cooling of the hypereutectoid alloys 2 and 3 is left as an exercise for the student.

6·24 The peritectoid reaction. This is a less common reaction in the solid state than the eutectoid reaction. Two equilibrium diagrams to illustrate the peritectoid reaction are shown in Figs. 6·43 and 6·44. In Fig. 6·43, two solid phases, the pure metal A and β solid solution, react at the peritectoid-temperature line CD to form a new solid phase, the terminal solid solution γ. The equation may be written as

$$A + \beta \underset{\text{heating}}{\overset{\text{cooling}}{\rightleftharpoons}} \gamma$$

In Fig. 6·44, two solid phases α and β react at the peritectoid-temperature line EF to form an intermediate phase γ. The equation may be written as

$$\alpha + \beta \underset{\text{heating}}{\overset{\text{cooling}}{\rightleftharpoons}} \gamma$$

The peritectoid reaction may be written in general as

$$\text{Solid} + \text{solid} \underset{\text{heating}}{\overset{\text{cooling}}{\rightleftharpoons}} \text{new solid}$$

A study of Table 6·4, which summarizes the various reactions studied

Table 6·4   Equilibrium-diagram reactions

Name of reaction	General equation	Appearance on diagram
Monotectic	$L_1 \underset{\text{heating}}{\overset{\text{cooling}}{\rightleftharpoons}} L_2 + \text{solid}$	L_1 over $L_2 + \text{solid}$
Eutectic	$\text{Liquid} \underset{\text{heating}}{\overset{\text{cooling}}{\rightleftharpoons}} \text{solid} + \text{solid}$	L over Solid + solid
Eutectoid	$\text{Solid} \underset{\text{heating}}{\overset{\text{cooling}}{\rightleftharpoons}} \text{solid} + \text{solid}$	Solid over Solid + solid
Peritectic	$\text{Liquid} + \text{solid} \underset{\text{heating}}{\overset{\text{cooling}}{\rightleftharpoons}} \text{new solid}$	Liquid + solid over New solid
Peritectoid	$\text{Solid} + \text{solid} \underset{\text{heating}}{\overset{\text{cooling}}{\rightleftharpoons}} \text{new solid}$	Solid + solid over New solid

and their appearance on the equilibrium diagram, shows that the peritectic and peritectoid reactions are related in the same way as the eutectic and eutectoid reactions.

6·25   Complex diagrams. Some of the equilibrium diagrams discussed under the simple types are the same as actual ones. Many alloy systems have diagrams which show more than one type of reaction and are generally more complex than the simple types. However, even the most complex diagrams show mainly the reactions that have been covered. The student should be able to label completely; understand the significance of every point, line, and area; determine the various reactions that occur at the horizontal lines; and describe the slow cooling and microstructure of any alloy on a binary equilibrium diagram. The Cu-Sb alloy system shown in Fig. 6·45 illustrates a

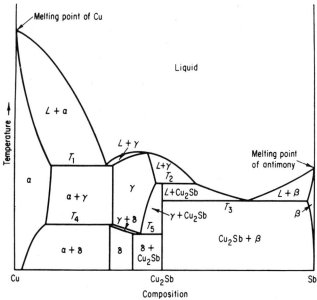

Fig. 6·45   The copper-antimony system.

complex equilibrium diagram completely labeled. The reactions that occur as the horizontal lines and the specific equations are as follows:

T_1 eutectic: $\text{Liquid} \xrightleftharpoons[\text{heating}]{\text{cooling}} \alpha + \gamma$

T_2 peritectic: $\text{Liquid} + \gamma \xrightleftharpoons[\text{heating}]{\text{cooling}} Cu_2Sb$

T_3 eutectic: $\text{Liquid} \xrightleftharpoons[\text{heating}]{\text{cooling}} Cu_2Sb + \beta$

T_4 peritectoid: $\alpha + \gamma \xrightleftharpoons[\text{heating}]{\text{cooling}} \delta$

T_5 eutectoid: $\gamma \xrightleftharpoons[\text{heating}]{\text{cooling}} \delta + Cu_2Sb$

QUESTIONS

6·1 What information may be obtained from an equilibrium diagram?
6·2 Explain the importance of equilibrium diagrams in the development of new alloys.

6·3   Platinum and gold are completely soluble in both the liquid and solid states.   The melting point of platinum is 3225°F and that of gold is 1945°F. An alloy containing 40 per cent gold starts to solidify at 2910°F by separating crystals of 15 per cent gold.   An alloy containing 70 per cent gold starts to solidify at 2550°F by separating crystals of 37 per cent gold.

   a. Draw the equilibrium diagram to scale and label all points, lines, and areas.

   b. For an alloy containing 70 per cent gold (1) give the temperature of initial solidification; (2) give the temperature of final solidification; (3) give the chemical composition and relative amounts of the phases present at 2440°F; (4) draw the cooling curve.

6·4   Bismuth and antimony are completely soluble in both the liquid and solid states.

   A. Check the crystal-structure factor and calculate the relative-size factor for these metals.

   B. Bismuth melts at 520°F and antimony melts at 1170°F.   An alloy containing 50 per cent bismuth starts to solidify at 940°F by separating crystals of 90 per cent antimony.   An alloy containing 80 per cent bismuth starts to solidify at 750°F by separating crystals of 75 per cent antimony.

   1. Draw the equilibrium diagram to scale, labeling all lines, points, and areas.

   2. For an alloy containing 40 per cent antimony (*a*) give the temperature of initial solidification; (*b*) give the temperature of final solidification; (*c*) give the chemical composition and relative amounts of the phases present at 800°F; (*d*) draw the cooling curve.

   6·5   Bismuth (melting point 520°F) and cadmium (melting point 610°F) are assumed to be completely soluble in the liquid state and completely insoluble in the solid state.   They form a eutectic at 290°F containing 40 per cent cadmium.

   1. Draw the equilibrium diagram to scale, labeling all points, lines, and areas.

   2. For an alloy containing 70 per cent cadmium (*a*) give the temperature of initial solidification; (*b*) give the temperature of final solidification; (*c*) give the chemical composition and relative amounts of the phases present at a temperature of 100°F below (*a*); (*d*) sketch the microstructure at room temperature; (*e*) draw the cooling curve.

   3. Same as part 2 but for an alloy containing 10 per cent cadmium.

   6·6   Lead melts at 620°F and tin melts at 450°F.   They form a eutectic containing 62 per cent tin at 360°F.   The maximum solid solubility of tin in lead at this temperature is 19 per cent; of lead in tin, 3 per cent.   Assume the solubility of each at room temperature is 1 per cent.

   1. Draw the equilibrium diagram to scale, labeling all points, lines, and areas.

   2. Describe the solidification of a 40 per cent tin alloy.   Sketch its microstructure of room temperature giving the chemical composition and relative amounts of the phases present.

   3. Draw the cooling curve for the above alloy.

   4. Repeat 2 and 3 for an alloy containing 90 per cent tin.

   6·7   Calcium (melting point 1560°F) and magnesium (melting point 1200°F) form a compound $CaMg_2$ which contains 45 per cent calcium and melts at 1320°F. This compound forms a eutectic with pure magnesium at 960°F and contains 16 per cent calcium.   The solubility of the compound in magnesium is about 2 per cent at the eutectic temperature and decreases to almost zero at room temperature.   Magnesium is not soluble in the compound.   A second eutectic is formed between the compound and calcium at 830°F containing 78 per cent calcium and there is no solid solubility between the compound and pure calcium.

   1. Draw the equilibrium diagram to scale, labeling all points, lines, and areas.

Fig. 6·46

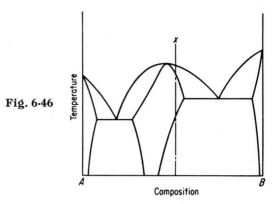

2. Describe the slow cooling of an alloy containing 30 per cent calcium. Sketch the microstructures at room temperature and give the relative amounts of the phases present.

3. Draw the cooling curve.

4. Write the specific equation of the reaction that takes place at each eutectic temperature.

6·8 1. Label Fig. 6·46 completely.

2. What type of intermediate phase is formed in this diagram?

3. Write the specific equation of the reaction that takes place at each horizontal line.

4. Sketch the microstructure of alloy x when slow-cooled to room temperature.

6·9 1. Describe the magnesium-nickel system so that it could be plotted from the description.

2. Plot this diagram to scale and label all the areas.

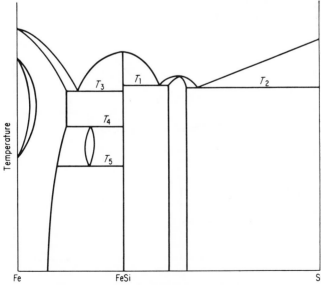

Fig. 6·47 The modified iron-silicon system.

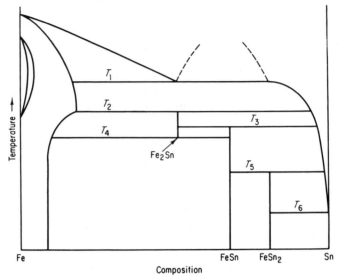

Fig. 6·48   The iron-tin system.

3. Write the reaction that takes place at each horizontal line.

4. Draw the cooling curve of a 40 per cent magnesium alloy.

5. Describe the slow cooling of this alloy, sketch its microstructure at room temperature, and give the relative amounts of the phases present.

6·10   1. Label completely the equilibrium diagrams given in Figs. 6·47, 6·48, and 6·49.

2. Give the name and write the specific equation of the reaction that takes place at each horizontal line.

3. Discuss the significance of each line on the diagrams.

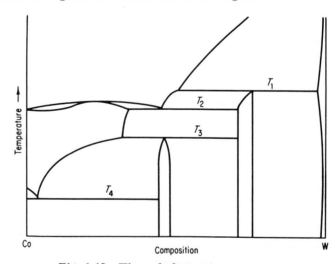

Fig. 6·49   The cobalt-tungsten system.

REFERENCES

American Society for Metals: "Metals Handbook," 1948 edition, Metals Park, Ohio.

Guy, A. G.: "Elements of Physical Metallurgy," Addison-Wesley Publishing Company, Inc., Reading, Mass., 1959.

Hansen, M., and K. Anderko: "Constitution of Binary Alloys," 2d ed., McGraw-Hill Book Company, Inc., New York, 1958.

Hume-Rothery, W., J. W. Christian, and W. B. Pearson: "Metallurgical Equilibrium Diagrams," The Institute of Physics, London, 1952.

Marsh, J. S.: "Principles of Phase Diagrams," McGraw-Hill Book Company, Inc., New York, 1935.

Mondolfo, L. F., and O. Zmeskal: "Engineering Metallurgy," McGraw-Hill Book Company, Inc., New York, 1955.

Rhines, F. H.: "Phase Diagrams in Metallurgy," McGraw-Hill Book Company, Inc., New York, 1956.

Van Vlack, L. H.: "Elements of Materials Science," Addison-Wesley Publishing Company, Inc., Reading, Mass., 1959.

Chapter 7

THE IRON–IRON CARBIDE
EQUILIBRIUM DIAGRAM

7·1 Introduction. Iron is an allotropic metal, which means that it can exist in more than one type of lattice structure depending upon temperature. A cooling curve for pure iron is shown in Fig. 7·1.

When iron first solidifies at 2800°F, it is in the b.c.c. (body-centered cubic) δ (delta) form. Upon further cooling, at 2554°F, a phase change occurs and the atoms rearrange themselves into the γ (gamma) form, which is f.c.c. (face-centered cubic) and nonmagnetic. When the temperature reaches 1666°F, another phase change occurs from f.c.c. nonmagnetic γ iron to b.c.c. nonmagnetic α (alpha) iron. Finally, at 1414°F, the α iron becomes magnetic without a change in lattice structure. Originally, nonmagnetic α iron was called β iron until subsequent X-ray studies showed no change in lattice structure at 1414°F. Since this magnetic transformation does not affect the heat treatment of iron-carbon alloys, it will be disregarded in our discussion. All the allotropic changes give off heat (exothermic) when iron is cooled and absorb heat (endothermic) when iron is heated.

7·2 The iron–iron carbide diagram. The temperature at which the above allotropic changes take place in iron is influenced by alloying elements, the most important of which is carbon. The iron–iron carbide diagram is shown in Fig. 7·2. Before going into a study of this diagram, it is important for the student to understand that this is not a true equilibrium diagram since equilibrium implies no change of phase with time. It is a fact, however, that the compound iron carbide will decompose into iron and carbon (graphite). This decomposition will take a very long time at room temperature, and even at 1300°F, it takes several years to form graphite. Iron carbide is called a *metastable* phase. Therefore, the iron–iron carbide diagram, even though it technically represents metastable conditions, can be considered as representing equilibrium changes, under conditions of relatively slow heating and cooling.

The diagram shows three horizontal lines which indicate isothermal reactions. Let us consider the portion of the diagram in the upper left-hand corner, expanded in Fig. 7·3. This is known as the *delta region*. The student should recognize the horizontal line at 2720°F

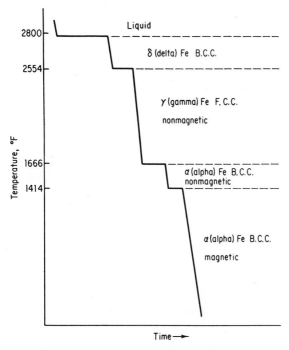

Fig. 7·1 Cooling curve for pure iron.

as being a peritectic reaction. The equation of the peritectic reaction may be written as

$$\text{Liquid} + \delta \underset{\text{heating}}{\overset{\text{cooling}}{\rightleftarrows}} \gamma$$

The maximum solubility of carbon in b.c.c. δ Fe is 0.10 per cent C while in f.c.c. γ Fe the solubility is much greater. Notice, too, the influence of carbon on the $\delta \rightleftharpoons \gamma$ allotropic change. As carbon is added to iron, the temperature of the allotropic change increases from 2554 to 2720°F at 0.10 per cent C. The delta region is of very little industrial value since no heat-treating process is carried out in that temperature range.

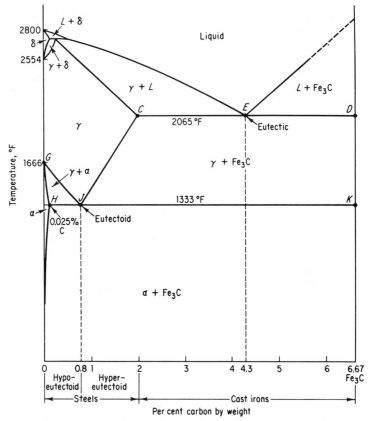

Fig. 7·2   The iron–iron carbide equilibrium diagram.

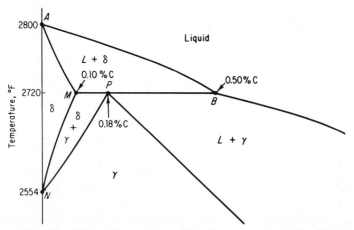

Fig. 7·3   The delta region of the iron–iron carbide diagram.

The next horizontal line is CD (Fig. 7·2) at 2065°F. This is the eutectic-temperature line at which the following reaction takes place:

$$\text{Liquid} \underset{\text{heating}}{\overset{\text{cooling}}{\rightleftharpoons}} \underbrace{\gamma + \text{Fe}_3\text{C}}_{\text{eutectic mixture}}$$

The eutectic mixture is usually not seen in the microstructure since the γ phase is not stable at room temperature and must undergo another reaction during cooling.

The last horizontal line HK occurs at 1333°F. This is the eutectoid-temperature line at which γ must disappear on slow cooling. The equation for the eutectoid reaction may be written as

$$\gamma \underset{\text{heating}}{\overset{\text{cooling}}{\rightleftharpoons}} \underbrace{\alpha + \text{Fe}_3\text{C}}_{\text{eutectoid mixture}}$$

On the basis of carbon content it is common practice to divide the iron–iron carbide diagram into two parts. Those alloys containing less than 2 per cent carbon are known as *steels* and those containing more than 2 per cent carbon are known as *cast irons*. The steel range is further subdivided by the eutectoid carbon content (0.8 per cent C). Steels containing less than 0.8 per cent C are called *hypoeutectoid steels* while those containing between 0.8 and 2.0 per cent C are called *hypereutectoid steels*.

7·3 Definition of structures. Although Fig. 7·2 has been labeled in general terms, it is common practice, for descriptive or commemorative reasons, to assign definite names to most of the structures.

Cementite or iron carbide, chemical formula Fe_3C, contains 6.67 per cent C by weight. It is a typical hard and brittle interstitial compound of low tensile strength but high compressive strength. It is the hardest structure that appears on the diagram.

Austenite is the name given to the γ solid solution. It is an interstitial solid solution of carbon dissolved in γ (f.c.c.) iron. Maximum solubility is 2 per cent C at 2065°F (point C). Average properties are: tensile strength, 150,000 psi; elongation, 10 per cent in 2 in.; hardness, Rockwell C 40, approx. It is normally not stable at room temperature. Under certain conditions it is possible to obtain austenite at room temperature, and its microstructure is shown in Fig. 7·4a.

Ledeburite is the eutectic mixture of austenite and cementite. It contains 4.3 per cent C and is formed at 2065°F.

Ferrite is the name given to the α solid solution. It is an interstitial solid solution of a small amount of carbon dissolved in α (b.c.c.) iron (Fig. 7·4b). The maximum solubility is 0.025 per cent C at 1333°F (point H), and it dissolves only 0.008 per cent C at room temperature.

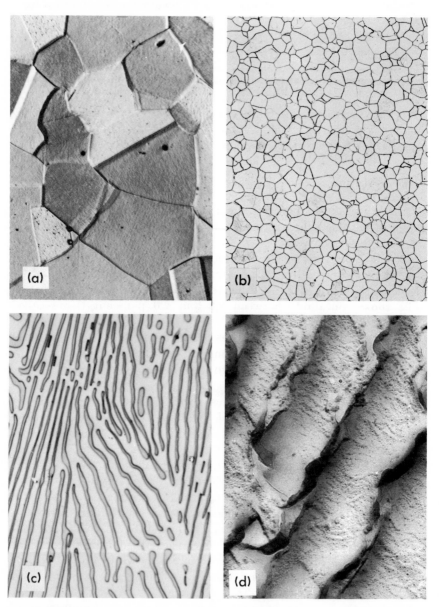

Fig. 7·4   The microstructure of (a) austenite, 500×; (b) ferrite, 100×; (c) pearlite, 2,500×; (d) pearlite, electron micrograph, 17,000×, enlarged 3× in printing.   (a, b, and c, Edgar C. Bain, Research Laboratory, U.S. Steel Corporation)

It is the softest structure that appears on the diagram. Average properties are: tensile strength, 40,000 psi; elongation, 40 per cent in 2 in.; hardness, less than Rockwell C 0.

Pearlite (point *J*) is the eutectoid mixture containing 0.80 per cent C, and is formed at 1333°F on very slow cooling. It is a very fine platelike or lamellar mixture of ferrite and cementite. The fine fingerprint mixture called pearlite is shown in Fig. 7·4c. The white ferritic background or matrix which makes up most of the eutectoid mixture contains thin plates of cementite. The same structure, magnified 17,000 times with the electron microscope, is shown in Fig. 7·4d. Average properties are: tensile strength, 120,000 psi; elongation, 20 per cent in 2 in.; hardness, Rockwell C 20, approx.

7·4   Carbon solubility in iron. Austenite, being f.c.c. with four atoms per unit cell, represents a much denser packing of atoms than ferrite, which is b.c.c. with two atoms per unit cell. This is shown by the expansion that takes place when austenite changes to ferrite on slow cooling. If the iron atoms are assumed to be spheres, it is possible, from the lattice dimensions and assuming the distance of closest approach to be equal to the atom diameter, to calculate the amount of empty space in both crystal structures. The calculation shows that the percentage of unfilled space in the f.c.c. lattice is 25 per cent and in the b.c.c. lattice 32 per cent. In both austenite and ferrite, the carbon atoms are dissolved interstitially, that is, in the unfilled spaces of the lattice structure. In view of the above calculations, it may seem strange that the solubility of carbon in austenite is so much greater than it is in ferrite. This seemingly unusual behavior may be explained by a study of Figs. 7·5 and 7·6. The largest hole in b.c.c. ferrite is halfway between the center of the face and the space between the two corner atoms (Fig. 7·5a). Two of the four possible positions for a carbon atom on the front face of a body-centered cube are shown in Fig. 7·6. The largest interstitial sphere that would just fit has a radius of $0.36(10^{-8})$ cm. The largest hole in f.c.c. austenite is midway along the edge between two corner atoms (Fig. 7·5b). One possible position for a carbon atom on the front face of a face-centered cube is shown in Fig. 7·6. The largest interstitial sphere that would just fit has a radius of $0.52(10^{-8})$ cm. Therefore, austenite will have a greater solubility for carbon than ferrite. Since the carbon atom has a radius of about $0.70(10^{-8})$ cm, the iron atoms in austenite are spread apart by the solution of carbon so that, at the maximum solubility of 2 per cent, only about 10 per cent of the holes are filled. The distortion of the ferrite lattice by the carbon atom is much greater than in the case of austenite; therefore, the carbon solubility is much more restricted.

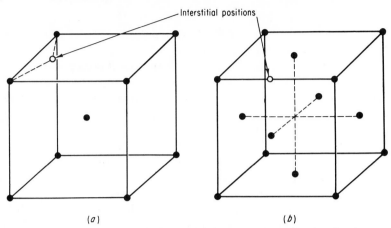

(*a*)   (*b*)

Fig. 7·5   Schematic picture of the interstitial positions in the f.c.c. and b.c.c. structures. (*a*) The largest hole in b.c.c.; (*b*) the largest hole in f.c.c. (*By permission from C. S. Barrett, "Structure of Metals," 2d ed., McGraw-Hill Book Company, Inc., New York,* 1952)

7.5   Slow cooling of steel.   The steel portion of the iron–iron carbide diagram is of greatest interest, and the various changes that take place during the very slow cooling, from the austenite range, of several steels will be discussed. Alloys containing more than 2 per cent carbon will be discussed in Chap. 11.

Alloy 1 (Fig. 7·7) is a hypoeutectoid steel containing 0.20 per cent carbon. In the austenite range, this alloy consists of a uniform interstitial solid solution. Each grain contains 0.20 per cent carbon dissolved in the spaces of the f.c.c. iron lattice structure. Upon slow cooling nothing happens until the line *GJ* is crossed at point x_1. This

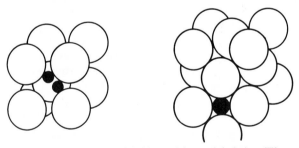

Fig. 7·6   Interstices of the b.c.c. (left) and f.c.c. (right).   The maximum-diameter foreign sphere (black) that can enter the b.c.c. lattice is indicated by the black atom with two of the four possible positions on one face shown here as filled. The f.c.c. lattice has far fewer holes, but as shown by the black sphere, the hole is much larger. (*By permission from R. M. Brick and A. Phillips, "Structure and Properties of Alloys," 2d ed., McGraw-Hill Book Company, Inc., New York,* 1949)

line is known as the *upper-critical-temperature* line on the hypoeutectoid side and is labeled A_3.   The allotropic change from f.c.c. to b.c.c.
iron takes place at 1666°F for pure iron and decreases in temperature
with increasing carbon content, as shown by the A_3 line.   Therefore,
at x_1, ferrite must begin to form from austenite.   Since ferrite can
dissolve very little carbon, in those areas that are changing to ferrite

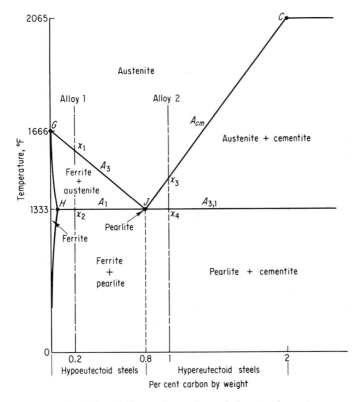

Fig. 7·7   Enlarged portion of the steel range.

the carbon must come out of solution before the atoms rearrange
themselves to b.c.c.   The carbon which comes out of solution is dissolved in the remaining austenite, so that, as cooling progresses and
the amount of ferrite increases, the remaining austenite becomes richer
in carbon.   Its carbon content is gradually moving down and to the
right along the A_3 line.   Finally, the line HJ is reached at point x_2.
This line is known as the *lower-critical-temperature line* on the hypoeutectoid side and is labeled A_1.   The A_1 line is the eutectoid-temperature line and is the lowest temperature at which f.c.c. iron can exist
under equilibrium conditions.   The remaining austenite, about 25 per

cent of the total material (Rule II) and containing 0.8 per cent carbon,
now experiences the eutectoid reaction

$$\text{Austenite} \xrightleftharpoons[\text{heating}]{\text{cooling}} \underbrace{\text{ferrite} + \text{cementite}}_{\text{pearlite}}$$

The carbon comes out of solution as cementite (iron carbide) plates,
and in the neighboring areas which are depleted of carbon, the iron
atoms rearrange themselves to form plates of ferrite. The reaction
continues by alternate precipitation of plates of cementite and ferrite
(Fig. 7·8) to give the very fine fingerprint mixture known as *pearlite*.

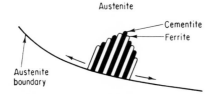

Fig. 7·8   Schematic picture of the
formation and growth of pearlite.

The microstructure remains substantially the same down to room temperature and consists of approximately 75 per cent free ferrite or
proeutectoid ferrite (formed between the A_3 and A_1 lines) and approximately 25 per cent pearlite (formed from austenite at the A_1 line)
(Fig. 7·9a). To show that the dark areas are actually pearlite, the
same sample has been magnified higher in Fig. 7·9b.

The slow cooling of any other hypoeutectoid steel would differ only
in the quantity of ferrite and pearlite. The closer the carbon content
is to the eutectoid composition (0.8 per cent C), the more pearlite will
be present in the microstructure (Fig. 7·9c).

Alloy 2 (Fig. 7·7) is a hypereutectoid steel containing 1 per cent
carbon. In the austenite range, this alloy consists of a uniform f.c.c.
solid solution with each grain containing 1 per cent carbon dissolved
interstitially. Upon slow cooling nothing happens until the line CJ
is crossed at point x_3. This line is known as the *upper-critical-temperature line* on the hypereutectoid side and is labeled A_{cm}. The A_{cm}
line shows the maximum amount of carbon that can be dissolved in
austenite as a function of temperature. Above the A_{cm} line, austenite is an unsaturated solid solution. At the A_{cm} line, point x_3, the
austenite is saturated in carbon. As the temperature is decreased,
the carbon content of the austenite, that is, the maximum amount of
carbon that can be dissolved in austenite, moves down along the A_{cm}
line toward point J. Therefore, as the temperature decreases from
x_3 to x_4, the excess carbon above the amount required to saturate

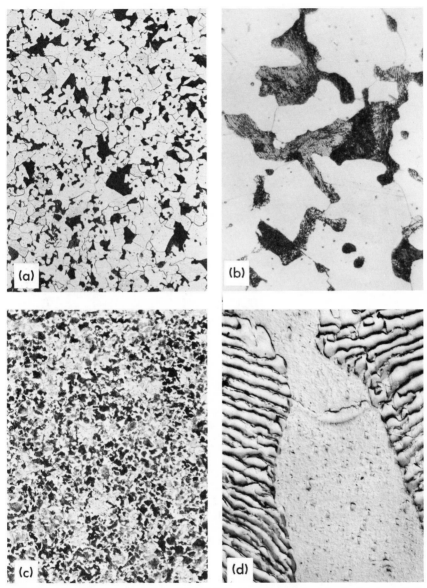

Fig. 7·9   Photomicrographs of (a) 0.20 per cent carbon steel, slow-cooled, 100×; (b) same as (a) but at 500×; (c) 0.40 per cent carbon steel, slow-cooled, 100×; (d) same as (c) but taken with the electron microscope; original magnification 3,000×, enlarged 3× in printing. All samples etched with 2 per cent nital. Dark areas are pearlite; light areas are proeutectoid ferrite.

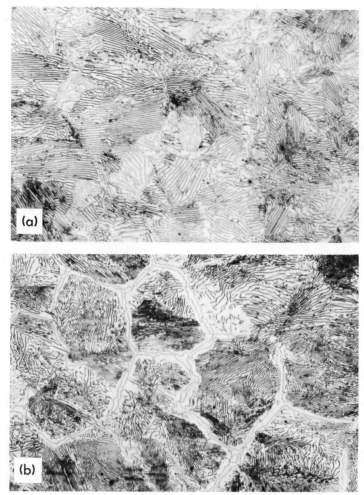

Fig. 7·10   Photomicrographs of (*a*) 1 per cent carbon steel, slow-cooled, 500×; (*b*) 1.2 per cent carbon steel, slow-cooled, 300×.   Pearlite areas surrounded by a white proeutectoid cementite network.   Note the increase in thickness of the cementite network with the increase in carbon content.

austenite is precipitated as cementite primarily along the grain boundaries.   Finally, the eutectoid-temperature line is reached at x_4.   This line is called the *lower-critical-temperature* line on the hypereutectoid side and is labeled $A_{3,1}$.   The remaining austenite, approximately 96.5 per cent of all the material and containing 0.8 per cent C, now experiences the eutectoid reaction to form pearlite by the same process described earlier.   At room temperature, the microstructure consists of approximately 96.5 per cent pearlite (formed from austenite at the $A_{3,1}$ line) and a network of approximately 3.5 per cent free cementite or proeutectoid cementite (formed between the A_{cm} and $A_{3,1}$ lines) (Fig. 7·10a).   As the carbon content of the alloy increases, the thickness of the proeutectoid cementite network generally increases (Fig. 7·10b).   Both photomicrographs show very clearly the lamellar (plate-like) structure of pearlite.

Note the difference in significance of the upper-critical-temperature lines, the A_3 and the A_{cm}.   The former line involves an allotropic change whereas the latter involves only a change in carbon solubility.

7·6   The critical-temperature lines.   In Fig. 7·7, the upper- and lower-critical-temperature lines are shown as single lines under equilibrium conditions and are sometimes indicated as Ae_3, Ae_1, etc. When the critical points of a steel are actually determined, it is found that they do not occur at the same temperature.   The critical point on heating is always higher than the critical point on cooling.   To distinguish critical points on heating from those occurring on cooling, the former are called Ac (c from the French word *chauffage*, which means heating) and the latter Ar (r from the French word *refroidissement*, which means cooling).   Therefore, the upper critical point of a hypoeutectoid steel on heating would be labeled Ac_3 and the same point on cooling Ar_3.

The rate of heating and cooling has a definite effect on the temperature gap between these points.   The slower the rate of heating and cooling the nearer will the two points approach each other, so that with infinitely slow heating and cooling they would probably occur at exactly the same temperature.

The results of thermal analysis of a series of carbon steels with an average heating and cooling rate of 11°F per min are shown in Fig. 7·11.   The diagram shows the effect of this rate of heating and cooling on the position of the critical lines.   Also shown are the Ac_2 and Ar_2 lines, which are due to the magnetic change in iron at 1414°F.

7·7   Classification of steels.   Several methods may be used to classify steels:

Method of Manufacture.   This gives rise to bessemer steel, open-hearth steel, electric-furnace steel, crucible steel, etc.

Use.   This is generally the final use for the steel such as machine steel, spring steel, boiler steel, structural steel, or tool steel.

Chemical Composition.   This method indicates, by means of a numbering system, the approximate content of the important elements in the steel.   This is the most popular method of classification and will be discussed in greater detail.

The steel specifications represent the results of the cooperative effort of the American Iron and Steel Institute (AISI) and the Society of Automotive Engineers (SAE) in a simplification program aimed at greater efficiency in meeting the steel needs of American industry.

The first digit of the four- or five-numeral designation indicates the type to which the steel belongs. Thus 1 indicates a carbon steel, 2 a nickel steel, 3 a nickel-chromium steel, etc. In the case of simple alloy steels, the second digit indicates the approximate percentage

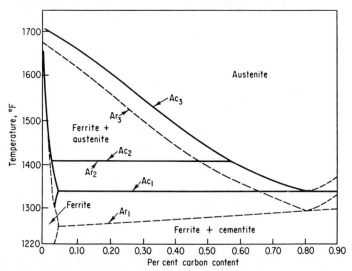

Fig. 7·11   Hypoeutectoid portion of the iron–iron carbide diagram. (*Reprinted with permission from Dowdell, "General Metallography," John Wiley & Sons, Inc., New York,* **1943**)

of the predominant alloying element. The last two or three digits usually indicate the mean carbon content divided by 100. Thus the symbol 2520 indicates a nickel steel of approximately 5 per cent nickel and 0.20 per cent carbon.

In addition to the numerals, AISI specifications may include a letter prefix to indicate the manufacturing process employed in producing the steel. SAE specifications now employ the same four-digit numerical designations as the AISI specifications, with the elimination of all letter prefixes.

The basic numbers for the four-digit series of the various grades of carbon and alloy steels are:

10xx   Basic open-hearth and acid bessemer carbon steels
11xx   Basic open-hearth and acid bessemer carbon steels, high sulfur, low phosphorus

Table 7·1   Some representative standard-steel specifications

AISI No.*	% C	% Mn	% P max	% S max	SAE No.
		Plain Carbon Steels			
C1010	0.08–0.13	0.30–0.60	0.04	0.05	1010
C1015	0.13–0.18	0.30–0.60	0.04	0.05	1015
C1020	0.18–0.23	0.30–0.60	0.04	0.05	1020
C1025	0.22–0.28	0.30–0.60	0.04	0.05	1025
C1030	0.28–0.34	0.60–0.90	0.04	0.05	1030
C1035	0.32–0.38	0.60–0.90	0.04	0.05	1035
C1040	0.37–0.44	0.60–0.90	0.04	0.05	1040
C1045	0.43–0.50	0.60–0.90	0.04	0.05	1045
C1050	0.48–0.55	0.60–0.90	0.04	0.05	1050
C1055	0.50–0.60	0.60–0.90	0.04	0.05	1055
C1060	0.55–0.65	0.60–0.90	0.04	0.05	1060
C1065	0.60–0.70	0.60–0.90	0.04	0.05	1065
C1070	0.65–0.75	0.60–0.90	0.04	0.05	1070
C1074	0.70–0.80	0.50–0.80	0.04	0.05	1074
C1080	0.75–0.88	0.60–0.90	0.04	0.05	1080
C1085	0.80–0.93	0.70–1.00	0.04	0.05	1085
C1090	0.85–0.98	0.60–0.90	0.04	0.05	1090
C1095	0.90–1.03	0.30–0.50	0.04	0.05	1095
		Free-machining Carbon Steels			
B1112	0.13 max	0.70–1.00	0.07–0.12	0.16–0.23	1112
B1113	0.13 max	0.70–1.00	0.07–0.12	0.24–0.33	1113
C1110	0.08–0.13	0.30–0.60	0.04	0.08–0.13	
C1113	0.10–0.16	1.00–1.30	0.04	0.24–0.33	
C1115	0.13–0.18	0.60–0.90	0.04	0.08–0.13	1115
C1120	0.18–0.23	0.70–1.00	0.04	0.08–0.13	1120
C1137	0.32–0.39	1.35–1.65	0.04	0.08–0.13	1137
C1141	0.37–0.45	1.35–1.65	0.04	0.08–0.13	1141
C1212	0.13 max	0.70–1.00	0.07–0.12	0.16–0.23	1112
C1213	0.13 max	0.70–1.00	0.07–0.12	0.24–0.33	1113
C12L14†	0.15 max	0.80–1.20	0.04–0.09	0.25–0.35	12L14

* Prefix AISI letters: B = acid bessemer carbon steel; C = basic open-hearth carbon steel.

† Lead, 0.15 to 0.35 per cent.

12xx   Basic open-hearth carbon steels, high sulfur, high phosphorus

13xx   Manganese 1.60 to 1.90 per cent

23xx   Nickel 3.50 per cent

Table 7·2   Some representative alloy-steel specifications

AISI No.	% C	% Mn	% Ni	% Cr	% Mo	% V	SAE No.	Type
1330	0.28–0.33	1.60–1.90	...	...	...	...	1330	} Mn
1340	0.38–0.43	1.60–1.90	...	...	...	...	1340	} steels
2317	0.15–0.20	0.40–0.60	3.25–3.75	...	...	...	2315	} 3% Ni
2330	0.28–0.33	0.60–0.80	3.25–3.75	...	...	...	2330	} steels
E2512*	0.09–0.14	0.45–0.60	4.75–5.25	...	...	...	...	} 5% Ni
2515	0.12–0.17	0.40–0.60	4.75–5.25	...	...	...	2515	} steels
3115	0.13–0.18	0.40–0.60	1.10–1.40	0.55–0.75	...	...	3115	\
3130	0.28–0.33	0.60–0.80	1.10–1.40	0.55–0.75	...	...	3130	Ni-Cr
3140	0.38–0.43	0.70–0.90	1.10–1.40	0.55–0.75	...	...	3140	steels
E3310	0.08–0.13	0.45–0.60	3.65–3.75	1.40–1.75	...	...	3310	/
4023	0.20–0.25	0.70–0.90	...	...	0.20–0.30	...	4023	\ Mo
4032	0.30–0.35	0.70–0.90	...	...	0.20–0.30	...	4032	steels
4042	0.40–0.45	0.70–0.90	...	...	0.20–0.30	...	4042	/
4118	0.18–0.23	0.20–0.90	...	0.40–0.60	0.08–0.15	...	4118	\
4130	0.28–0.33	0.40–0.60	...	0.80–1.10	0.15–0.25	...	4130	Cr-Mo
4140	0.38–0.43	0.75–1.00	...	0.80–1.10	0.15–0.25	...	4140	steels
4150	0.48–0.53	0.75–1.00	...	0.80–1.10	0.15–0.25	...	4150	/
4320	0.17–0.22	0.45–0.60	1.65–2.00	0.40–0.60	0.20–0.30	...	4320	} Ni-Cr-Mo
4340	0.38–0.43	0.60–0.80	1.65–2.00	0.70–0.90	0.20–0.30	...	4340	} steels
4620	0.17–0.22	0.45–0.60	1.65–2.00	...	0.20–0.30	...	4620	\
4640	0.38–0.43	0.60–0.80	1.65–2.00	...	0.20–0.30	...	4640	Ni-Mo
4820	0.18–0.23	0.50–0.70	3.25–3.75	...	0.20–0.30	...	4820	steels
5120	0.17–0.22	0.70–0.90	...	0.70–0.90	...	...	5120	\
5130	0.28–0.33	0.70–0.90	...	0.80–1.10	...	...	5130	
5140	0.38–0.43	0.70–0.90	...	0.70–0.90	...	...	5140	Cr steels
5150	0.48–0.53	0.70–0.90	...	0.70–0.90	...	...	5150	
E52100*	0.95–1.10	0.25–0.45	...	1.30–1.60	...	...	52100	/
6120	0.17–0.22	0.70–0.90	...	0.70–0.90	...	0.10	6120	} Cr-V
6150	0.48–0.53	0.70–0.90	...	0.80–1.10	...	0.15	6150	} steels
8620	0.17–0.24	0.60–0.95	0.35–0.75	0.35–0.65	0.15–0.25	...	8620	\ Low
8630	0.27–0.34	0.60–0.95	0.35–0.75	0.35–0.65	0.15–0.25	...	8630	Ni-Cr-Mo
8640	0.37–0.45	0.70–1.05	0.35–0.75	0.35–0.65	0.15–0.25	...	8640	steels
8720	0.17–0.24	0.60–0.95	0.35–0.75	0.35–0.65	0.20–0.30	...	8720	
8740	0.37–0.45	0.70–1.05	0.35–0.75	0.35–0.65	0.20–0.30	...	8740	
E9310*	0.08–0.13	0.45–0.65	3.00–3.50	1.00–1.40	0.08–0.15	...	9310	
9840	0.38–0.43	0.70–0.90	0.85–1.15	0.70–0.90	0.20–0.30	...	9840	
9850	0.48–0.53	0.70–0.90	0.85–1.15	0.70–0.90	0.20–0.30	...	9850	

* E = basic electric-furnace process.   All others are normally manufactured by the basic open-hearth process.

25xx   Nickel 5 per cent

31xx   Nickel 1.25 per cent, chromium 0.60 per cent

32xx   Nickel 1.75 per cent, chromium 1.00 per cent

33xx   Nickel 3.50 per cent, chromium 1.50 per cent

40xx   Molybdenum 0.25 per cent

41xx   Chromium 1.00 per cent, molybdenum 0.20 per cent

43xx   Nickel-chromium-molybdenum

46xx   Nickel 1.75 per cent, molybdenum 0.25 per cent

48xx   Nickel 3.50 per cent, molybdenum 0.25 per cent

51xx   Chromium 0.80 per cent
52xx   Chromium 1.50 per cent
61xx   Chromium-vanadium
86xx   Nickel 0.55 per cent, chromium 0.50 per cent, molybdenum
       0.20 per cent
87xx   Nickel 0.55 per cent, chromium 0.50 per cent, molybdenum
       0.25 per cent
92xx   Manganese 0.80 per cent, silicon 2.00 per cent
93xx   Nickel 3.25 per cent, chromium 1.20 per cent, molybdenum
       0.12 per cent
98xx   Nickel 1.00 per cent, chromium 0.80 per cent, molybdenum
       0.25 per cent

Some representative standard steel specifications are given for plain carbon and free-machining steels in Table 7·1 and for alloy steels in Table 7·2.

Chapter 8

THE HEAT TREATMENT OF STEEL

8.1 Introduction. The definition of heat treatment given in the "Metals Handbook" is: "A combination of heating and cooling operations, timed and applied to a metal or alloy in the solid state in a way that will produce desired properties." All basic heat-treating processes for steel involve the transformation or decomposition of austenite. The nature and appearance of these transformation products determine the physical and mechanical properties of any given steel.

The first step in the heat treatment of steel is to heat the material to some temperature in or above the critical range in order to form austenite. In most cases, the rate of heating to the desired temperature is less important than other factors in the heat-treating cycle. Highly stressed materials produced by cold work should be heated more slowly than stress-free materials to avoid distortion. The difference in temperature rise within thick and thin sections of articles of variable cross section should be considered, and whenever possible, provision should be made for slowing the heating of the thinner sections to minimize thermal stress and distortion. Usually less overall damage will be done to the steel by utilizing as slow a heating rate as is practical.

8.2 Full annealing. This process consists in heating the steel to the proper temperature and then cooling slowly through the transformation range, preferably in the furnace or in any good heat-insulating material. The slow cooling is generally continued to low temperatures.

The purpose of annealing may be to refine the grain, induce softness, improve electrical and magnetic properties, and, in some cases, to improve machinability.

Since the entire mass of the furnace must be cooled down along with the material, annealing is a very slow cooling process and therefore comes closest to following the iron–iron carbide equilibrium diagram.

The proper annealing temperature for a hypoeutectoid steel is 50°F above the upper-critical-temperature (A_3) line. The microstructure will consist of a mixture of proeutectoid ferrite and coarse lamellar pearlite (see Fig. 7·9).

Refinement of the grain size of hypereutectoid steel will occur about 50°F above the lower-critical-temperature ($A_{3,1}$) line. Heating above this temperature will coarsen the austenitic grains, which, on cooling, will transform to large pearlitic areas. The microstructure of annealed hypereutectoid steel will consist of coarse lamellar pearlite areas surrounded by a network of proeutectoid cementite (see Fig. 7·10).

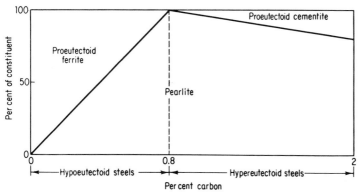

Fig. 8·1 Proportion of the constituents present in the microstructure of annealed steels as a function of carbon content.

Because this excess cementite network is brittle and tends to be a plane of weakness, annealing should never be a final heat treatment for hypereutectoid steels. The presence of a thick, hard, grain boundary will also result in poor machinability.

A careful microscopic study of the proportions of ferrite and pearlite or pearlite and cementite present in an annealed steel can enable one to determine the approximate carbon content of the steel (Fig. 8·1).

The approximate tensile strength of annealed hypoeutectoid steels may be determined by the proportion of ferrite and pearlite present:

Approx tensile strength

$$= \frac{40{,}000(\text{per cent ferrite}) + 120{,}000(\text{per cent pearlite})}{100}$$

For example, an annealed 0.20 per cent carbon steel contains approximately 25 per cent pearlite and 75 per cent ferrite. Applying the above formula,

Approx tensile strength $= 40{,}000(0.75) + 120{,}000(0.25) = 60{,}000$ psi

This same idea cannot be applied to hypereutectoid steels, since their strength is determined by the cementite network which forms the continuous phase. The presence of the brittle network results in a drop in tensile strength above 0.8 per cent carbon (see Table 8·1).

Table 8·1   Mechanical properties of normalized and annealed steels*

Carbon, %	Yield point, 1,000 psi	Tensile strength, 1,000 psi	Elongation, % in 2 in.	Reduction in area, %	BHN
Normalized (hot-rolled steel):					
0.01	26	45	45	71	90
0.20	45	64	35	60	120
0.40	51	85	27	43	165
0.60	60	109	19	28	220
0.80	70	134	13	18	260
1.00	100	152	7	11	295
1.20	100	153	3	6	315
1.40	96	148	1	3	300
Annealed:					
0.01	18	41	47	71	90
0.20	36	59	37	64	115
0.40	44	75	30	48	145
0.60	49	96	23	33	190
0.80	52	115	15	22	220
1.00	52	108	22	26	195
1.20	51	102	24	39	200
1.40	50	99	19	25	215

* By permission from R. M. Brick and A. Phillips, "The Structure and Properties of Alloys," 2d ed., McGraw-Hill Book Company, Inc., New York, 1949.

8·3   Spheroidizing. As was pointed out earlier, an annealed hypereutectoid steel will give poor machinability because of the presence of hard cementite plates. A heat-treating process which will improve the machinability is known as *spheroidize annealing*. This process will produce a spheroidal or globular form of carbide. The methods most frequently used are:

1. Prolonged holding at a temperature just below the lower critical line

2. Heating and cooling alternately between temperatures that are just above and just below the lower critical line

This treatment allows the carbide to assume the form of round particles (spheroids) instead of plates as in pearlite (Fig. 8·2). This structure gives not only good machinability but also high ductility.

Spheroidize annealing is sometimes applied to hypoeutectoid steels for forming applications that require maximum ductility.

8·4 Stress-relief annealing. This process, sometimes called *subcritical* annealing, is useful in removing residual stresses due to heavy machining or other cold-working processes. It is usually carried out at temperatures below the lower critical line (1000 to 1200°F).

8·5 Process annealing. This heat treatment is used in the sheet and wire industries and is carried out by heating the steel to a

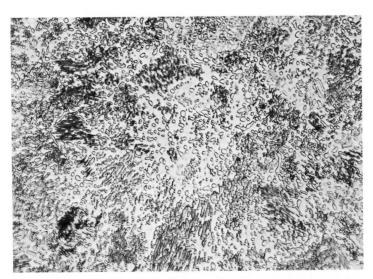

Fig. 8·2   A 1 per cent carbon steel spheroidize-annealed showing sphe-roidized cementite in a ferrite matrix.   Etched in 2 per cent nital, 750×.

temperature below the lower critical line (1000 to 1250°F). It is applied after cold working and softens the steel, by recrystallization, for further working. It is very similar to stress-relief annealing.

8·6 Normalizing. The normalizing of steel is carried out by heating approximately 100°F above the upper-critical-temperature (A_3 or A_{cm}) line followed by cooling in still air to room temperature (Fig. 8·3). The purpose of normalizing is to produce a harder and stronger steel than full annealing, to refine the grain, homogenize the structure, and improve machinability, particularly in lower-carbon steels. The increase in cooling rate due to air cooling as compared with furnace cooling affects the transformation of austenite and the resultant micro-structure in several ways. The austenite transforms at a lower tem-perature, resulting in a finer pearlite structure as compared with annealing. This is shown schematically in Fig. 8·4. There is less time for the formation of the proeutectoid constituent; consequently there

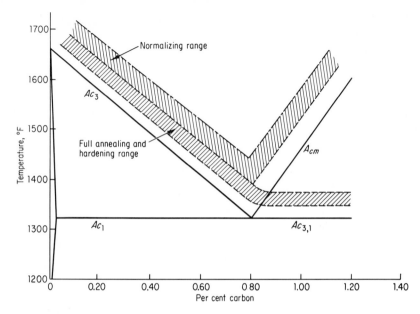

Fig. 8·3   Normalizing, annealing, and hardening temperature range for carbon steels.

will be less proeutectoid ferrite in normalized hypoeutectoid steels and less proeutectoid cementite in hypereutectoid steels as compared with annealed material.   This is shown in Fig. 8·5 of a 0.40 per cent C steel normalized.   Compare this with Fig. 7·9c, which is the same steel annealed.   Air cooling has produced much less than the expected 50 per cent proeutectoid ferrite determined by the equilibrium diagram. It is possible, in thin sections of hypereutectoid steels, to suppress the formation of proeutectoid cementite entirely.   Nonequilibrium cooling

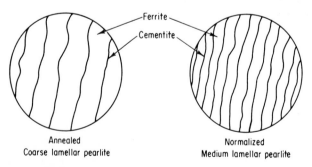

Fig. 8·4   Schematic picture of the difference in pearlitic structure due to annealing and normalizing.

also shifts the eutectoid point toward lower carbon content in hypo-eutectoid steels and toward higher carbon content in hypereutectoid steels.

The net effect is that normalizing produces a finer and more abundant pearlitic structure than is obtained by annealing. This results in a harder and stronger steel (Table 8·1).

8·7   Hardening.   Under slow or moderate cooling rates, the carbon atoms are able to diffuse out of the austenite structure.   The iron atoms then move slightly to become b.c.c. (body-centered cubic).

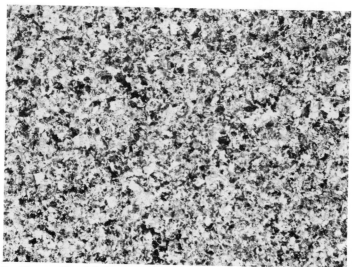

Fig. 8·5   **Normalized 0.40 per cent carbon steel.   Etched in 2 per cent nital, 100✕.   Pearlite dark with white proeutectoid ferrite network.**

This gamma-to-alpha transformation takes place by a process of nucleation and growth and is time-dependent.   With a still further increase in cooling rate, insufficient time is allowed for the carbon to diffuse out of solution, and although some movement of the iron atoms takes place, the structure cannot become b.c.c. while the carbon is trapped in solution.   The resultant structure, called *martensite*, is a super-saturated solid solution of carbon trapped in a body-centered tetragonal structure.   Two dimensions of the unit cell are equal, but the third is slightly expanded because of the trapped carbon.   The axial ratio c/a increases with carbon content to a maximum of 1.08.   This highly distorted lattice structure is the prime reason for the high hardness of martensite.   Since the atoms of martensite are less densely packed than in austenite, an expansion occurs during the transformation.   This expansion during the formation of martensite produces high localized stresses which result in plastic deformation of the matrix. After drastic cooling (quenching), martensite appears microscopically as a white needlelike or acicular structure sometimes described as a pile of straw.   In most steels, the martensitic structure appears vague and unresolvable (Fig. 8·6).   In high-carbon alloys where the background is retained austenite, the acicular structure of martensite is more clearly defined (Fig. 8·7).

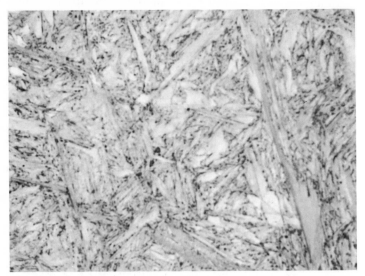

Fig. 8·6   The structure called martensite, 2,500×. (*Edgar C. Bain Research Laboratory, U.S. Steel Corporation*)

There are several important characteristics of the martensite transformation:

1. The transformation is diffusionless and there is no change in chemical composition.   Small volumes of austenite suddenly change crystal structure by a combination of two shearing actions.

2. The transformation proceeds only during cooling and ceases if cooling is interrupted.   Therefore, the transformation depends only upon the decrease in temperature and is independent of time.   The amount of martensite formed with decreasing temperature is not linear. The number of martensite needles produced at first is small; then the number increases, and finally, near the end, it decreases again (Fig. 8·8).   The temperature of the start of martensite formation is known as M_s and that of the end of martensite formation as M_f.

3. The martensite transformation for a given alloy cannot be suppressed nor can the M_s temperature be changed by changing the cooling rate.   The M_s temperature seems to be a function of chemical

Fig. 8·7   A 1 per cent carbon steel water-quenched.   Etched in 2 per cent nital, 750×.   Martensitic needles in a retained austenite matrix.

composition only, and several formulas have been developed by which it may be calculated.   One such formula (R. A. Grange and H. M. Stewart, *Metals Technology*, June, 1946) is

$$M_s \, (°F) = 1,000 - (650 \times \% \; C) - (70 \times \% \; Mn)$$
$$- (35 \times \% \; Ni) - (70 \times \% \; Cr) - (50 \times \% \; Mo)$$

The influence of carbon on the M_s and M_f temperatures is shown in Fig. 8·9.

4. Martensite is probably never in a condition of real equilibrium, although it may persist indefinitely at or near room temperature.   The structure can be considered as a transition between the unstable austenite phase and the final equilibrium condition of ferrite.

5. Although martensite is always harder than the austenite from which it forms, extreme hardnesses are possible only in steels that

Fig. 8·8   Schematic representation of percentage of martensite formed as a function of temperature. (*From "Metals Handbook," 1948 edition, American Society for Metals, Metals Park, Ohio*)

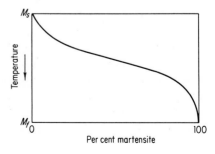

contain sufficient carbon. The maximum hardness obtainable from a steel in the martensitic condition is a function of carbon content only (Fig. 8·10).

The martensite transformation, for many years, was believed to be unique for steel. However, in recent years, this martensite type of transformation has been found in a number of other alloy systems, including nonferrous alloys, and it undoubtedly occurs also in pure metals and compounds. The transformation is therefore recognized

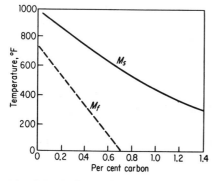

Fig. 8·9   Influence of carbon on the martensite range. (*From "Metals Handbook," 1948 edition, American Society for Metals, Metals Park, Ohio*)

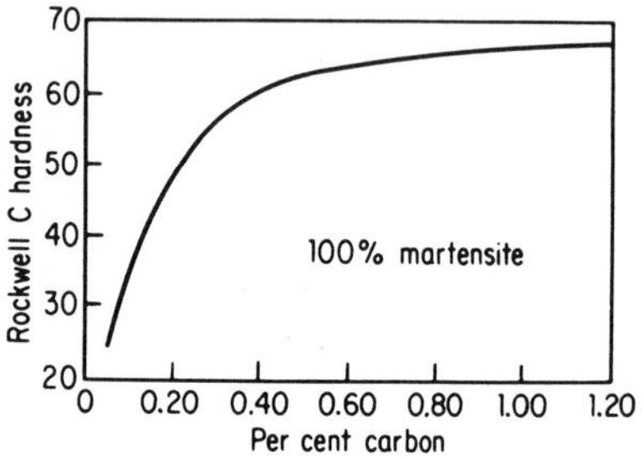

Fig. 8·10   Influence of carbon content on the hardness of fully martensitic steel, as quenched. (*From "Metals Handbook," 1948 edition, American Society for Metals, Metals Park, Ohio*)

as a basic type of reaction in the solid state, and the term *martensite* is no longer confined only to the metallurgy of steel.

The basic purpose of hardening is to produce a fully martensitic structure, and the minimum cooling rate (°F per second) that will avoid the formation of any of the softer products of transformation is known as the *critical cooling rate.* The critical cooling rate, determined by chemical composition and austenitic grain size, is an important property of a steel since it indicates how fast a steel must be cooled in order to form only martensite.

8·8   The isothermal-transformation diagram.   It is apparent from the previous discussion that the iron–iron carbide equilibrium diagram is of little value in the study of steels cooled under nonequilibrium conditions. Many metallurgists realized that time and temperature of austenite transformation had a profound influence on the transformation products and the subsequent properties of the steel. However, this was not given scientific basis until E. S. Davenport and E. C. Bain published their classic paper (*Trans. AIME*, vol.

90, p. 117, 1930) on the study of the transformation of austenite at constant subcritical temperature. Since austenite is unstable below the lower critical temperature Ae_1, it is necessary to know at a particular subcritical temperature how long it will take for the austenite to start to transform, how long it will take to be completely transformed, and what will be the nature of the transformation product. Two facts should be kept in mind:

1. Martensite is formed only from austenite almost instantaneously at relatively low temperatures.

2. If austenite transforms at higher temperature to a structure which

Fig. 8·11 A typical sample which is used to determine an I-T diagram.

is stable at room temperature, rapid cooling will not change the transformation product.

The best way to understand the isothermal-transformation diagrams is to study their derivation. The eutectoid composition of 0.8 per cent carbon is the simplest one to study since there is no proeutectoid constituent present in the microstructure.

A large number of small samples cut from the same bar are prepared. These are handled during heat treatment by means of a wire threaded through a hole in the sample, as illustrated in Fig. 8·11. A number of samples are placed in a furnace and heated to the proper austenitizing temperature. They are then placed in a second furnace which is held at an arbitrarily selected subcritical transformation temperature, say 1300°F. They are held there, and then at successive time intervals, preferably in geometric progression—as 5, 10, 20, 40, 80, etc., min—a sample is quenched in iced water or iced brine. The quenched samples are examined for hardness and microstructure. If the holding time for any sample is insufficient for the start of transformation, the hardness of that sample will be the same as that of a sample quenched directly from the austenitizing temperature and the structure will be completely martensitic. At the beginning of transformation the sample at 1300°F will have small areas of coarse lamellar pearlite in an austenitic matrix. This sample, when quenched, will show small areas of coarse lamellar pearlite in a martensitic matrix. The hardness will also be less than that of a fully martensitic sample. At the end of transformation the sample will be entirely coarse lamellar pearlite, and it will remain unchanged even after rapid quenching to room temperature (Fig. 8·12). As a result of this study, two points may be plotted at 1300°F, namely, the time for the beginning and

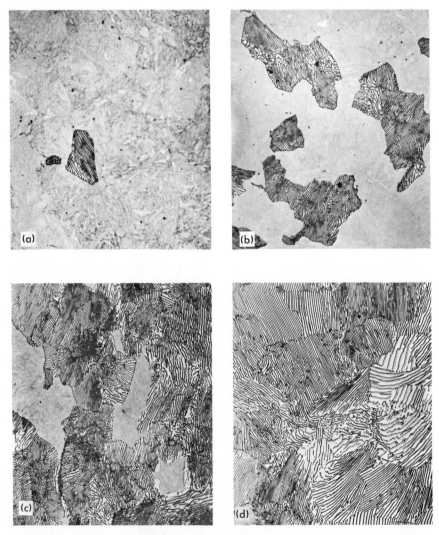

Fig. 8·12 **The progress of isothermal transformation of austenite at 1300°F, 500×.** (*a*) 350 sec, (*b*) 1,150 sec, (*c*) 1,450 sec, (*d*) 4,000 sec. (*Edgar C. Bain Research Laboratory, U.S. Steel Corporation*)

the time for the end of the transformation. The entire experiment is repeated at different subcritical temperatures until sufficient points are determined to draw two curves, one showing the beginning of transformation and the other showing the end of transformation (Fig. 8·13). Time is plotted on a logarithmic scale so that times of 1 min or less, as well as times of 1 day or week, can be fitted into a reasonable

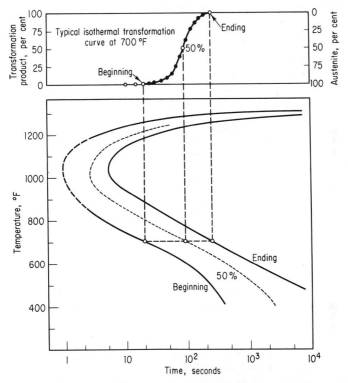

Fig. 8·13 **Diagram showing how measurements of isothermal transformation are summarized by the I-T diagram.** (*From "Atlas of Isothermal Transformation Diagrams," U.S. Steel Corporation*)

space and yet permit an open scale in the region of short times. The diagram is known as an *I-T* (*isothermal-transformation*) *diagram.* Other names for the same curves are TTT (transformation, temperature, time) curves or S curves. Construction of a reasonably accurate diagram requires the heat treatment and metallographic study of more than one hundred individual samples.

The I-T diagram for a 1080 eutectoid steel is shown in Fig. 8·14. Above the Ae_1 austenite is stable. The area to the left of the beginning of transformation consists of unstable austenite. The area to the right

of the end of the transformation line is labeled $F + C$ to indicate
that only ferrite and carbide are present, all austenite having been
transformed to a combination of these phases.   The area between the
two lines labeled $A + F + C$ consists of three phases, austenite, ferrite,
and carbide, or austenite plus the product to which it is transforming.
The point on the beginning of the transformation line farthest to the
left is known as the *nose* of the diagram.   In all diagrams, except

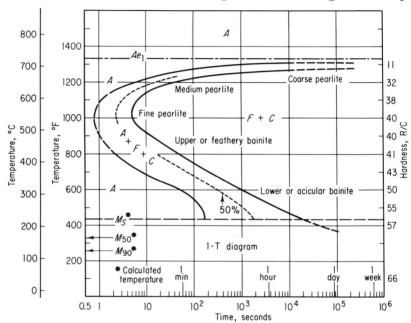

Fig. 8·14   I-T diagram for a 1080 eutectoid steel, C 0.79 per cent, Mn
0.76 per cent, austenitized at 1650°F, grain size 6. A = austenite, F =
ferrite, C = carbide, M = martensite. (*From "Atlas of Isothermal
Transformation Diagrams," U.S. Steel Corporation*)

the one for eutectoid steel, there is an additional line above the nose
region (see Fig. 8·23).   The first line to the left indicates the beginning
of austenite transformation to proeutectoid ferrite in hypoeutectoid
steels or proeutectoid cementite in hypereutectoid steels.   The second
line indicates the beginning of austenite transformation to pearlite.
The area between the two lines is labeled $A + F$ (austenite plus proeutectoid ferrite), or $A + C$ (austenite plus proeutectoid cementite).
The two lines generally merge at the nose region.   The principal curves
of the I-T diagram are drawn as broad lines to emphasize that their
exact location on the time scale is not highly precise.   Portions of
these lines are often shown as dashed lines to indicate a much higher
degree of uncertainty.

The line labeled "50%" and located between the beginning and ending lines represents the time required at each temperature for transformation of half of the total austenite.

The M_s temperature is indicated as a horizontal line. Arrows pointing to the temperature scale indicate the temperature at which

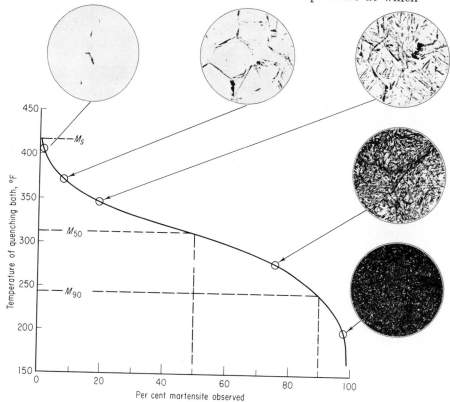

Fig. 8·15   Typical example of the transformation of austenite to martensite. Microstructures at 500×. (*From "Atlas of Isothermal Transformation Diagrams," U.S. Steel Corporation*)

50 and 90 per cent of the total austenite will, on quenching, have transformed to martensite. In some diagrams, the data on martensite formation were obtained by direct measurement using an involved metallographic technique. In other diagrams, the temperatures were calculated by an empirical formula. To determine the progress of martensite formation metallographically, let us drastically quench a sample to a temperature below the M_s line, say 370°F. Approximately 20 per cent of the austenite will have transformed to martensite. If this sample is now reheated for a short time to a temperature below the lower critical line, say 800°F, the martensite just formed will

become dark. The austenite will remain unchanged. Upon quenching, this sample will show 20 per cent dark martensite and 80 per cent fresh or white martensite, and the amount formed at 370°F may therefore be determined microscopically. A typical example of the transformation of austenite to martensite determined by the heat-treating procedure described above is shown in Fig. 8·15.

8·9   Pearlite and bainite. Returning to Fig. 8·14, the transformation product above the nose region is pearlite. The fineness of the pearlite formed and the resulting hardness vary with the temperature of transformation. Just below the Ae_1 line, coarse lamellar pearlite is formed with a hardness of Rockwell C 15. As the temperature decreases, the fineness of the pearlite and the hardness both increase, reaching a maximum at the nose region (Fig. 8·16). Between the nose region and the M_s line, a new, dark-etching aggregate of ferrite and carbide appears. This structure, named after E. C. Bain, is called *bainite*. At 900°F, it resembles pearlite and is known as *upper* or *feathery bainite* (Fig. 8·17). At low temperatures it resembles martensite and is known as *lower* or *acicular* (needlelike) *bainite* (Fig. 8·18). The hardness of bainite Rockwell C 40 to 60 is between the hardnesses of pearlite and martensite.

8·10   Cooling curves and the I-T diagram. A cooling curve is determined experimentally by placing a thermocouple at a definite location in a steel sample and then measuring the variation of temperature with time. Since the coordinates of the I-T diagram are the same as those for a cooling curve, it is possible to superimpose various cooling curves on the I-T diagram. This was done in Fig. 8·19.

Cooling curve 1 shows a very slow cooling rate typical of conventional annealing. The diagram indicates that the material will remain austenitic for a relatively long period of time. Transformation will start when the cooling curve crosses the beginning of transformation at point x_1. The transformation product at that temperature will be very coarse pearlite. Transformation will continue until point x_1'. Since there is a slight difference in temperature between the beginning and end of transformation, there will be a slight difference in the fineness of pearlite formed at the beginning and at the end. The overall product will be coarse pearlite with low hardness. Below the temperature of x_1' the rate of cooling will have no effect on the microstructure or properties. The material may now be cooled rapidly without any change occurring. This is of great value to companies doing commercial annealing, since the diagram indicates that it is not necessary to cool in the furnace to room temperature but that the material may be removed at a relatively high temperature after transformation and cooled in air.

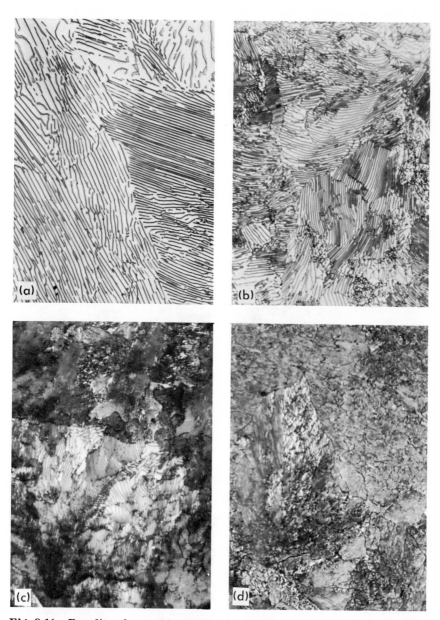

Fig. 8·16   Pearlites formed by the isothermal transformation of austenite at various subcritical temperatures. (a) 1300°F, (b) 1225°F, (c) 1150°F, (d) 1075°F, magnified 1,500×. Note the increase of fineness of pearlite with decreasing transformation temperature. (*Edgar C. Bain Research Laboratory, U.S. Steel Corporation*)

Cooling curve 2 illustrates "isothermal" or "cycle annealing" and was developed directly from the I-T diagram. The process is carried out by cooling the material rapidly from above the critical range to a predetermined temperature in the upper portion of the I-T diagram and holding for the time indicated to produce complete transformation. In contrast to conventional annealing, this treatment produces a more

Fig. 8·17 Feathery bainite and fine pearlite in a martensitic (white) matrix, 1,000×. (*Edgar C. Bain Research Laboratory, U.S. Steel Corporation*)

Fig. 8·18 Acicular or lower bainite, 2,500×. (*Edgar C. Bain Research Laboratory, U.S. Steel Corporation*)

uniform microstructure and hardness, in many cases with a shorter time cycle.

Cooling curve 3 is a faster cooling rate than annealing and may be considered typical of normalizing. The diagram indicates that transformation will start at x_3, with the formation of coarse pearlite, in a much shorter time than annealing. Transformation will be complete at x_3' with the formation of medium pearlite. Since there is a greater temperature difference between x_3 and x_3' than there is between x_1 and x_1', the normalized microstructure will show a greater variation in the fineness of pearlite and a smaller proportion of coarse pearlite than the annealed microstructure.

Cooling curve 4, typical of a slow oil quench, is similar to the one just described, and the microstructure will be a mixture of medium and fine pearlite.

Cooling curve 5, typical of an intermediate cooling rate, will start to transform (at x_5) to fine pearlite in a relatively short time. The

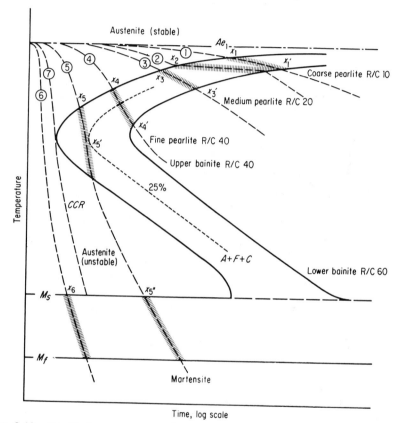

Fig. 8·19 Cooling curves superimposed on a hypothetical I-T diagram for a eutectoid steel. Zigzag portion of the cooling curve indicates transformation.

transformation to fine pearlite will continue until the curve becomes tangent to some percentage transformed, say 25 per cent, at x_5'. Below this temperature, the cooling curve is going in a direction of decreasing per cent transformed. Since pearlite cannot form austenite on cooling, the transformation must stop at x_5'. The microstructure at this point will consist 25 per cent of fine, nodular pearlite largely surrounding the existing austenitic grains. It will remain in this condition until the M_s line is crossed at x_5''. The remaining austenite now transforms to martensite. Figure 8·20 shows the microstructure of fine nodular pearlite in a martensitic matrix typical of an intermediate cooling rate.

Cooling curve 6, typical of a drastic quench, is rapid enough to avoid transformation in the nose region. It remains austenitic until the M_s line is reached at x_6. Transformation to martensite will take place between the M_s and M_f lines. The final microstructure will be entirely martensite of high hardness.

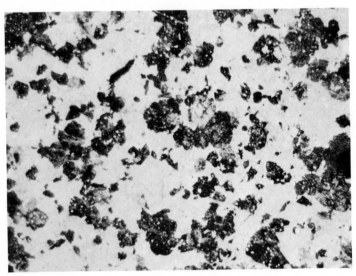

Fig. 8·20 Microstructure illustrating an intermediate cooling rate. High-carbon steel, oil-quenched. Fine pearlite (dark) in a martensitic matrix. Etched in 2 per cent nital, 500×.

It is apparent that to obtain a fully martensitic structure it is necessary to avoid transformation in the nose region. Therefore, cooling rate 7, which is tangent to the nose, would be the approximate critical cooling rate (CCR) for this steel.

8·11 Transformation on continuous cooling. Theoretically, cooling-rate curves should not be superimposed on the I-T diagram as was done in the previous section. The I-T diagram shows the time-temperature relationship for austenite transformation only as it occurs at constant temperature, but most heat treatments involve transformation on continuous cooling. It is possible to derive from the I-T diagram another diagram which will show the transformation under continuous cooling. This is referred to as the C-T diagram (cooling-transformation diagram) (Fig. 8·21). Consideration of the I-T diagram in relation to the location of lines of the C-T diagram in

Fig. 8·21 shows that the nose and the fields of the I-T diagram have been moved downward and to the right by continuous cooling. The derivation of a C-T diagram is a tedious task and is really not essential provided the fundamental relationship of the C-T diagram to the corresponding I-T diagram is understood.

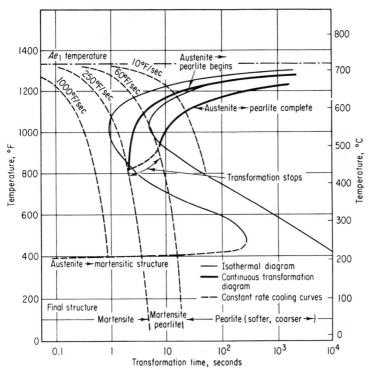

Fig. 8·21 Continuous cooling-transformation diagram derived from the isothermal diagram for a plain-carbon eutectoid steel. (*From "Atlas of Isothermal Transformation Diagrams," U.S. Steel Corporation*)

It should be noted that a particular I-T diagram exactly represents only one sample; samples from other heats, or even from other locations in the same heat, are likely to have slightly different I-T diagrams. When used with its limitations in mind, the I-T diagram is useful in interpreting and correlating observed transformation phenomena on a rational basis, even though austenite transforms during continuous cooling rather than at constant temperature.

8·12 Position of the I-T curves. There are only two factors that will change the position of the curves of the I-T diagram, namely, chemical composition and austenitic grain size. With few exceptions, an increase in carbon or alloy content or in grain size of the austenite

always retards transformation (moves the curves to the right),[1] at least
at temperatures at or above the nose region.   This in turn slows up
the critical cooling rate, making it easier to form martensite.   This
retardation is also reflected in the greater hardenability, or depth of

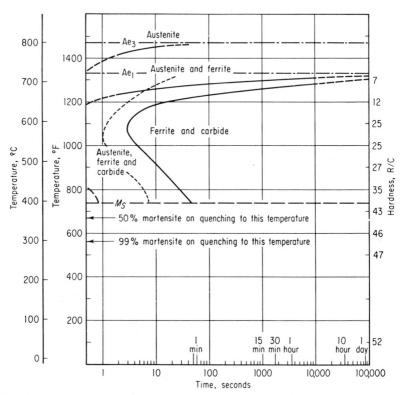

**Fig. 8·22   I-T diagram of a 0.35 per cent carbon, 0.37 per cent manganese
steel.   Grain size: 75 per cent, 2 to 3; 25 per cent, 7 to 8.   Austenitized at
1550°F.   (*From "Atlas of Isothermal Transformation Diagrams," U.S.
Steel Corporation*)**

penetration of hardness, of steel with higher alloy content or larger
austenitic grain size.   Although alloy additions tend in general to
delay the start of transformation and to increase the time for its
completion, they differ greatly in both the magnitude and nature of
their effects.   Figure 8·22 represents the I-T diagram of a 0.35 per
cent carbon, 0.37 per cent manganese steel.   Figure 8·23 shows the
effect of increasing the manganese content to 1.85 per cent, and Fig.
8·24 shows the effect of the addition of about 2 per cent chromium.
The addition of manganese has shifted the entire curve to the right.

The addition of 2 per cent chromium not only has shifted the curve to the right but has changed its shape, particularly in the region of 900 to 1200°F. The effect of alloy additions is cumulative. This is illustrated in the C-T diagram for a triple-alloy steel (Fig. 8·25). The critical cooling rate for this steel is shown to be approximately 54,000°F

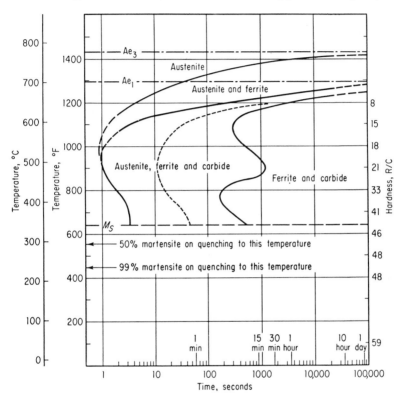

Fig. 8·23 I-T diagram of a 0.35 per cent carbon, 1.85 per cent manganese steel. Grain size: 70 per cent, 7; 30 per cent, 2. Austenitized at 1550°F. (*From "Atlas of Isothermal Transformation Diagrams," U.S. Steel Corporation*)

per hr, or about 15°F per sec as compared with the critical cooling rate of 250°F per sec for the eutectoid steel shown in Fig. 8·21. It is apparent that this eutectoid steel has a very fast critical cooling rate and low hardenability. The triple-alloy steel has a slow critical cooling rate, is deep-hardening, and illustrates how much easier it is to form martensite by the addition of alloying elements. This is one of the principal reasons for alloying steel. In general, the relative effect of the common alloying elements on the movement of the nose of the I-T diagram to the right is: vanadium (strongest), tungsten, molybdenum, chromium, manganese, silicon, and nickel (weakest).

The effect on the retardation of the critical cooling rate by coarsening the grain size of the austenite is shown in Fig. 8·26. The numbers

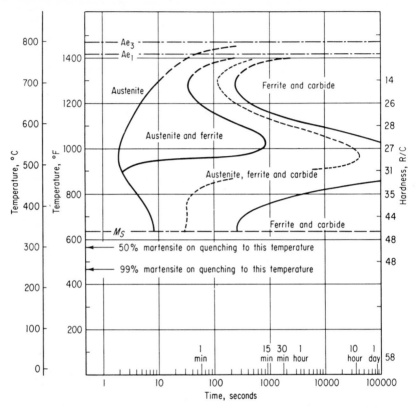

Fig. 8·24   I-T diagram of a 0.33 per cent carbon, 0.45 per cent manganese, 1.97 per cent chromium steel. Grain size: 6 to 7. Austenitized at 1600°F. (*From "Atlas of Isothermal Transformation Diagrams," U.S. Steel Corporation*)

that indicate grain size are related to the number of grains in a unit area so that the higher the number the finer the grain size.

8·13   Hardening or austenitizing temperature.   The recommended austenitizing temperature for hypoeutectoid steels is about 50°F above the upper critical temperature (A_3) line.   This is the same as the recommended annealing temperature.   At any temperature below the A_3 line there will be some proeutectoid ferrite present which will remain after quenching, giving rise to soft spots and lower hardness.

For plain-carbon hypereutectoid steels the recommended austenitizing temperature is usually between the A_{cm} and $A_{3,1}$ lines (Fig. 8·3). The A_{cm} line rises so steeply that an excessively high temperature may be required to dissolve all the proeutectoid cementite in

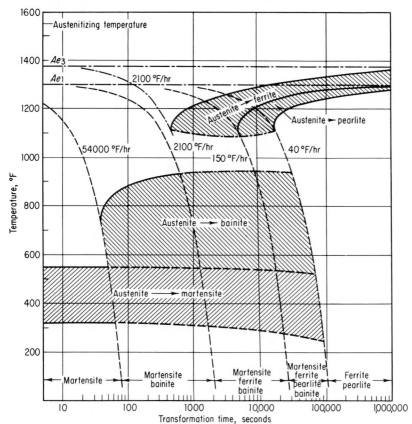

Fig. 8·25 C-T diagram of a triple alloy steel. 0.42 per cent carbon, 0.78 per cent manganese, 1.79 per cent nickel, 0.80 per cent chromium, 0.33 per cent molybdenum. (*From "U.S.S. Carilloy Steels," U.S. Steel Corporation*)

the austenite. This tends to develop undesirable coarse austenitic grain size, with danger of cracking on cooling.

8·14 Homogeneity of austenite. This refers to the uniformity in carbon content of the austenite grains. If a hypoeutectoid steel is heated for hardening, when the A_1 line is crossed, the austenite grains formed from pearlite will contain 0.8 per cent carbon. With continued heating, the austenite grains formed from proeutectoid ferrite will contain very little carbon, so that, when the A_3 line is crossed, the austenite grains will not be uniform in carbon content. Upon quenching, the austenite grains leaner in carbon, having a fast critical cooling rate, tend to transform to nonmartensitic structures while those richer in carbon, having a slower critical cooling rate, tend to form martensite. This results in a nonuniform microstructure with variable hardness. This condition may be avoided by very slow heating

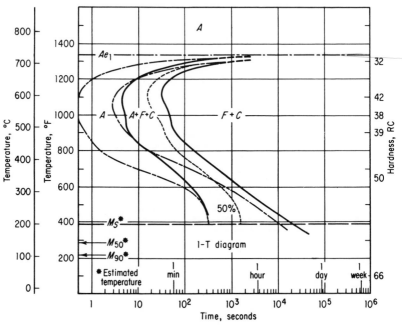

Fig. 8·26   I-T diagram of a 0.87 per cent carbon, 0.30 per cent manganese, 0.27 per cent vanadium steel. ———— Grain size: 2 to 3. Austenitized at 1925°F. – – – – Grain size: 11. Austenitized at 1500°F. (*From "Atlas of Isothermal Transformation Diagrams," U.S. Steel Corporation*)

so that uniformity is established by carbon diffusion during heating. However, the excessive time required by this method does not make it commercially practical. A more suitable method is to soak the material at the austenitizing temperature. At this temperature diffusion of carbon is rapid and uniformity will be established in a short time. To be on the safe side, it is recommended that the material be held at the austenitizing temperature 1 hr for each inch of thickness or diameter.

8·15 Mechanism of heat removal during quenching. The actual structure, hardness, and strength resulting from a heat-treating operation are determined by the actual cooling rate obtained by the quenching process. If the actual cooling rate exceeds the critical cooling rate, martensite will result.   If the actual cooling rate is less than the critical cooling rate, the part will not completely harden. The greater the difference between the two cooling rates the softer will be the transformation products and the lower the hardness.   At this point, it is necessary to understand the mechanism of heat removal during quenching.

To illustrate, a typical cooling curve for a small steel cylinder quenched in warm water is shown in Fig. 8·27.   Instead of showing

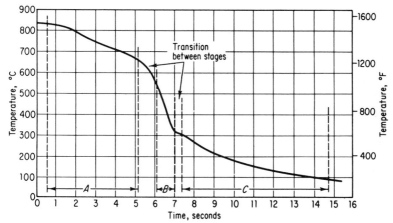

Fig. 8·27   **Typical cooling curve for a small cylinder quenched in warm water.**   (*Gulf Oil Corp.*)

a constant cooling rate throughout the quench, the cooling curve shows three distinct stages.

Stage A—Vapor-blanket Cooling Stage.   In this first stage, the temperature of the metal is so high that the quenching medium is vaporized at the surface of the metal and a thin stable film of vapor surrounds the hot metal.   Cooling is by conduction and radiation through the gaseous film, and since vapor films are poor heat conductors, the cooling rate is relatively slow through this stage.

Stage B—Vapor-transport Cooling Stage.   This stage starts when the metal has cooled to a temperature at which the vapor film is no longer stable.   Wetting of the metal surface by the quenching medium and violent boiling occur.   Heat is removed from the metal very rapidly as the latent heat of vaporization.   This is the fastest stage of cooling.

Stage C—Liquid Cooling Stage.   This stage starts when the surface temperature of the metal reaches the boiling point of the quenching liquid.   Vapor no longer forms; so cooling is by conduction and convection through the liquid.   The rate of cooling is slowest in this stage.

The actual cooling rate is obtained experimentally from a cooling curve by drawing a tangent to the curve at a particular temperature and determining the slope of the tangent. The more nearly horizontal the tangent, the slower is the cooling rate. Applying this to Fig. 8·27 shows that the cooling rate of a quenching medium is constantly changing.

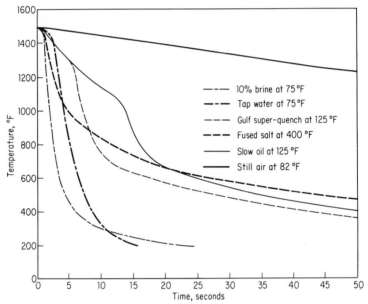

Fig. 8·28 **Center-cooling curves for stainless-steel specimens, ½ in. diameter by 2½ in. long. No agitation. (*Gulf Oil Corp.*)**

Many factors determine the actual cooling rate. The most important are the type of quenching medium, the temperature of the quenching medium, the surface condition of the part, and the size and mass of the part.

8·16 Quenching medium. In view of the mechanism of heat removal, the ideal quenching medium would show a high initial cooling rate to avoid transformation in the nose region of the I-T diagram and then a slow cooling rate throughout the lower-temperature range to minimize distortion. Unfortunately, there is no quenching medium that exhibits these ideal properties. Water and water solutions of inorganic salts have high initial cooling rates through the A and B stages, but these high cooling rates persist to low temperatures where distortion and cracking tend to occur. Conventional quenching oils have a longer A, or vapor-blanket, stage and a shorter B stage with a slower rate of cooling.

The following industrial quenching media are listed in order of decreasing quenching severity:

1. Water solution of 10 per cent sodium chloride (brine)
2. Tap water
3. Fused or liquid salts
4. Soluble oil and water solutions
5. Oil
6. Air

The cooling curves obtained by different media in the center of a ½-in.-diameter stainless-steel bar are shown in Fig. 8·28.

The usual methods of comparing the quenching speed of different

Table 8·2   Cooling rates at center of ½-in.-diameter by 2½-in.-long stainless-steel specimen when quenched from 1500°F in various media*

Bath	Rate at 1300°F, °F per sec		Rate at 1200°F, °F per sec		Average rate 1250–900°F, °F per sec	
	75°	125°	75°	125°	75°	125°
Brine (10%)	382	296	382	325	383	287
Tap water	211	46	223	117	220	176
Gulf Super-Quench	80	85	170	180	135	137
Slow oil	36	32	30	26	39	44
10% soluble oil, 90% water	36	30	36	30	34	28
Still air	5	...	4	...	3	
Fused salt (at 400°F)	162		130		66	

* Courtesy of Gulf Oil Corp.

media are by determining the rate of cooling at some fixed temperature or the average rate between two temperatures. Cooling rates of several media are given in Table 8·2.

8·17   Temperature of quenching medium. Generally, as the temperature of the medium rises, the cooling rate decreases (Fig. 8·29; Table 8·2). This is due to the increase in persistence of the vapor-blanket stage. Since the medium is closer to its boiling point, less heat is required to form the vapor film. This is particularly true of water and brine. In the case of oil, however, an increase in bath temperature decreases the viscosity of the oil and tends to produce a slightly faster cooling rate. The optimum rates of cooling are obtained with conventional quenching oils at bath temperatures between 120 and 150°F. To prevent a temperature rise in the medium during quenching, it is always necessary to provide sufficient volume of

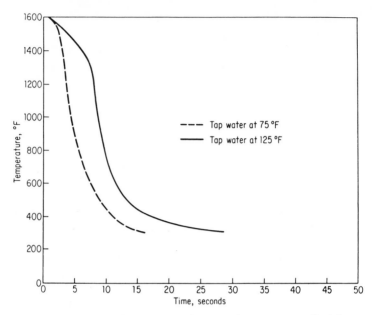

Fig. 8·29   Center-cooling curves for specimens quenched in tap water at bath temperatures of 75 and 125°F.   No agitation.   (*Gulf Oil Corp.*)

medium.   In some cases, cooling coils are inserted in the quenching tank to control the temperature of the medium.

The cooling rate may be improved and the temperature of the medium kept constant by circulation of the medium and agitation of the piece.   This effectively wipes off the vapor film as quickly as it forms, reducing the length of the vapor-blanket stage, and results in faster cooling (Fig. 8·30).   The quenching severity, relative to still water as 1.0, is shown in Table 8·3 for various conditions of quench.

Table 8·3   Quenching severity relative to still water as 1.0 for various conditions of quench*

Method of cooling	Oil	Water	Brine
No circulation of liquid or agitation of piece	0.25–0.30	0.9–1.0	2
Mild circulation or agitation	0.30–0.35	1.0–1.1	2–2.2
Moderate circulation	0.35–0.40	1.2–1.3	
Good circulation	0.40–0.50	1.4–1.5	
Strong circulation	0.50–0.80	1.6–2.0	
Violent circulation	0.80–1.10	4	5

* From M. A. Grossmann, "Principles of Heat Treatment," American Society for Metals, Metals Park, Ohio, 1953.

Circulation is a factor which is sometimes overlooked in the quenching process. It is possible, by proper choice of circulation, to obtain a wide variety of cooling rates with an oil quench.

8·18 Surface condition. When steel is exposed to an oxidizing atmosphere because of the presence of water vapor or oxygen in the furnace, a layer of iron oxide called *scale* is formed. Scale acts as an

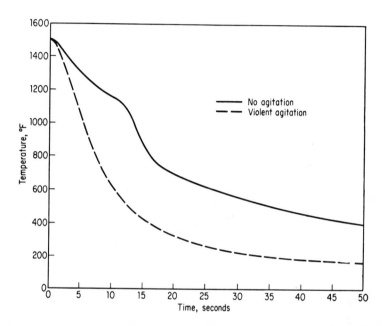

Fig. 8·30 **Effect of agitation on center-cooling curves of a stainless-steel specimen quenched in conventional quenching oil. Oil temperature 125°F. (*Gulf Oil Corp.*)**

insulator and seriously retards the flow of heat from the steel to the quenching medium. Thus, in some cases, the actual cooling rate with scale on the surface of the part may be reduced below the critical cooling rate, resulting in softer transformation products and lower hardness.

Many methods are used industrially to minimize the formation of scale. The choice of method depends upon the part being heat-treated, type of furnace used, availability of equipment, and cost.

Copper Plating. A flash coating of only a few ten-thousandths of an inch of copper will protect the surface of a steel against the formation of scale. This method is economical when copper-plating tanks are available in the plant.

Protective Atmosphere.   An atmosphere that is inert with respect to steel may be introduced under pressure into the furnace.   Gases used for this purpose are hydrogen, dissociated ammonia, and combusted gas resulting from the partial or complete combustion of hydrocarbon-fuel gases such as methane and propane in special generators.

Liquid-salt Pots.   The part to be heat-treated may be immersed in a liquid-salt furnace that is neutral with respect to the steel.   The

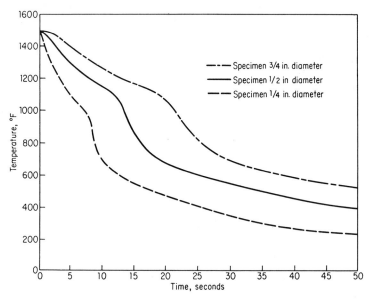

Fig. 8·31   **Effect of mass on center-cooling curves of stainless-steel specimens quenched in conventional quenching oil.   Oil temperature 125°F.   (*Gulf Oil Corp.*)**

piece, being completely surrounded by the neutral liquid salt, cannot be oxidized to form scale.

Cast-iron Chips.   The part is buried in a container having cast-iron chips.   Any oxygen entering the furnace reacts with the cast iron before it reaches the steel.

8·19   Size and mass.   Since it is only the surface of a part which is in contact with the quenching medium, the ratio of surface area to mass is an important factor in determining the actual cooling rate. This ratio is a function of the geometric shape of the part and is smallest for a spherical part.   Thin plates and small-diameter wires have a large ratio of surface area to mass and therefore rapid cooling rates.   Consider a long cylinder so that the surface area of the ends is negligible.   The surface area is equal to the circumference times the length of the cylinder, and the mass is equal to the cross-sectional area times the length times the density of the material. The ratio is

$$\frac{\text{Surface area}}{\text{Mass}} = \frac{\pi DL}{(\pi/4)D^2 L \rho} = \frac{4}{D\rho}$$

where ρ = density.

The calculation shows that the ratio is inversely proportional to diameter. If the diameter is increased, the ratio of surface area to mass decreases and the cooling rate decreases. In other words, with a fixed quenching medium, a large piece will be cooled more slowly than a small piece (Fig. 8·31). As the diameter increases, the duration of the vapor-blanket stage increases. The vapor-transport stage is less distinct, and the transition from the vapor-transport stage to the last stage becomes more gradual. The rate of cooling in all three stages decreases sharply (Fig. 8·32).

Let us now perform an experiment on a medium-carbon steel of about 0.45 per cent carbon. A series of pieces ranging from ½ to 5 in. diameter are heated to the proper austenitizing temperature and quenched in water. When the surface hardness was determined on these pieces, the following results were obtained:

Diameter of Piece Water-quenched, in.	Surface Hardness, Rockwell C
0.5	59
1	58
2	41
3	35
4	30
5	24

From the above data we can conclude that the actual cooling rate at the surface of the ½- and 1-in. pieces exceeded the critical cooling rate for this steel so that a fully martensitic structure was obtained with maximum hardness. The surface of the 2- and 3-in. pieces received intermediate cooling, and the structure is probably a mixture of martensite, fine pearlite, and a small amount of ferrite. The surface of the 4- and 5-in. pieces received slow cooling, with a resulting structure of pearlite and ferrite. As a matter of fact, for the 5-in. piece, the amount of heat to be removed is so large compared with the surface area available that the water quench is ineffective, and very nearly the same hardness would have been obtained if that piece had been cooled in the furnace. The approximate relation of the actual cooling curves of the surface to the I-T diagram is shown in Fig. 8·33.

Up to this point, the discussion has concerned itself only with the surface hardness. The surface, being in actual contact with the

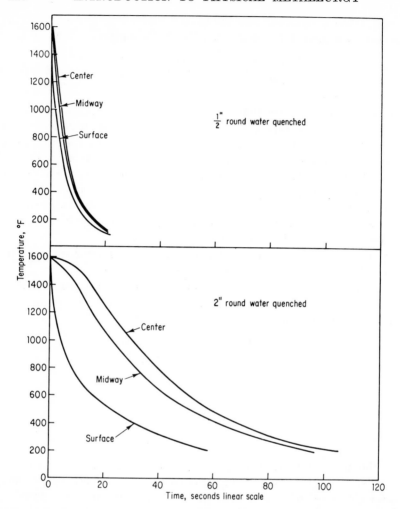

Fig. 8·32   Cooling curves at the surface, midway on the radius, and the center of two different-sized bars when water-quenched.   (From "Suiting the Heat Treatment to the Job," U.S. Steel Corporation)

quenching medium, was cooled most rapidly in quenching.   The heat in the interior of the piece must be removed by conduction, through the body of the piece, eventually reaching the surface and the quenching medium.   Therefore, the cooling rate in the interior is less than that at the surface.   Figure 8·34 shows the time-temperature cooling curves at different positions in a 1-in.-diameter bar during a drastic quench. If such a variation in cooling rates exists across the radius of a bar during cooling, it is to be anticipated that variations in hardness

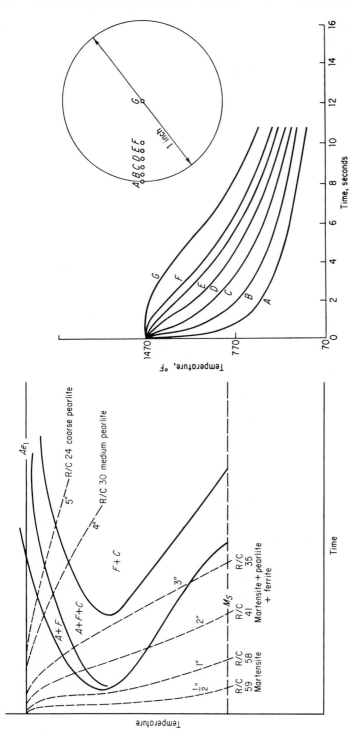

Fig. 8.34 Time-temperature cooling curves at different positions in a 1-in.-diameter bar quenched drastically in water. (*From M. A. Grossmann, "Principles of Heat Treatment," American Society for Metals, Metals Park, Ohio, 1955*)

Fig. 8.33 Surface-cooling curves, the final structure and hardness of different-sized rounds related to the I-T diagram of a 0.45 per cent carbon steel.

221

would be evident when the bars are cut and hardness surveys made on the cross section.

The results of a hardness survey on the different diameters, whose surface hardness was previously mentioned, are shown in Fig. 8·35a. This may be called a *hardness-penetration diagram*, since it shows at

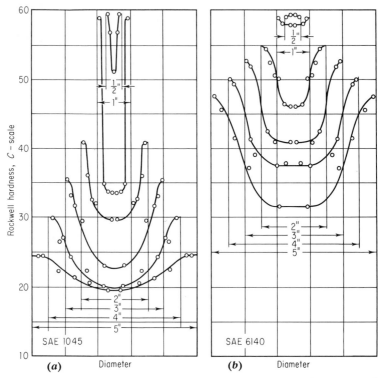

Fig. 8·35 Hardness-penetration curves for various sizes quenched in water. (a) SAE 1045 steel; (b) SAE 6140 chrome-vanadium steel. (*From M. A. Grossmann, "Principles of Heat Treatment," American Society for Metals, Metals Park, Ohio, 1955*)

a glance to what extent the steel has hardened during quenching. Hardenability is related to the depth of penetration of the hardness, and in no case has the hardness penetrated deeply, so that this steel is said to have *low hardenability*. As anticipated, it is seen that the hardness of the quenched piece is less as its size increases, and also that each piece is lower in hardness at the center than at the surface.

A study of the curves of Fig. 8·35a shows an interesting situation. The hardness of Rockwell C 30 was obtained (1) at the surface of a 4-in. round, (2) at about ½ in. under the surface of a 3-in. round, and (3) at almost the center of a 2-in. round. These three points are equivalent and have reached the same hardness because the actual cooling rate was the same at each location. This leads to a very important conclusion: *that for a steel of fixed composition and austenitic grain size, regardless of the shape or size of the piece and the quenching conditions, wherever the actual cooling rate is the same, the hardness must be the same.* The student should realize that the converse of this statement is not necessarily true. Wherever the hardness is the same in a steel of fixed composition and austenitic grain size, the actual cooling rate may or may not have been the same. If the actual cooling rate at the center of a piece exceeds the critical cooling rate for the steel, the hardness at the center will be the same as that at the surface but the actual cooling rate at both locations will be different. This is shown in Fig. 8·35*b* for a ½-in. bar.

Increase in the hardenability or depth of penetration of the hardness may be accomplished by either of two methods:

1. With the actual cooling rates fixed, slow up the critical cooling rate (shift the I-T curve to the right) by adding alloying elements or coarsening the austenitic grain size.

2. With the I-T curve fixed, increase the actual cooling rates by using a faster quenching medium or increasing circulation.

Since increasing cooling rates increase the danger of distortion or cracking, the addition of alloying elements is the more popular method of increasing hardenability. Figure 8·35*b* shows the hardness-penetration diagrams, after water quenching, for different-size rounds of a chromium-vanadium steel of about the same carbon content as Fig. 8·35*a*. The hardness level of all sizes has been raised appreciably, and notice that the 1-in. size has almost achieved a fully martensitic structure across its diameter. If the actual cooling rate is reduced by using an oil quench, the hardness level of all pieces made of the plain-carbon steel will drop, as shown by Fig. 8·36*a*. Even the chromium-vanadium steel (Fig. 8·36*b*) shows a drop in hardness level in an oil quench as compared with the water quench, but note that the ½-in. round still attained full hardness.

During the entire discussion of cooling rates, it was assumed that the thermal conductivity of all steels is the same. This is not technically true, but the variation in thermal conductivity between different steels is so small compared with the other variables in the quenching process that it may be considered constant with little error.

8·20 Hardenability. The usual method of purchasing steel is on the basis of chemical composition. This allows a considerable variation in the carbon and alloy content of the steel. For example, AISI 4340 steel has the following composition range: 0.38 to 0.43 per cent C, 0.60 to 0.80 per cent Mn, 0.20 to 0.35 per cent Si, 1.65 to 2.00 per cent Ni, 0.70 to 0.90 per cent Cr, and 0.20 to 0.30 per cent Mo. This variation in chemical composition within a particular grade will cause a variation in the critical cooling rate and in turn a variation in the response of the steel to heat treatment. Since strength is the primary factor in design, unless special properties are desired, it would

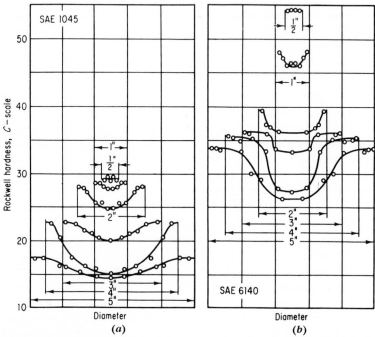

Fig. 8·36   Hardness-penetration curves for various sizes quenched in oil. (*a*) SAE 1045 steel; (*b*) SAE 6140 chrome-vanadium steel. (*From M. A. Grossmann, "Principles of Heat Treatment," American Society for Metals, Metals Park, Ohio, 1955*)

seem more economical to base the material specification on the response to heat treatment (hardenability) rather than chemical composition. It is therefore necessary to have a test that will predict the hardenability of the steel. The most widely used method of determining hardenability is the *end-quench hardenability test*, or the *Jominy test*.

The test has been standardized by the ASTM, SAE, and AISI. In conducting this test, a 1-in. round specimen 4 in. long is heated uniformly to the proper austenitizing temperature. It is then removed from the furnace and placed on a fixture where a jet of water impinges on the bottom face of the specimen (Fig. 8·37). The size of the orifice, the distance from the orifice to the bottom of the specimen, and the temperature and circulation of the water are all standardized, so that every specimen quenched in this fixture receives the same rate of cooling. After 10 min on the fixture, the specimen is removed and two parallel flat surfaces are ground longitudinally to a depth of 0.015 in. Rockwell C scale hardness readings are taken at $\frac{1}{16}$-in. intervals

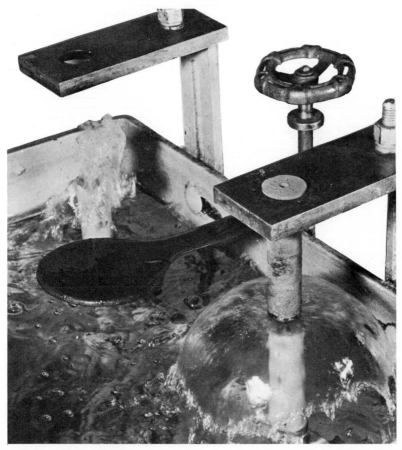

Fig. 8-37   End-quench hardenability specimen being quenched. (*Bethlehem Steel Company*)

from the quenched end. The results are expressed as a curve of hardness values vs. distance from the quenched end. A typical hardenability curve is shown in Fig. 8·38. Details pertaining to the testing procedure may be obtained by referring to ASTM Designation A255-48T End Quench Test for Hardenability of Steel.

Each location on the Jominy test piece, quenched in a standard manner, represents a certain cooling rate, and since the thermal conductivity of all steels is assumed to be the same, this cooling rate is

A.S.T.M. END QUENCH TEST
FOR HARDENABILITY
OF STEEL (A 255-48T)

DATE_____
LABORATORY_____
TYPE SPECIMEN_____
TEST NO._____

TYPE	HEAT NO.	GRAIN SIZE	C	Mn	P	S	Si	Ni	Cr	Mo	Cu	NORMAL TEMP °F	QUENCH TEMP °F
4620	35862	8	.18	.55	.018	.018	.27	1.79	.47	.23	.14		1700

REMARKS:

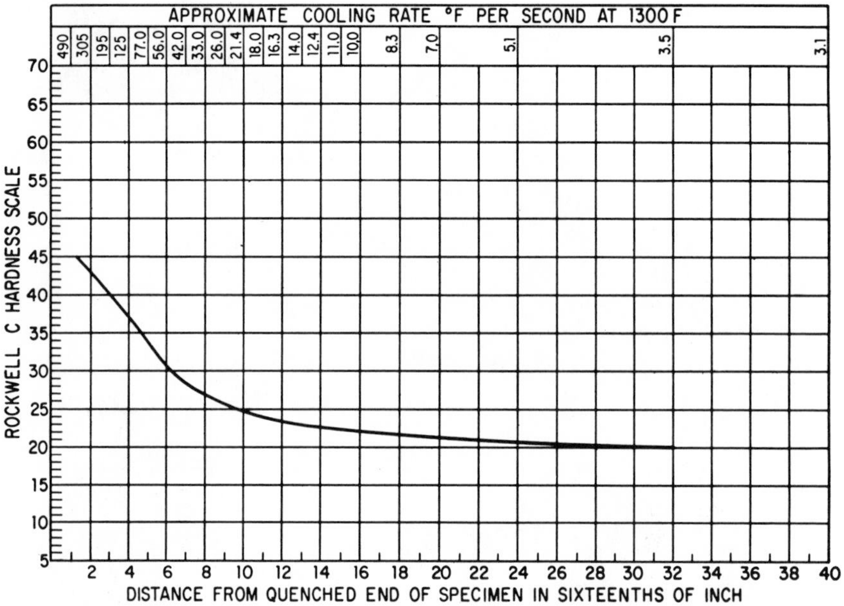

Fig. 8·38   A typical end-quench hardenability curve.

the same for a given position on the test piece regardless of the composition of the steel from which the test piece is made.   Each specimen is thus subjected to a series of cooling rates varying continuously from very rapid at the quenched end to very slow at the air-cooled end (Table 8·4).

Figure 8·39 shows the continuous cooling-transformation diagram for an alloy steel of the 8630 type on which cooling curves, representing those at selected locations along the end-quench test bar, have been superimposed.   This serves to clarify the relationship between the

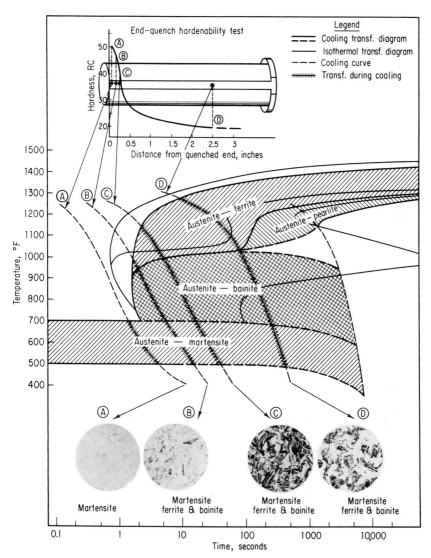

Fig. 8·39 Correlation of continuous-cooling and I-T diagrams with end-quench hardenability test data for an 8630 type steel. (*From "U.S.S. Carilloy Steels," U.S. Steel Corporation*)

end-quench hardenability test and the transformation behavior previously discussed.

Analyzing the microstructural changes on cooling at these various rates, it will be seen that rate A, which represents the rate nearest the quenched end, exceeds the critical cooling rate and will result in transformation to martensite. Rates B, C, and D all result in transformation to various mixtures of ferrite, bainite, and martensite, the amount of martensite decreasing with the decrease in cooling rate.

Table 8·4   Cooling rates at distances from the water-cooled end of the standard end-quench hardenability test bar

Distance from quenched end, in.	Cooling rate, °F per sec at 1300°F	Distance from quenched end, in.	Cooling rate, °F per sec at 1300°F
$\frac{1}{16}$	489	$1\frac{1}{16}$	19.5
$\frac{1}{8}$	307	$\frac{3}{4}$	16.3
$\frac{3}{16}$	195	$1\frac{3}{16}$	14.5
$\frac{1}{4}$	124	$\frac{7}{8}$	12.4
$\frac{5}{16}$	77.2	$1\frac{5}{16}$	11.5
$\frac{3}{8}$	56.3	1	10.0
$\frac{7}{16}$	41.9	$1\frac{1}{4}$	7.0
$\frac{1}{2}$	32.3	$1\frac{1}{2}$	5.1
$\frac{9}{16}$	25.0	$1\frac{3}{4}$	4.0
$\frac{5}{8}$	21.4	2	3.5

It should be noted that a very slow cooling rate is necessary to obtain pearlite in this steel.

Although hardenability is usually expressed in terms of hardness changes, it is the changes in microstructure reflected by those hardness values which are of importance in the properties of steel.   Alloying elements, in general, increase hardenability by delaying transformation in the pearlite and bainite regions, thus permitting the formation of martensite with slower rates of cooling.

The end-quench curves of three alloy steels, each containing 0.40 per cent carbon but of different hardenability, are shown in Fig. 8·40. All three steels develop the same maximum hardness of Rockwell C 52.5 at the water-quenched end since this is primarily a function of carbon content only.   However, in the high-hardenability steel 4340, this hardness is maintained for a distance of ten-sixteenths, whereas in the lower-hardenability steels 4140 and 5140 the hardness drops off almost immediately.

By the analysis of data collected from hundreds of heats of each grade of steel, the AISI has established minimum and maximum hardenability curves known as *hardenability bands*. A typical hardenability band is shown in Fig. 8·41. The suffix H denotes steels that may be bought on the basis of a hardenability specification, with chemical composition, grain size, etc., being of secondary importance.

Two points are usually designated in specifying hardenability by one of the following methods:

1. The minimum and maximum hardness values at any desired distance. The distance selected should be that distance on the end-quench test bar which corresponds to the section used by the purchaser.

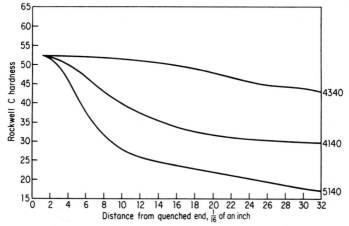

Fig. 8·40 End-quench hardenability curves for individual samples of 4340, 4140, and 5140 alloy steels.

For example, in Fig. 8·41, the specification could be J50/58 = $\frac{6}{16}$ in.

2. The minimum and maximum distances at which any desired hardness value occurs. This method of specification, in Fig. 8·41, could be J50 = $\frac{6}{16}$ to $2\frac{1}{16}$ in.

8·21 Use of hardenability data. To select a steel to meet a minimum hardness at a given location in a part quenched under given conditions, the cooling rate at the given location must first be known and the reference point on the end-quench test bar having the same cooling rate must be determined. If the part is simple in cross section, such as round, flat, or square, numerous charts are available in the literature which give the cooling rate at different locations under various quenching conditions or the equivalent point on the end-quench test bar that has the same cooling rate. The relation between the end-quench test bar and the center and mid-radius locations of various sizes of rounds quenched under different conditions is shown in Figs. 8·42 and 8·43. The severity of quench is designated by Table 8·5. Let us assume that a minimum hardness of Rockwell C 40 is

Hardness limits for specification purposes		
"J" distance 1/16"	4140H	
	Max	Min
1	60	53
2	60	53
3	60	52
4	59	51
5	59	51
6	58	50
7	58	48
8	57	47
9	57	44
10	56	42
11	56	40
12	55	39
13	55	38
14	54	37
15	54	36
16	53	35
18	52	34
20	51	33
22	49	33
24	48	32
26	47	32
28	46	31
30	45	31
32	44	30

Heat treating temperatures recommended by SAE
*Normalize 1600 °F
Austenitize 1550 °F
*For forged or rolled specimens only

Hardenability band 4140 H

C	Mn	Si		Cr	Mo	
0.37/0.44	0.65/1.10	0.20/0.35		0.75/1.20	0.15/0.25	

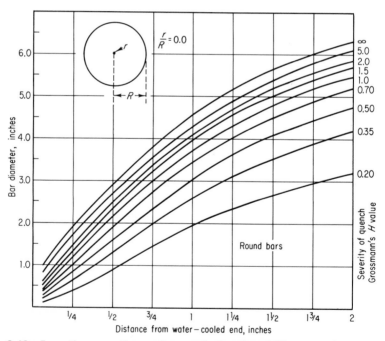

Rockwell hardness, C scale vs. Distance from quenched end, 1/16"

Fig. 8·41 Test data and standard hardenability band for 4140H steel. (*American Iron and Steel Institute*)

Fig. 8·42 Location on the end-quench hardenability test bar corresponding to the center of round bars under various quenching conditions. (*From "U.S.S. Carilloy Steels," U.S. Steel Corporation*)

230

Table 8·5   H or severity of quench values for various quenching conditions*

H Value	Quenching Condition
0.20	Poor oil quench—no agitation
0.35	Good oil quench—moderate agitation
0.50	Very good oil quench—good agitation
0.70	Strong oil quench—violent agitation
1.00	Poor water quench—no agitation
1.50	Very good water quench—strong agitation
2.00	Brine quench—no agitation
5.00	Brine quench—violent agitation
∞	Ideal quench

* From "U.S.S. Carilloy Steels," U.S. Steel Corporation.

required at the center of a 2-in. round with a good oil quench and moderate agitation (H = 0.35, Table 8·5). Reference to Fig. 8·42 shows that the center of a 2-in. round and severity of quench of 0.35 correspond to three-fourths on the end-quench hardenability test bar. The specification should be J40 min = $^{12}/_{16}$. Examination of published minimum-hardenability limits will result in the selection of several steels to meet the above requirements. The final selection

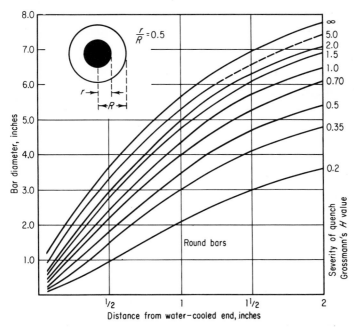

Fig. 8·43   Location on the end-quench hardenability test bar corresponding to the mid-radius position of round bars under various quenching conditions. (*From "U.S.S. Carilloy Steels," U.S. Steel Corporation*)

will be based on other manufacturing requirements and will show the greatest overall economy.

The typical U curves (Fig. 8·35) or hardness-penetration curves of rounds quenched under given conditions may be calculated from the standard hardenability band (Fig. 8·41) and a series of curves such as Figs. 8·42 and 8·43. The calculated results will show the maximum and minimum hardness variation across the cross section of various sizes of rounds.

It is possible to show the relation between the minimum as-quenched hardness at the center location and the diameter of different-sized rounds quenched under the same conditions, by means of the standard hardenability band (Fig. 8·41) and the curves of Fig. 8·42. The same may be done at other locations by curves similar to Fig. 8·42.

The approximate cooling rate, under fixed quenching conditions, at any location in an irregularly shaped part may be determined if the hardenability curve for that steel is available. Assume that a hardness of Rockwell C 40 was obtained at a particular location in a part made of 4140 steel whose hardenability curve is shown in Fig. 8·40. Rockwell C 40 is obtained at a distance of ten-sixteenths on the end-quench test bar, and Table 8·4 gives the cooling rate at that location as 21.4°F per sec.

When steel is purchased on the basis of a hardenability specification, the purchaser is certain that he will obtain the desired mechanical properties after heat treatment. This results in fewer rejections or retreatments and greater economy.

8·22 Tempering. In the as-quenched martensitic condition, the steel is too brittle for most applications. The formation of martensite also leaves high residual stresses in the steel. Therefore, hardening is almost always followed by tempering or drawing, which consists in heating the steel to some temperature below the lower critical temperature A_1. The purpose of tempering is to relieve residual stresses and to improve the ductility and toughness of the steel. This increase in ductility is usually attained at the sacrifice of the hardness or strength.

In general, over the broad range of tempering temperatures, hardness decreases and toughness increases as the tempering temperature is increased. This is true if toughness is measured by reduction of area in a tensile test. However, this is not entirely true if the notched bar such as Izod or Charpy is used as a measure of toughness. Most steels actually show a decrease in notched-bar toughness when tempered between 400 and 800°F even though the piece at the same time loses hardness and strength. The reason for this decrease in toughness is not fully understood. The variation of hardness and notched-bar toughness with tempering temperature shown in Fig. 8·44 is typical of plain-carbon and low-alloy steels.

The tempering range of 400 to 800°F is a dividing·line between applications that require high hardness and those requiring high toughness. If the principal desired property is hardness or wear resistance, the part is tempered below 400°F; if the primary requirement is toughness, the part is tempered above 800°F. If the part does not have any "stress raisers" or notches, the change in ductility may be a better indication of toughness than the notched-bar test, and tempering in the range of 400 to 800°F may not be detrimental. The effect of

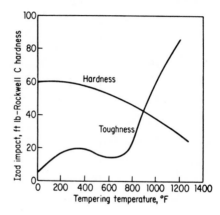

Fig. 8·44 Hardness and notched-bar toughness of 4140 steel after tempering 1 hr at various temperatures. (*From "Suiting the Heat Treatment to the Job," U.S. Steel Corporation*)

tempering temperature on the mechanical properties of a low-alloy steel 4140 is shown in Fig. 8·45.

Residual stresses are relieved to a large extent when the tempering temperature reaches 400°F, and by 900°F they are almost completely gone.

Certain alloy steels exhibit a phenomenon known as *temper brittleness*, which is a loss of notched-bar toughness when tempered in the range of 1000 to 1250°F followed by relatively slow cooling. Toughness is maintained, however, if the part is quenched in water from the tempering temperature. The precise mechanism which causes temper brittleness has not been established, although the behavior suggests some phase which precipitates along the grain boundaries during slow cooling. High manganese, phosphorus, and chromium appear to promote susceptibility while molybdenum seems to have a definite retarding effect.

Martensite, as defined previously, is a supersaturated solid solution of carbon trapped in a body-centered tetragonal structure. This is a metastable condition, and as energy is applied by tempering, the carbon will be precipitated as carbide and the iron will become b.c.c.

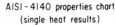

AISI - 4140 properties chart
(single heat results)

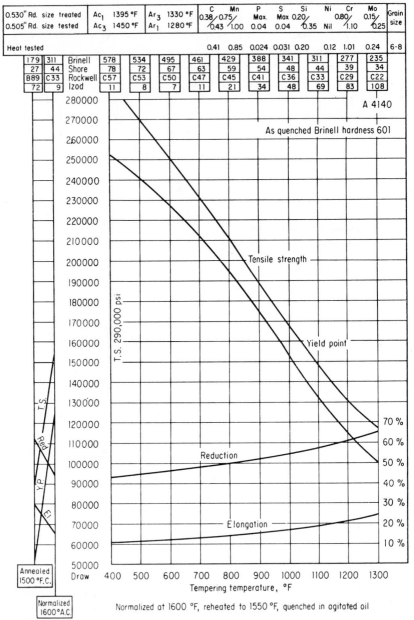

| 0.530" Rd. size treated | Ac₁ 1395 °F | Ar₃ 1330 °F | C Mn | P | S | Si | Ni | Cr | Mo | Grain |
| 0.505" Rd. size tested | Ac₃ 1450 °F | Ar₁ 1280 °F | 0.38/0.75 /0.43 /1.00 | Max. 0.04 | Max 0.04 | 0.20 /0.35 | Nil | 0.80/ 1.10 | 0.15/ 0.25 | size |

| Heat tested | | | | 0.41 | 0.85 | 0.024 0.031 0.20 | 0.12 1.01 0.24 | 6-8 |

179	311	Brinell	578	534	495	461	429	388	341	311	277	235
27	44	Shore	78	72	67	63	59	54	48	44	39	34
B89	C33	Rockwell	C57	C53	C50	C47	C45	C41	C36	C33	C29	C22
72	9	Izod	11	8	7	11	21	34	48	69	83	108

A 4140

As quenched Brinell hardness 601

Tensile strength

Yield point

70 %
60 %
50 %
Reduction
40 %
30 %
Elongation 20 %
10 %

Annealed 1500 °F.C. Draw 400 500 600 700 800 900 1000 1100 1200 1300
Tempering temperature, °F

Normalized 1600 °A.C.   Normalized at 1600 °F, reheated to 1550 °F, quenched in agitated oil

Fig. 8·45 Mechanical properties of 4140 steel after oil quenching and tempering at various temperatures. (*Bethlehem Steel Company*)

There will be diffusion and coalescence of the carbide as the tempering temperature is raised.

When steel is tempered in the range of 100 to 400°F, the martensite progressively loses its tetragonal structure to become cubic, and the first precipitation of a carbide appears. X-ray study has shown that this first precipitate, known as *transition carbide*, is quite different

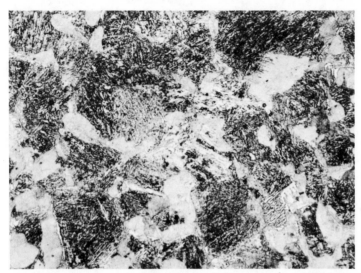

Fig. 8·46   1045 steel water-quenched and tempered at 600°F for 1 hr. Tempered martensite (dark) and untempered martensite (gray).   Etched in 2 per cent nital, 500×.

from cementite and that it may possibly be of a composition approaching Fe_2C. The precipitation of this compound causes a slight but measurable increase in hardness, particularly in high-carbon steels.

Heating in the range of 450 to 750°F continues the precipitation and growth of transition carbide, and any retained austenite is transformed to lower bainite. The carbides are too small to be resolved by the optical microscope, and the entire structure etches rapidly to a black mass formerly called *troostite* (Fig. 8·46). If the sample is magnified 9,000 diameters using the electron microscope, the carbide precipitate is clearly seen. Some of the carbide has come out along original martensitic plate directions (Fig. 8·47).

Tempering in the range of 750 to 1200°F causes the carbide to become cementite (Fe_3C) and continues the growth of the carbides. This coalescence of the carbide particles allows more of the ferrite matrix to be seen, causing the sample to etch lighter than the lower-temperature product. In this structure, formerly known as *sorbite*, the carbide

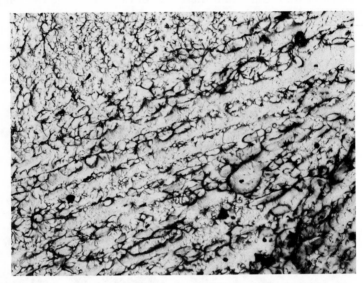

Fig. 8·47   Same sample as Fig. 8·46 taken with the electron microscope, 9,000×.

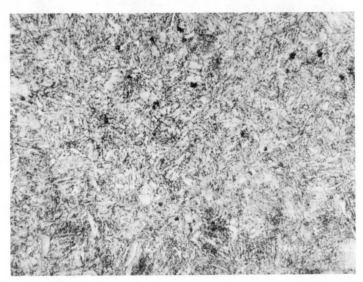

Fig. 8·48   1045 steel water-quenched and tempered at 1150°F for 1 hr. Precipitated carbide particles in a ferrite matrix.   Etched in 2 per cent nital, 500×.

is just about resolvable at 500× (Fig. 8·48) and is clearly seen in the electron micrograph (Fig. 8·49).

Heating in the range from 1200 to 1333°F produces large, globular cementite particles. This structure is very soft and tough and is similar to the spheroidized cementite structure obtained directly from austenite by a spheroidize anneal.

For many years, metallurgists divided the tempering process into definite stages. The microstructure appearing in these stages was given

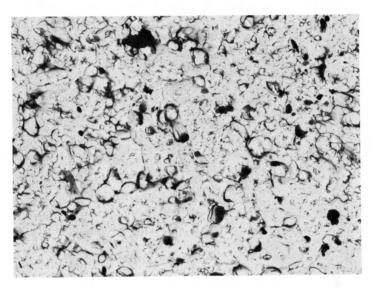

Fig. 8·49   Same sample as Fig. 8·48 taken with the electron microscope, 9,000×.

names like troostite and sorbite. However, the changes in microstructure are so gradual that it is more realistic to call the product of tempering at any temperature simply *tempered martensite.*

In the above discussion, time of tempering has been assumed to be constant. Since tempering is a process that involves energy, both time and temperature are factors. The same effect can be achieved by using a shorter time at a higher temperature as by using a longer time at a lower temperature. Figure 8·50 shows the effect of time at four tempering temperatures for a eutectoid steel. Note that most of the softening action occurs in the first few minutes and that little further reduction in hardness results from increasing the time of tempering from say 1 to 5 hr.

It is important to realize that, when toughness measurements are made in order to compare different steels, the comparisons must be made at the same hardness or strength levels, and at the same temperature of testing.

If a medium tensile strength is desired, one may ask why it is necessary first to form a fully martensitic structure and then to reduce the strength substantially in tempering, when the same tensile strength may be obtained, with less difficulty in quenching, from mixtures of martensite and bainite or martensite and pearlite. Samples of a medium-carbon alloy steel were heat-treated in three different ways: (1) quenched to martensite, (2) partially transformed isothermally to bainite and quenched to form a mixture of bainite and martensite, (3) partially transformed isothermally to ferrite and pearlite and then

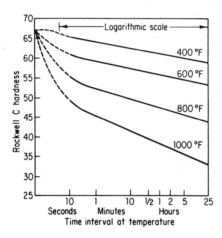

Fig. 8·50   Effect of time interval at four tempering temperatures upon the softening of a quenched 0.82 per cent carbon steel. (*From E. C. Bain and H. W. Paxton, "Alloying Elements in Steel," American Society for Metals, Metals Park, Ohio, 1961*)

quenched, resulting in a mixture of largely pearlite and martensite. The three samples were then tempered to the same tensile strength of 125,000 psi and tested. The sample that was fully martensitic before tempering had the highest yield strength, the highest ductility, the highest fatigue strength, and the greatest toughness. Figure 8·51 shows the notched-bar toughness of the three structures at different testing temperatures.

As a further aid in the selection of a steel for a given application, it is possible to extend the usefulness of the end-quench hardenability test by subjecting additional end-quench samples to various tempering temperatures (Fig. 8·52).

8·23   Austempering. This is a heat-treating process developed from the I-T diagram to obtain a structure which is 100 per cent bainite. It is accomplished by first heating the part to the proper austenitizing temperature followed by cooling rapidly in a salt bath held in the bainite range (usually between 400 and 800°F). The piece is left in the bath until the transformation to bainite is complete.

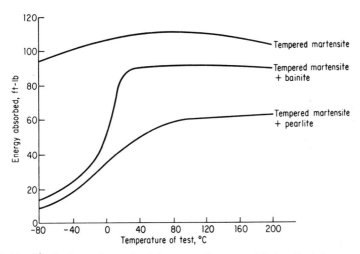

Fig. 8·51 Variation of notched-bar toughness with testing temperature for three structures tempered to the same tensile strength of 125,000 psi. (*By permission from R. M. Brick and A. Phillips, "Structure and Properties of Alloys," 2d ed., McGraw-Hill Book Company, Inc., New York, 1949*)

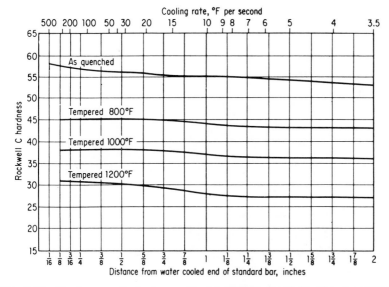

Fig. 8·52 End-quench test results of 4340H steel in the as-quenched condition and after tempering at the indicated temperatures. (*Joseph T. Ryerson & Son, Inc.*)

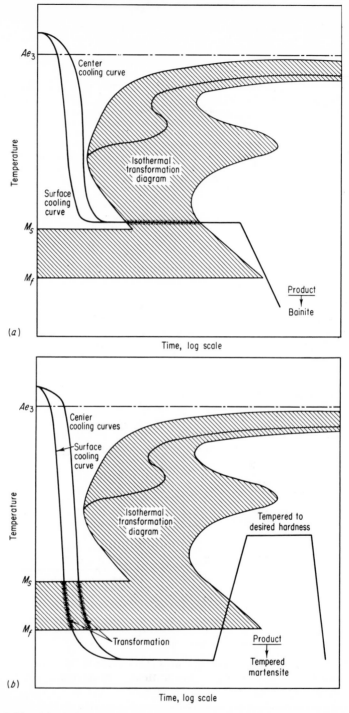

Fig. 8·53 (*a*) Schematic transformation diagram for austempering; (*b*) schematic transformation diagram for conventional quench and temper method. (*From "U.S.S. Carilloy Steels," U.S. Steel Corporation*)

The steel is caused to go directly from austenite to some particular desired structure, and at no time is the steel in the fully hardened martensitic state.   Actually, austempering is a complete heat treatment, and no reheating is involved as in tempering.   Figure 8·53 illustrates austempering schematically, showing the difference between austempering and the conventional quench and temper method.

The comparison of mechanical properties developed by austempering

Table 8·6   Summary of tensile and impact properties of 0.180-in. round rods heat-treated by quench and temper method and by austempering*

Property measured	Quench and temper method	Austempering
Rockwell C hardness	49.8	50.0
Ultimate tensile strength, psi	259,000	259,300
Elongation, % in 2 in.	3.75	5.0
Reduction in area, %	26.1	46.4
Impact, ft-lb (unnotched round specimen)	14.0	36.6
Free-bend test	Ruptured at 45°	Greater than 150° without rupture

Analysis: 0.78% C; 0.58% Mn; 0.146% Si; 0.042% P; 0.040% S
Heat treatment resulting in grain size (1450°F) 5 to 6 with 6 predominating:

Quench and Temper	*Austempering*
Pb bath 1450°F, 5 min	Pb bath 1450°F, 5 min
Oil quench	Transformed in Pb-Bi bath at 600°F, 20 min
Tempered 650°F, 30 min	

* Research Laboratory, U.S. Steel Corporation.

and the quench and temper method is usually made at the same hardness or strength (Table 8·6).   The superiority of austempering shows up in such properties as reduction of area in tension, resistance to impact, and the slow-bend test (Fig. 8·54).   A striking demonstration of the resiliency of an austempered shovel is shown in Fig. 8·55. The marked improvement in the impact strength of austempered parts is most pronounced in the hardness range of Rockwell C 45 to 55 (Fig. 8·56).

Aside from the advantage of greater ductility and toughness along with high hardness as a result of austempering, there is also less distortion and danger of quenching cracks because the quench is not so drastic as that of the conventional method.

The primary limitation of austempering is the effect of mass of the part being heat-treated.   Only sections which can be cooled fast

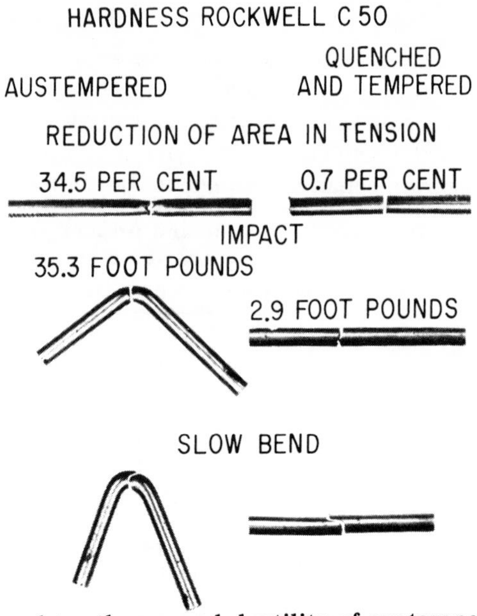

HARDNESS ROCKWELL C 50

AUSTEMPERED

QUENCHED
AND TEMPERED

REDUCTION OF AREA IN TENSION

34.5 PER CENT   0.7 PER CENT

IMPACT

35.3 FOOT POUNDS

2.9 FOOT POUNDS

SLOW BEND

Fig. 8·54 Improved toughness and ductility of austempered rods compared with quenched and tempered rods at the same hardness. (*Edgar C. Bain Research Laboratory, U.S. Steel Corporation*)

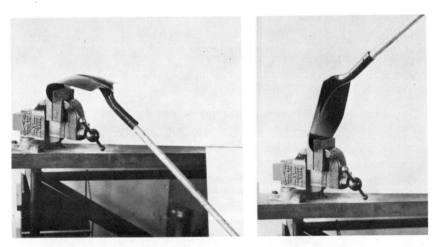

Fig. 8·55 A striking demonstration of an austempered shovel. The picture on the left shows the extent to which the shovel can be bent without failure, and that on the right shows how the bent shovel, after removal of the bending force, returns to its original position without permanent deformation. (*Edgar C. Bain Research Laboratory, U.S. Steel Corporation*)

enough to avoid transformation to pearlite, in the temperature range of 900 to 1200°F, are suitable. Therefore, most industrial applications have been in sections less than ½ in. thick (Fig. 8·57). This thickness may be increased somewhat by the use of alloy steels, but then the time for completion of transformation to bainite may become excessive.

8·24 Surface heat treatment or case hardening. Numerous industrial applications require a hard wear-resistant surface called the

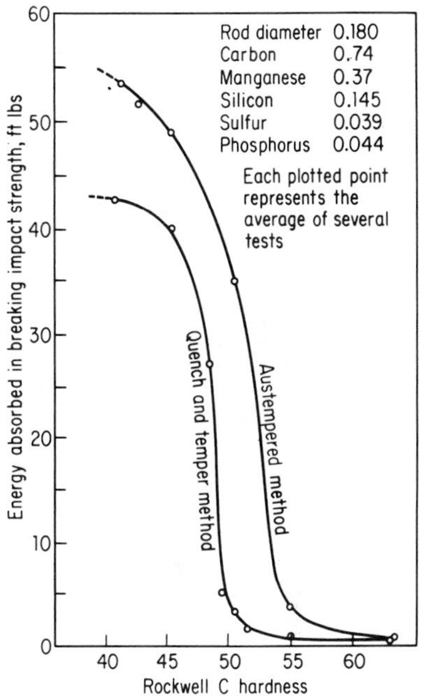

Fig. 8·56 Comparison between austempered and quenched and tempered steel. (*From "Suiting the Heat Treatment to the Job," U.S. Steel Corporation*)

case, and a relatively soft, tough inside called the *core*. There are five principal methods of case hardening:

1. Carburizing
2. Nitriding
3. Cyaniding or carbonitriding
4. Flame hardening
5. Induction hardening

The first three methods change the chemical composition, carburizing by the addition of carbon, nitriding by the addition of nitrogen, and cyaniding by the addition of both carbon and nitrogen. The last two methods do not change the chemical composition of the steel and are essentially shallow-hardening methods. In flame and induction hardening the steel must be capable of being hardened; therefore, the carbon content must be about 0.35 per cent or higher.

8.25 Carburizing. This is the oldest and one of the cheapest methods of case hardening. A low-carbon steel, usually about 0.20 per cent carbon or lower, is placed in an atmosphere that contains

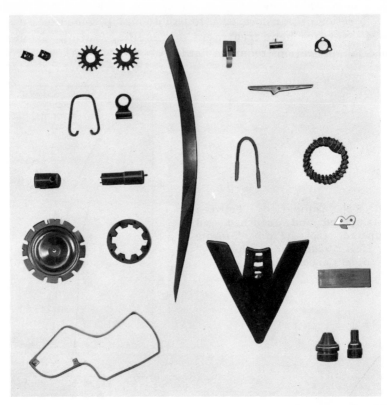

Fig. 8.57 Variety of industrial articles that are austempered: (*Ajax Electric Co.*)

substantial amounts of carbon monoxide. The usual carburizing temperature is 1700°F. At this temperature, the following reaction takes place:

$$Fe + 2CO \rightarrow Fe_{(C)} + CO_2$$

where $Fe_{(C)}$ represents carbon dissolved in austenite. The maximum amount of carbon that can be dissolved in austenite at 1700°F is indicated on the iron–iron carbide equilibrium diagram at the A_{cm} line. Therefore, very quickly, a surface layer of high carbon (about 1.2 per cent) is built up. Since the core is of low carbon content, the carbon atoms trying to reach equilibrium will begin to diffuse inward. The rate of diffusion of carbon in austenite, at a given

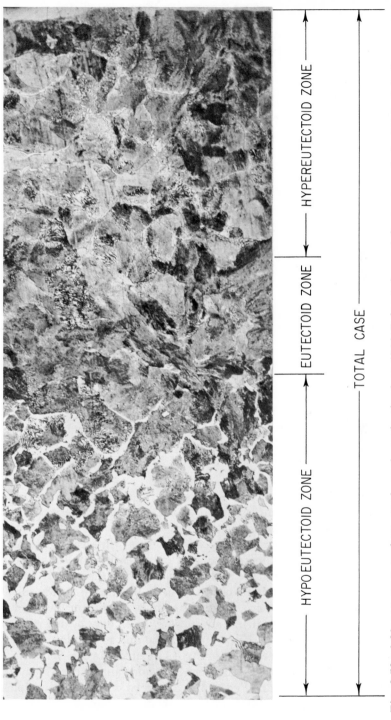

Fig. 8-58 0.20 per cent carbon steel, pack-carburized at 1700°F for 6 hr and furnace-cooled. Etched in 2 per cent nital, 30×.

temperature, is dependent upon the diffusion coefficient and the carbon-concentration gradient. Under known and standard operating conditions, with the surface at a fixed carbon concentration, the form of the carbon gradient may be predicted, with reasonable accuracy, as a function of elapsed time. After diffusion has taken place for the required amount of time depending upon the case depth desired, the

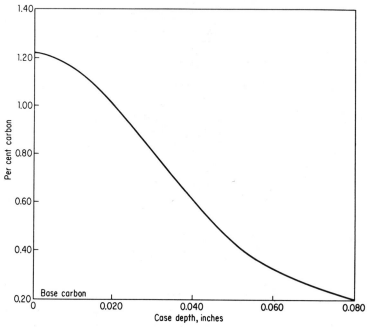

Fig. 8·59   Carbon-concentration gradient in a carburized steel with 0.080 in. total case.

part is removed from the furnace and cooled. If the part is furnace-cooled and examined microscopically, the carbon gradient will be visible in the gradual change of the structure. At the surface is the hypereutectoid zone consisting of pearlite with a white cementite network, followed by the eutectoid zone of only pearlite and finally the hypoeutectoid zone of pearlite and ferrite, with the amount of ferrite increasing until the core is reached. This is illustrated in Fig. 8·58. The case depth may be measured microscopically with a micrometer eyepiece. The carbon gradient and the case depth may be determined experimentally by placing the part in a lathe and machining samples for chemical analysis at increments of 0.005 in. until the core is reached. Analysis to determine carbon content is made, and the results can be plotted graphically as in Fig. 8·59. The relation of time and temperature to case depth is shown in Fig. 8·60 and Table 8·7.

The carburizing equation given previously, $Fe + 2CO \rightarrow Fe_{(C)} + CO_2$, is reversible and may proceed to the left, removing carbon from the surface layer if the steel is heated in an atmosphere containing

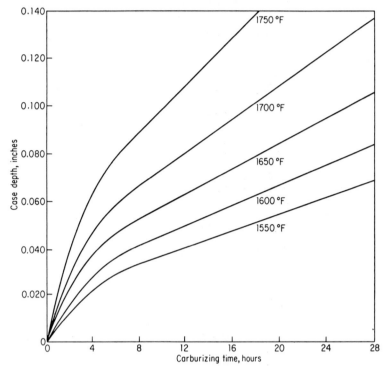

Fig. 8·60   **Relation of time and temperature to carbon penetration.**

carbon dioxide (CO_2).   This is called *decarburization*.   Other possible decarburizing reactions are

$$Fe_{(C)} + H_2O \rightarrow Fe + CO + H_2$$

$$Fe_{(C)} + O_2 \rightarrow Fe + CO_2$$

Decarburization is a problem primarily with high-carbon steels and tool steels.   The surface, depleted of carbon, will not transform to martensite on subsequent hardening, and the steel will be left with a soft skin.   For many tool applications, the stresses to which the part is subjected in service are maximum at or near the surface, so that decarburization is harmful.   Figure 8·61 shows decarburization on the surface of a high-carbon steel.

Commercial carburizing may be accomplished by pack carburizing, gas carburizing, and liquid carburizing.   In pack carburizing, the work is surrounded by a carburizing compound in a closed container. The container is heated to the proper temperature for the required amount of time and then slow-cooled. This is essentially a batch method and does not lend itself to high production. Commercial carburizing

Table 8·7   Case depth in inches by carburizing*

Time, hr	Temp, °F					
	1500	1550	1600	1650	1700	1750
1	0.012	0.015	0.018	0.021	0.025	0.029
2	0.017	0.021	0.025	0.030	0.035	0.041
3	0.021	0.025	0.031	0.037	0.043	0.051
4	0.024	0.029	0.035	0.042	0.050	0.059
5	0.027	0.033	0.040	0.047	0.056	0.066
6	0.030	0.036	0.043	0.052	0.061	0.072
7	0.032	0.039	0.047	0.056	0.066	0.078
8	0.034	0.041	0.050	0.060	0.071	0.083
9	0.036	0.044	0.053	0.063	0.075	0.088
10	0.038	0.046	0.056	0.067	0.079	0.093
11	0.040	0.048	0.059	0.070	0.083	0.097
12	0.042	0.051	0.061	0.073	0.087	0.102
13	0.043	0.053	0.064	0.076	0.090	0.106
14	0.045	0.055	0.066	0.079	0.094	0.110
15	0.047	0.057	0.068	0.082	0.097	0.114
16	0.048	0.059	0.071	0.084	0.100	0.117
17	0.050	0.060	0.073	0.087	0.103	0.121
18	0.051	0.062	0.075	0.090	0.106	0.125
19	0.053	0.064	0.077	0.092	0.109	0.128
20	0.054	0.066	0.079	0.094	0.112	0.131
21	0.055	0.067	0.081	0.097	0.114	0.134
22	0.056	0.069	0.083	0.099	0.117	0.138
23	0.058	0.070	0.085	0.101	0.120	0.141
24	0.059	0.072	0.086	0.103	0.122	0.144

* Courtesy of Republic Steel Corp.

compounds usually consist of hardwood charcoal, coke, and about 20 per cent of barium carbonate as an energizer. The carburizing compound is in the form of coarse particles or lumps, so that, when the cover is sealed on the container, sufficient air will be trapped inside to form carbon monoxide. The principal disadvantages of pack carburizing are the time consumed in heating and cooling the charge, the high cost of labor for packing and unpacking, and the difficulty of direct quenching from the carburizing temperature.

Gas carburizing may be either batch or continuous and lends itself better to production heat treatment.   The pieces are placed in contact with gases rich in carbon monoxide, and hydrocarbons such as methane, butane, and propane.   Natural gas is a good carburizing source.   These gases are generally mixed with a definite amount of air prior to entering the furnace.   The air acts as a diluent and also provides oxygen for

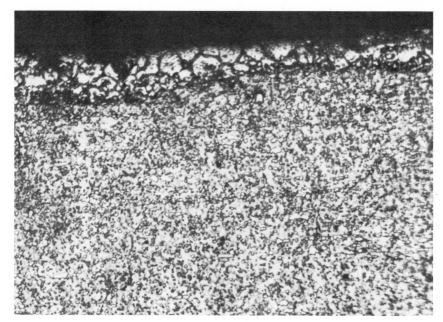

Fig. 8·61   Decarburization on the surface of a high-carbon tool steel, 200×.

the formation of carbon monoxide from the hydrocarbons.   Gas carburizing allows quicker handling by direct quenching, lower cost, cleaner surroundings, closer quality control, and greater flexibility of operation as compared with pack carburizing.

Carburized parts usually have a thin outer layer of high carbon (1.2 per cent) which on subsequent hardening may lead to surface cracks.   Gas carburizing, by using a *diffusion period* during which the gas is turned off but the temperature maintained, allows the surface carbon to be reduced to any desired value.   Use of the diffusion period also produces much cleaner work by dissipation of carbon deposit during the time when no gas is flowing.

Liquid carburizing is performed in a bath of molten salt containing up to 20 per cent sodium cyanide.   The cyanide (CN) acts as a source

of carbon and nitrogen. The case obtained by this method is composed largely of carbon with only a small amount of nitrogen. Operating temperatures are usually in the range of 1600 to 1750°F. It

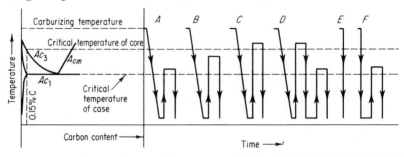

Treatment	Case	Core
A—best adapted to fine-grained steels	Refined; excess carbide not dissolved	Unrefined; soft and machinable
B—best adapted to fine-grained steels	Slightly coarsened; some solution of excess carbide	Partially refined; stronger and tougher than A
C—best adapted to fine-grained steels	Somewhat coarsened; solution of excess carbide favored; austenite retention promoted in highly alloyed steels	Refined; maximum core strength and hardness; better combination of strength and ductility than B
D—best treatment for coarse-grained steels	Refined; solution of excess carbide favored; austenite retention minimized	Refined; soft and machinable; maximum toughness and resistance to impact
E—adapted to fine-grained steels only	Unrefined with excess carbide dissolved; austenite retained; distortion minimized	Unrefined but hardened
F—adapted to fine-grained steels only	Refined; solution of excess carbide favored; austenite retention minimized	Unrefined; fair toughness

Fig. 8·62   Various heat treatments for carburized steels.   (*From "Metals Handbook," 1948 edition, American Society for Metals, Metals Park, Ohio*)

is used mainly for case depths up to 0.030 in., and its chief limitation
is the cost of the carburizing salt.

8·26   Heat treatment after carburizing.   Since steel is carburized in the austenite region, direct quenching from the carburizing
temperature will harden both the case and core if the cooling rate is
greater than the critical cooling rate. Direct quenching of coarse-
grained steels often leads to brittleness and distortion, so that this

treatment should be applied only to fine-grained steels. Alloy steels are rarely used in the direct-quenched condition because of the large amount of retained austenite in the hardened case. Figure 8·62 shows a diagrammatic representation of various hardening treatments for carburized steels together with case and core properties.

When a carburized part is hardened, the case will appear as a light martensite zone followed by a darker transition zone (Fig. 8·63). The *hard case* or *effective case* is measured from the outer edge to the middle

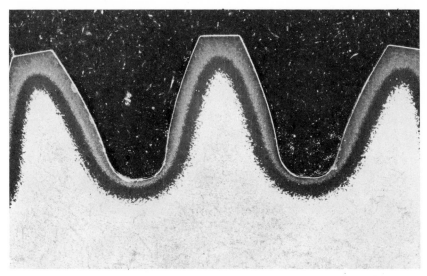

Fig. 8·63   A properly carburized, hardened, and tempered gear.   Etched in 2 per cent nital, 7×.

of the dark zone. From the nature of the carbon gradient, the hard case contains the portion of the case above 0.50 per cent carbon and is approximately equal to two-thirds of the total case.

8·27   Cyaniding. A thin case of high hardness and good wear resistance can be given to carbon and alloy steels by cyaniding. This process consists in immersing the steel in a molten bath containing about 30 per cent sodium cyanide at temperatures between 1450 and 1600°F, usually followed by water quenching. Cyaniding differs from liquid carburizing in the composition and character of the case. The cyanide case is high in nitrogen and low in carbon; the reverse is true of liquid-carburized cases. Cyaniding is used extensively to produce light cases on small parts. Since the case depths produced during the usual immersion times (up to 1 hr) are up to 0.010 in., the carbon concentration alone does not account for the high hardness obtained. Nitrogen, like carbon, combines with iron to form iron nitride needles of submicroscopic size which contribute to the high hardness.

Carbonitriding, also known as *gas cyaniding*, utilizes a mixture of ammonia (NH_3) and hydrocarbon gas to produce the same effect as cyaniding. It is used mainly as a low-cost substitute for cyaniding. Figure 8·64 shows a carbonitrided case obtained by heating C1213 steel in an ammonia-propane atmosphere at 1550°F for 20 min followed by oil quenching. Each division of the micrometer eyepiece is 0.001 in., and the case depth, measured to the middle of the dark zone, is therefore approximately 0.0025 in.

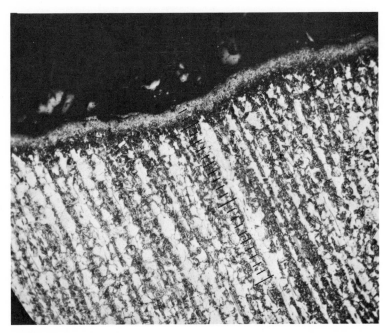

Fig. 8·64 Carbonitrided case on AISI C1213 steel. Heated at 1550°F for 20 min in an ammonia-propane atmosphere followed by oil quenching. Etched in 2 per cent nital, 125×. Case depth approximately 0.0025 in.

8·28 Nitriding. Parts to be nitrided are placed in an airtight container through which ammonia is passed continuously at a temperature between 900 and 1150°F. Under these conditions, the ammonia partially decomposes into nitrogen and hydrogen. The nitrogen penetrates the steel surface, combining with iron and alloying elements to form nitrides. Figure 8·65 shows a nitrided gear with a heavy case. Nitriding produces the hardest case (above Rockwell C 70) obtainable on steel. Special alloy steels have been developed for use in nitriding. These are called *nitralloy* steels and are essentially medium-carbon steels with aluminum, chromium, and molybdenum in amounts up to 3 per cent total. Nitriding cycles are quite long (a 50-hr cycle will give approximately 0.015-in. case), and it is rarely used for case depths exceeding 0.020 in.   Since nitriding temperatures are below the critical range of the steel, there will be very little distortion or dimensional change.   The steel is usually hardened and tempered above 1100°F (above the nitriding temperature) to achieve

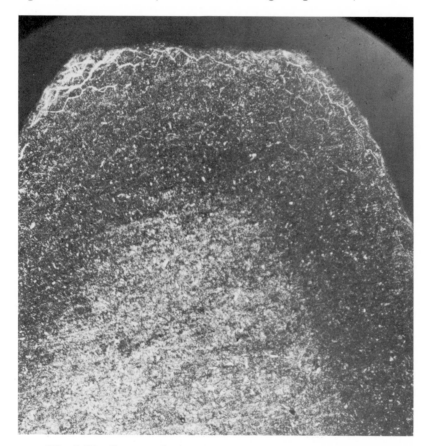

Fig. 8·65   Gear tooth showing a heavy nitrided case, 50×.

maximum core toughness and then nitrided.   Many parts are finish-machined or ground before nitriding.   The principal disadvantages are the brittle case and increased cost compared with carburizing. Nitriding is used extensively for aviation engine parts, gauges, cylinder liners, cams, valve parts, etc.

8·29   Flame hardening.   This process consists in rapidly heating a selected surface area of medium- or high-carbon steel and immediately cooling in water or an air blast.   Heat may be applied by a single oxyacetylene torch or can be part of an elaborate apparatus which automatically heats, quenches, and indexes parts. Since only a small section of the steel is hardened at a time, there is practically no distortion. Parts that are to be flame-hardened are usually quenched and tempered first to obtain desired core properties. Although parts of uniform section lend themselves most readily to flame hardening, it is also useful for large pieces where it would be cumbersome to heat the entire piece for quenching. Flame hardening is used to improve surface hardness and wear resistance of piston pins, shafts, large gears, cams, and hand tools.

8·30 Induction hardening. This method is similar to flame hardening in principle. They are both shallow-hardening methods and do not change the chemical composition of the steel. Induction hardening is applied mainly to medium-carbon steels. The part to be induction-hardened is made the secondary of a high-frequency induction apparatus. The primary, or work, coil consists of several turns of copper tubing which is water-cooled during operation. When a high-frequency alternating current passes through the work coil, a high-frequency magnetic field is set up. This magnetic field induces high-frequency eddy currents and hysteresis currents in the metal. The losses due to these currents provide the energy for heating the metal. Of primary importance for induction surface hardening is the fact that high-frequency current tends to travel at the surface of the conductor. This is known as *skin effect*. The total depth of heat penetration depends upon both the frequency employed and the time allowed for conduction of heat from the surface. Frequencies used range from 2,000 to 500,000 cps. Extremely rapid, the heating is completed in a matter of seconds, the current shuts off automatically, and the part is immediately quenched with a water spray. Progressive surface hardening by induction heating may be applied successfully to relatively long pieces of uniform cross section such as chain-saw blades and long lead screws.

8·31 Residual stresses. These are stresses that remain in the part after the force has disappeared. Residual stresses always arise from a nonuniform deformation. In the case of heat treatment, this nonuniform deformation may be caused by the temperature gradient or the phase change or usually a combination of both factors during cooling. Residual stresses are a very serious problem in heat treatment since they often result in distortion or cracking and in some cases in premature failure of the part in service. Actually the problem of residual stresses is quite complex, but it is hoped that the following discussion, although simplified, will give the student some insight into and appreciation of the factors that give rise to these stresses.

Consider first the effect of temperature gradient alone. It was shown earlier, under the effect of size and mass, that during quenching the surface is cooled more rapidly than the inside. This results in a temperature gradient across the cross section of the piece or a temperature difference between the surface and the center. For example, let us examine the cooling curves of a 2-in. round water-quenched (Fig. 8·32). At the end of 10 sec the surface has cooled to about 700°F while the center is at about 1500°F. Almost all solids expand as they are heated and contract as they are cooled. This means that at the end of 10 sec the surface, since it is at a much lower temperature, should have contracted much more than the inside. However, since the outside and inside are attached to each other, the inside, being longer, will prevent the outside from contracting as much as it should. It will therefore elongate the outside layers, putting them in tension while the inside in turn will be in compression. The approximate magnitude of this thermal stress may be calculated from the following formula:

$$s = \alpha E \ \Delta T$$

where s = thermal stress, psi
α = coefficient of linear expansion, in./(in.) (°F)
E = modulus of elasticity, psi
ΔT = difference in temperature, °F

Assuming an average value for the coefficient of expansion for steel as 6.5×10^{-6} in./(in.)(°F) and $E = 30 \times 10^6$ psi, insertion of these values in the above equation with $\Delta T = 800$ (1500 to 700°F) gives

$$s = 6.5 \times 10^{-6} \times 30 \times 10^6 \times 800 = 156{,}000 \text{ psi}$$

This is the approximate value of the thermal stress existing between the outside and inside layers because of the temperature difference of 800°F. This total stress of 156,000 psi must now be distributed between the inside and outside layers, and the average stress is inversely proportional to the area available to support this stress. Assuming that the outside layers constitute one-fourth of the cross-sectional area, the average tensile stress on the outside would be equal to $\frac{3}{4} \times 156{,}000$, or 117,000 psi, while the average compressive stress on the inside would be $\frac{1}{4} \times 156{,}000$, or 39,000 psi. This stress distribution is plotted schematically in Fig. 8·66. The area in tension must balance the area in compression in order for the stresses to be in equilibrium across the cross section. The plot in Fig. 8·66 shows a sharp drop in stress at the junction of the inside and outside layers due to a sharp drop in temperature from 1500 to 700°F. Actually the temperature does not drop sharply but changes gradually across the cross section, as shown by the curves of Fig. 8·34. A truer representation of the stress distribution is shown by the dotted curve in Fig. 8·66. The above discussion shows that the tensile stress on the

surface may reach a very high value.   If this stress exceeds the ultimate strength of the material, cracking will occur.   This is what
usually happens when glass is subjected to a large temperature difference.   In the case of steel, however, thermal stresses alone very rarely
lead to cracking.   If the stress is below the yield strength of the steel,
the stress will be borne elastically.   When the entire piece has reached
room temperature, $\Delta T = 0$ and therefore, since the thermal stress

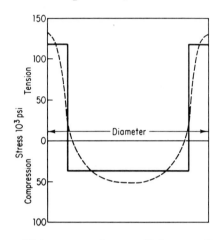

Fig. 8·66 Schematic representation of the stress distribution across the diameter due to a temperature gradient. Dotted curve indicates a truer representation of the stress distribution.

will be zero, there will be no distortion.   If the stress exceeds the
yield strength, the surface layer will be plastically deformed or permanently elongated.   At room temperature the surface will have
residual compressive stress and the inside, residual tensile stress.   If
the piece was originally cylindrical, it will now be barrel-shaped.

Austenite, being f.c.c. (face-centered cubic), is a denser structure
than any of its transformation products.   Therefore, when austenite
changes to pearlite, bainite, or martensite, an expansion occurs.   The
austenite-to-martensite expansion is the largest and amounts to a
volume increase of about 4.6 per cent.   The martensite expansion
will be greater the lower the M_s temperature.   Figure 8·67 shows the
changes in length, during cooling, of a small-diameter cylinder as
measured in a dilatometer.   The piece is austenitic at the elevated
temperature, and normal contraction of the austenite takes place until
the M_s temperature is reached.   Between the M_s and M_f the transformation of austenite to martensite causes an expansion in length.
After the M_f temperature, the martensite undergoes normal contraction.

Let us now consider the combined effect of temperature gradient
and phase change for two possibilities: (1) through-hardened steel and
(2) shallow-hardened steel.

Figure 8·68 shows the surface- and center-cooling curves superimposed on the I-T diagram for the through-hardened steel.   Since the

center-cooling rate exceeds the critical cooling rate, the part will be fully martensitic across its diameter. During the first stage, up to time t_1, the stresses present are due to the temperature gradient. The surface, prevented from contracting as much as it should by the center, will be in tension while the center will be in compression. During the second stage, between times t_1 and t_2, the surface, having reached the M_s temperature, transforms to martensite and expands. The

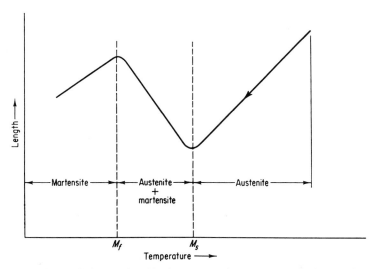

Fig. 8·67 **Schematic dilation curve for martensite formation.**

center, however, is undergoing normal contraction due to cooling. The center contracting will prevent the surface from expanding as much as it should, and the surface will tend to be in compression while the center will tend to be in tension. After t_2, the surface has reached room temperature and will be a hard, brittle, martensitic structure. During the third stage, the center finally reaches the M_s temperature and begins to expand, forming martensite. The center, as it expands, will try to pull the surface along with it, putting the surface in tension. The stress condition in the three stages is summarized below.

Stage	Stress condition	
	Surface	Center
First (temperature gradient)	Tension	Compression
Second ($A \rightarrow M$ of surface)	Compression	Tension
Third ($A \rightarrow M$ of center)	Tension	Compression

To initiate and propagate a crack it is necessary for tensile stress to be present.   Let us examine the three stages with regard to the danger of cracking.   In the first stage, the surface is in tension; however, it is austenitic and if the stress is high enough, rather than cracking, it will deform plastically, relieving the stress.   In the second stage, the center is in tension and is austenitic, so that the tendency

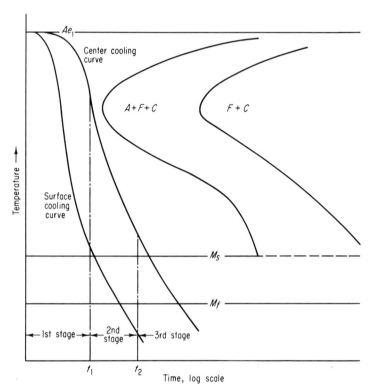

Fig. 8·68   Center- and surface-cooling curves superimposed on the I-T diagram to illustrate the through-hardened condition.

is to produce plastic deformation rather than cracking.   In the last stage, the surface is again in tension.   Now, however, the surface is hard, unyielding martensite.   As the center expands, there is little likelihood of plastic deformation.   It is during this stage that the greatest danger of cracking exists.   Depending upon the difference in time between the transformation of the surface and center, the cracking may occur soon after the quench or sometimes many hours later.

One heat-treating rule which minimizes the danger of cracking is that parts should be tempered immediately after hardening.   Tempering will give the surface martensite some ductility before the center transforms.

Another very effective method of minimizing distortion and cracking is by *martempering*, illustrated in Fig. 8·69. It is carried out by heating to the proper austenitizing temperature, quenching rapidly in a liquid-salt bath held just above the M_s temperature, and holding for a period of time. This allows the surface and the center to reach the same temperature and is then followed by air cooling to room

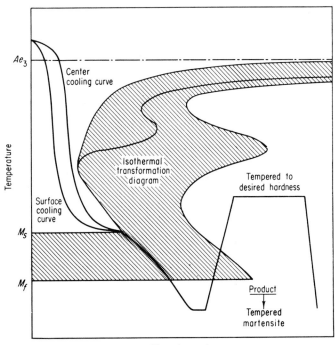

Fig. 8·69 Schematic transformation diagram for martempering. (*From "U.S.S. Carilloy Steels," U.S. Steel Corporation*)

temperature. Since air cooling from just above the martensite-formation range introduces very little temperature gradient, the martensite will be formed at nearly the same time throughout the piece. Thus martempering minimizes residual stresses and greatly reduces the danger of distortion and cracking. The heat treatment is completed by tempering the martensite to the desired hardness.

Figure 8·70 shows the surface- and center-cooling curves superimposed on the I-T diagram for the shallow-hardened steel. During the first stage, up to time t_1, the stresses present are due only to the temperature gradient, and as in the through-hardened condition, the surface will be in tension while the center will be in compression. During the second stage, between times t_1 and t_2, both the surface and center will transform. The surface will transform to martensite while the center will transform to a softer product, like pearlite. The entire piece is expanding, but since the expansion resulting from the formation of martensite is greater than that resulting from the formation of pearlite, the surface tends to expand more than the center.

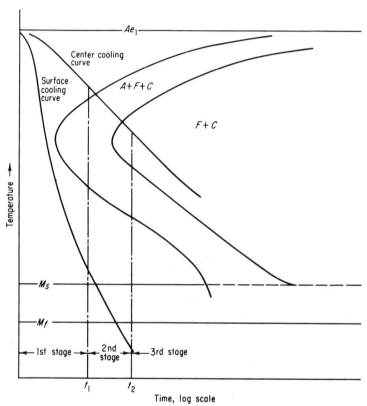

Fig. 8-70 Center- and surface-cooling curves superimposed on the I-T diagram to illustrate the shallow-hardened condition.

This tends to put the center in tension while the surface is in compression. After t_2, the center will contract on cooling from the transformation temperature to room temperature. The surface, being martensitic and having reached room temperature much earlier, will prevent the center from contracting as much as it should. This will result in higher tensile stresses in the center. The stress condition in the three stages is summarized below.

Let us examine the three stages with regard to the danger of cracking. In the first stage, the surface is in tension, but being austenitic, if the stress is high enough, it will yield rather than crack. In the second stage, the center is in tension. However, since both the surface and center are expanding, the tensile stress will be small. During the third stage, the surface, as a hard, rigid shell of martensite, will prevent the center from contracting as it cools to room temperature. The tensile stresses in the center may reach a high value, and since the center is pearlite of relatively low tensile strength, it is during this stage that the greatest danger of cracking exists. The cracks that appear in the center do not go through the surface compressive layer

Stage	Stress condition	
	Surface	Center
First (temperature gradient)	Tension	Compression
Second ($A \to M$ of surface, $A \to P$ of center)	Compression	Tension
Third (cooling of center to room temperature)	Greater compression	Greater tension

and are difficult to detect. X-ray testing or in some cases Magnaflux inspection may show the presence of internal fissures. Very often these parts are placed in service without knowledge of the internal quenching cracks. As soon as there is the slightest bit of tensile stress in the surface due to the external load, the crack will come through and the part will fail.

In many applications, the tensile stress developed by the external force is maximum at or near the surface. For these applications, shallow-hardened or case-hardened parts are preferred, since the surface residual stresses are usually compressive. In order for the surface to be in tension, the residual compressive stresses must first be brought to zero. This effectively increases the strength of the surface. The same beneficial effect and greatly increased life have been found for leaf springs where residual surface compressive stresses were induced by shot peening before the springs were placed in service.

QUESTIONS

8·1 Describe completely the changes that take place during the slow cooling of a 0.5 per cent carbon steel from the austenite range.

8·2 Calculate the relative amounts of the structural constituents present in furnace-cooled steels containing (a) 0.30 per cent carbon, (b) 0.60 per cent carbon, (c) 0.80 per cent carbon, (d) 1.2 per cent carbon, (e) 1.7 per cent carbon.

8·3 What are the limitations on the use of the iron–iron carbide diagram?

8·4 What is the effect of increasing cooling rate on (a) temperature of austenite transformation, (b) fineness of pearlite, (c) amount of proeutectoid constituent?

8·5 Is it possible to determine the approximate carbon content of a normalized steel from microscopic study? Explain.

8·6 In Table 8·1, why do annealed steels show a decrease in tensile strength above 0.80 per cent carbon?

8·7 In Table 8·1, why do normalized steels show an increase in tensile strength up to 1.2 per cent and then a decrease?

8·8 Define "critical cooling rate."

8·9 What factors influence the critical cooling rate?   Explain.

8·10 Define actual cooling rate.

8·11 What factors influence the actual cooling rate?   Explain.

8·12 How is the actual cooling rate determined?

8·13 Calculate the surface-area-to-mass ratio of a 2-in-diameter 10-ft-long cylinder and compare it with a sphere of the same mass.

8·14 Explain why the cooling rate of oil may be increased by increasing the oil temperature.

8·15 Explain two ways in which the hardness-traverse curve of a given steel may show a straight horizontal line.

8·16 Explain why the surface hardness of quenched high-carbon steel may be less than the hardness under the surface.

8·17 What are the advantages of specifying steel on the basis of hardenability?

8·18 How will the microstructure differ for three samples of a 0.20 per cent C steel after the following heat treatments?   (a) Heated to 1700°F and furnace-cooled; (b) heated to 1800°F and furnace-cooled; (c) heated to 1700°F and air-cooled.

8·19 How will the microstructure differ in four samples of a 0.40 per cent carbon steel after the following heat treatments?   (a) Heated to 1500°F and air-cooled; (b) heated to 1500°F and oil-quenched; (c) heated to 1500°F and water-quenched; (d) heated to 1350°F and water-quenched.

8·20 If the samples in Question 8·19 are 2 in. in diameter, sketch the approximate hardness-traverse curves after the given heat treatments.

8·21 Give two different methods of obtaining a spheroidized cementite structure.

8·22 Sketch the I-T diagram of a 1080 steel (Fig. 8·14) and (a) show a cooling curve that will result in a structure of 50 per cent martensite and 50 per cent pearlite; (b) show a cooling curve that will result in a uniform pearlitic structure of Rockwell C 40.

8·23 A steel showed a hardness of Rockwell C 40 at the quenched end of a hardenability test.   What was the approximate carbon content?

8·24 What will be the approximate hardness at the quenched end of (a) a 1050 hardenability test specimen; (b) a 6150 hardenability test specimen; (c) a 4150 hardenability test specimen?

8·25 Describe how an I-T diagram is determined experimentally.

8·26 What are the limitations on the use of the I-T diagram?

8·27 What will be the hardness at the center and mid-radius position of (a) 2-in.-diameter 4140 steel with a poor oil quench, strong oil quench, brine quench—no agitation; (b) same as (a) for 5140 steel; (c) same as (a) and (b) for a $2\frac{1}{2}$-in.-diameter bar; (d) same as (a) and (b) for a 3-in.-diameter bar?

8·28 Plot the change in hardness and Izod impact strength as a function of tempering from the data in Fig. 8·45.

8·29 What are the principal advantages of austempering compared with the conventional quench and temper method?

8·30 What are the limitations of austempering?

8·31   From the data in Table 8·7, plot case depth vs. time at 1500, 1600, and 1700°F.   What conclusions may be drawn from the shape of these curves?

8·32   From the data in Table 8·7, plot case depth vs. temperature at 4, 10, and 20 hr.   What conclusions may be drawn from these curves?

8·33   What are the limitations on the use of high carburizing temperatures such as 1900 and 2000°F?

8·34   What are the advantages of gas carburizing compared with pack carburizing?

8·35   Define "hard case" or " effective case."

8·36   Describe an application and the heat treatment used so that advantage may be taken of the residual stresses resulting from heat treatment.

8·37   What will be the nature of the residual stresses after carburizing? Explain.

8·38   What are the limitations of martempering?

8·39   You have been given a gear with a broken tooth that has failed prematurely in service.   The normal heat treatment is carburize, harden, and temper. Describe completely how this gear would be studied to determine possible metallurgical cause for failure.

REFERENCES

American Society for Metals: "Metals Handbook," 1948 edition, Metals Park, Ohio.

Bullens, D. K.: "Steel and Its Heat Treatment," vols. 1, 2, and 3, John Wiley & Sons, Inc., New York, 1948–1949.

Carpenter, H., and J. M. Robertson: "Metals," Oxford University Press, Fair Lawn, N.J., 1944.

Crafts, W., and J. L. Lamont: "Hardenability and Steel Selection," Pitman Publishing Corporation, New York, 1949.

DuMond, T. C.: "Quenching of Steels," American Society for Metals, Metals Park, Ohio, 1959.

Grossmann, M. A.: "Elements of Hardenability," American Society for Metals, Metals Park, Ohio, 1952.

————: "Principles of Heat Treatment," American Society for Metals, Metals Park, Ohio, 1953.

Hultgren, R.: "Fundamentals of Physical Metallurgy," Prentice-Hall, Inc., Englewood Cliffs, N.J., 1952.

Rogers, B. A.: "The Nature of Metals," American Society for Metals, Metals Park, Ohio, 1951.

Sachs, G., and K. R. Van Horn: "Practical Metallurgy," American Society for Metals, Metals Park, Ohio, 1940.

Sauveur, A.: "The Metallography and Heat Treatment of Iron and Steel," McGraw-Hill Book Company, Inc., New York, 1935.

Smith, M. C.: "Alloy Series in Physical Metallurgy," Harper & Row, Publishers, Incorporated, New York, 1956.

U.S. Steel Corporation: "Atlas of Isothermal Transformation Diagrams," Pittsburgh, 1951.

Williams, R. S., and V. O. Homerberg: "Principles of Metallography," 5th ed., McGraw-Hill Book Company, Inc., New York, 1948.

Chapter 9

ALLOY STEELS

9·1 Introduction. An *alloy steel* may be defined as one whose characteristic properties are due to some element other than carbon. Although all plain-carbon steels contain moderate amounts of manganese (up to about 0.90 per cent) and silicon (up to about 0.30 per cent), they are not considered alloy steels because the principal function of the manganese and silicon is to act as deoxidizers. They combine with oxygen and sulfur to reduce the harmful effect of those elements.

9·2 Purpose of alloying. Alloying elements are added to steels for many purposes. Some of the most important are:

1. Increase hardenability
2. Improve strength at ordinary temperatures
3. Improve physical properties at either high or low temperatures
4. Improve toughness at any minimum hardness or strength
5. Increase wear resistance
6. Increase corrosion resistance
7. Improve magnetic properties

Alloying elements may be classified according to the way they may be distributed in the two main constituents of annealed steel.

Group 1. Elements which dissolve in ferrite

Group 2. Elements which combine with carbon to form simple or complex carbides

9·3 Effect of alloying elements upon ferrite. Technically, there is probably some solubility of all the elements in ferrite, but some elements are not found extensively in the carbide phase. Thus nickel, aluminum, silicon, copper, and cobalt are all found largely dissolved in ferrite. In the absence of carbon, considerable proportions of the group 2 elements will be found dissolved in ferrite. Therefore, the carbide-forming tendency is apparent only when there is a significant amount of carbon present. The behavior of the individual elements is shown in Table 9·1, and the relative tendency of certain

264

elements to exist in both groups is shown by the size of the arrowhead.

Any element dissolved in ferrite increases its hardness and strength in accordance with the general principles of solid solution hardening. The order of increasing effectiveness in strengthening iron, based upon equal additions by weight, appears to be about as follows: chromium, tungsten, vanadium, molybdenum, nickel, manganese, and silicon (Fig. 9·1). The hardening effect of the dissolved element is actually small

Table 9·1 Behavior of the individual elements
in annealed steel*

Alloying element	Group 1 dissolved in ferrite		Group 2 combined in carbide
Nickel	Ni		
Silicon	Si		
Aluminum	Al		
Copper	Cu		
Manganese	Mn	⟵⟶	Mn
Chromium	Cr	⟵⟶	Cr
Tungsten	W	⟵⟶	W
Molybdenum	Mo	⟵⟶	Mo
Vanadium	V	⟵⟶	V
Titanium	Ti	⟵⟶	Ti

* Adapted from E. C. Bain and H. W. Paxton, "Alloying Elements in Steel," 2d ed., American Society for Metals, Metals Park, Ohio, 1961.

and illustrates how relatively little is the contribution of the strengthening of the ferrite to the overall strength of the steel. This is shown in Fig. 9·2 for low-carbon chromium alloys. The upper curve indicates the influence of chromium to change the tensile strength by changing the structure, while the lower curve indicates the minor influence of chromium in essentially constant structures.

9·4 Effects of alloying elements upon carbide. The influence of the amount of carbide and the form and dispersion of the carbide on the properties of steel has been discussed in Chap. 8. Since all carbides found in steel are hard and brittle their effect on the room-temperature tensile properties is similar regardless of the specific composition.

The presence of elements that form carbides influences the hardening temperature and soaking time. Complex carbides are sluggish to dissolve and tend to remain out of solution in austenite. This serves to lower the carbon and alloy content of austenite below that of the steel as a whole. Undissolved carbides also act to reduce grain growth.

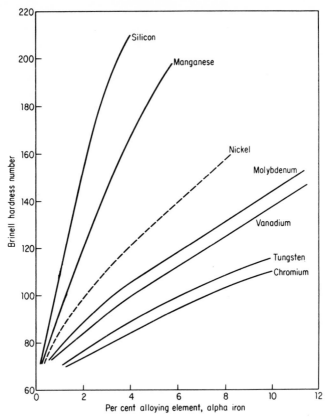

Fig. 9·1 Probable hardening effect of the various elements as dissolved in pure iron. (*From E. C. Bain and H. W. Paxton, "Alloying Elements in Steel," American Society for Metals, Metals Park, Ohio, 1961*)

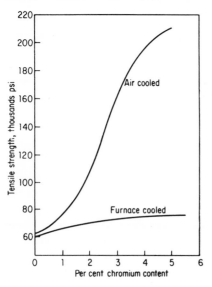

Fig. 9·2 The minor effect of chromium in annealed steels as compared with its strong effect as a strengthener through its influence on structure in air-cooled steels. (*From E. C. Bain and H. W. Paxton, "Alloying Elements in Steel," American Society for Metals, Metals Park, Ohio, 1961*)

266

Both effects tend to reduce hardenability. When dissolved in austenite, the carbide-forming elements are very powerful deep-hardening elements.

While all the carbides found in steel are hard, brittle compounds, chromium and vanadium carbides are outstanding in hardness and wear resistance. The hardness and wear resistance of alloy steels rich in carbides are in a large measure determined by the amount, size, and distribution of these hard particles. These factors, in turn, are controlled by chemical composition, method of manufacture, and heat treatment.

9·5 Influence of alloying elements on the iron–iron carbide diagram. Although no mention was made in Chap. 7 of the possible modification of the iron–iron carbide diagram by the presence of elements other than carbon, in determining the effects of alloying elements this possibility must be given due consideration. When a third element is added to steel, the binary iron–iron carbide diagram no longer represents equilibrium conditions. Although the construction and interpretation of ternary equilibrium diagrams are outside the scope of this book, the presence of alloying elements will change the critical range, the position of the eutectoid point, and the location of the alpha and gamma fields indicated by the binary iron–iron carbide diagram.

Nickel and manganese tend to lower the critical temperature on heating, while molybdenum, aluminum, silicon, tungsten, and vanadium tend to raise it. The change in critical temperature produced by the presence of alloying elements is important in the heat treatment of alloy steels since it will either raise or lower the proper hardening temperature as compared with the corresponding plain-carbon steel.

The eutectoid point is shifted from the position it normally has in the iron–iron carbide diagram. Nickel and manganese tend to reduce the eutectoid temperature, and all alloying elements tend to reduce the carbon content of the eutectoid (Fig. 9·3).

Certain alloying elements, notably molybdenum, chromium, silicon, and titanium, in increasing amounts, tend to contract the pure austenitic region and enlarge the field in which alpha (α) or delta (δ) iron is found. This change is shown in Fig. 9·4, where the solid lines represent the contraction of the austenitic field with increasing amounts of the alloying element. Alloy compositions to the right of the "triangles" will be largely austenite with increasing amounts of carbide, while to the left of the austenite areas, austenite with more or less ferrite (solutions in α or δ iron) will be found.

9·6 Effect of alloying elements in tempering. In the discussion of tempering of plain-carbon steels, it was shown that hardened

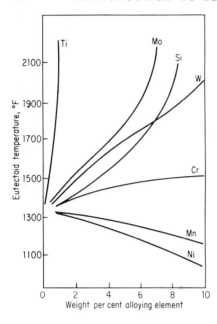

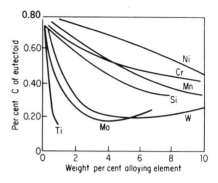

Fig. 9·3 Eutectoid composition and eutectoid temperature as influenced by several alloying elements. (*From E. C. Bain and H. W. Paxton, "Alloying Elements in Steel," American Society for Metals, Metals Park, Ohio,* 1961)

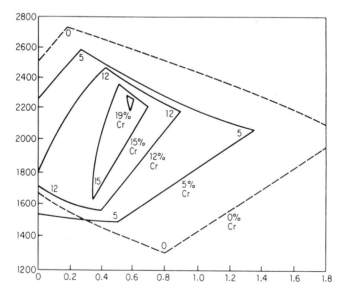

Fig. 9·4   Range of austenite in chromium steels.   (*From "Metals Handbook,"* 1948 *edition, American Society for Metals, Metals Park, Ohio*)

steels are softened by reheating. As the tempering temperature is increased, the hardness drops continuously. The general effect of alloying elements is to retard the softening rate so that alloy steels will require a higher tempering temperature to obtain a given hardness. The elements that remain dissolved in ferrite, such as nickel, silicon, and to some extent manganese, have very little effect on the hardness of tempered steel.

The complex carbide-forming elements such as chromium, tungsten, molybdenum, and vanadium, however, have a very noticeable effect on the retardation of softening. Not only do they raise the tempering temperature but, when they are present in higher percentages, the softening curves for these steels will show a range in which the hardness may actually increase with increase in tempering temperature. This characteristic behavior of alloy steels containing carbide-forming elements is known as *secondary hardness* and is believed to be due to delayed precipitation of fine alloy carbides. The effect of increasing chromium content is illustrated in Fig. 9·5.

The specific effects of the alloying elements in steel are summarized in Table 9·2.

Classification of alloy steels according to chemical composition as in the AISI series has been covered in Chap. 7, and compositions of some representative alloy steels are given in Table 7·1.

The preceding sections were devoted to a general discussion of the alloying elements in steel. Since a large number of alloy steels are manufactured, it is not feasible to discuss the individual alloy steels; however, a brief consideration of the specific effects of the common alloy elements and their application will be given.

9·7 Nickel steels. Nickel is one of the oldest and fundamental steel-alloying elements. It has unlimited solubility in gamma (γ) iron and is highly soluble in ferrite, contributing to the strength and toughness of this phase. Nickel lowers the critical temperatures of steel, widens the temperature range for successful heat treatment, retards the decomposition of austenite, and does not form any carbides which might be difficult to dissolve during austenitizing. Nickel also reduces the carbon content of the eutectoid; therefore, the structure of unhardened nickel steels contains a higher percentage of pearlite than similarly treated plain-carbon steels. Since the pearlite forms at a lower temperature, it is finer and tougher than the pearlite in unalloyed steels. These factors permit the attainment of given strength levels at lower carbon contents, thus increasing toughness, plasticity, and fatigue resistance. Nickel steels are highly suited for high-strength structural steels which are used in the as-rolled condition, or large forgings which are not adapted to quenching. The 3.5 per

Table 9.2 Specific effects of alloying elements in steel*

Element	Solid solubility		Influence on ferrite	Influence on austenite (hardenability)	Influence exerted through carbide		Principal functions
	In gamma iron	In alpha iron			Carbide-forming tendency	Action during tempering	
Aluminum	1.1% (increased by C)	36%	Hardens considerably by solid solution	Increases hardenability mildly, if dissolved in austenite	Negative (graphitizes)	. . .	1. Deoxides efficiently 2. Restricts grain growth (by forming dispersed oxides or nitrides) 3. Alloying element in nitriding steel
Chromium	12.8% (20% with 0.5% C)	Unlimited	Hardens slightly; increases corrosion resistance	Increases hardenability moderately	Greater than Mn; less than W	Mildly resists softening	1. Increases resistance to corrosion and oxidation 2. Increases hardenability 3. Adds some strength at high temperatures 4. Resists abrasion and wear (with high carbon)
Cobalt	Unlimited	75%	Hardens considerably by solid solution	Decreases hardenability as dissolved	Similar to Fe	Sustains hardness by solid solution	1. Contributes to red hardness by hardening ferrite
Manganese	Unlimited	3%	Hardens markedly; reduces plasticity somewhat	Increases hardenability moderately	Greater than Fe; less than Cr	Very little, in usual percentages	1. Counteracts brittleness from the sulfur 2. Increases hardenability inexpensively
Molybdenum	3% ± (8% with 0.3% C)	37.5% (less with lowered temperature)	Provides age-hardening system in high Mo-Fe alloys	Increases hardenability strongly (Mo > Cr)	Strong; greater than Cr	Opposes softening, by secondary hardening	1. Raises grain-coarsening temperature of austenite 2. Deepens hardening 3. Counteracts tendency toward temper brittleness 4. Raises hot and creep strength, red hardness 5. Enhances corrosion resistance in stainless steel 6. Forms abrasion-resisting particles

270

Element							Principal functions
Nickel	Unlimited	10% (irrespective of carbon content)	Strengthens and toughens by solid solution	Increases hardenability mildly, but tends to retain austenite with higher carbon	Negative (graphitizes)	Very little in small percentages	1. Strengthens unquenched or annealed steels 2. Toughens pearlitic-ferritic steels (especially at low temperature) 3. Renders high-chromium iron alloys austenitic
Phosphorus	0.5%	2.8% (irrespective of carbon content	Hardens strongly by solid solution	Increases hardenability	- Nil	...	1. Strengthens low-carbon steel 2. Increases resistance to corrosion 3. Improves machinability in free-cutting steels
Silicon	2% ± (9% with 0.35% C)	18.5% (not much changed by carbon)	Hardens with loss in plasticity (Mn < Si < P)	Increases hardenability moderately	Negative (graphitizes)	Sustains hardness by solid solution	1. Used as general-purpose deoxidizer 2. Alloying element for electrical and magnetic sheet 3. Improves oxidation resistance 4. Increases hardenability of steels carrying nongraphitizing elements 5. Strengthens low-alloy steels

Titanium	0.75% (1% ± with 0.20% C)	6% ± (less with lowered temperature)	Provides age-hardening system in high Ti:Fe alloys	Probably increases hardenability very strongly as dissolved. The carbide effects reduce hardenability	Greatest known (2% Ti renders 0.50% carbon steel unhardenable)	Persistent carbides probably unaffected. Some secondary hardening	1. Fixes carbon in inert particles
							  a. Reduces martensitic hardness and hardenability in medium-chromium steels
							  b. Prevents formation of austenite in high-chromium steels
							  c. Prevents localized depletion of chromium in stainless steel during long heating

Tungsten	6% (11% with 0.25% C)	33% (less with lowered temperature)	Provides age-hardening system in high W-Fe alloys	Increases hardenability strongly in small amounts	Strong	Opposes softening by secondary hardening	1. Forms hard, abrasion-resistant particles in tool steels 2. Promotes hardness and strength at elevated temperature
Vanadium	1% (4% with 0.20% C)	Unlimited	Hardens moderately by solid solution	Increases hardenability very strongly, as dissolved	Very strong (V < Ti or Cb)	Maximum for secondary hardening	1. Elevates coarsening temperature of austenite (promotes fine grain) 2. Increases hardenability (when dissolved) 3. Resists tempering and causes marked secondary hardening

* "Metals Handbook," 1948 edition, American Society for Metals, Metals Park, Ohio.

271

cent nickel steels with low carbon are used extensively for carburizing of drive gears, connecting-rod bolts, studs, and kingpins. The 5 per cent nickel steels provide increased toughness and are used for heavy-duty applications such as bus and truck gears, cams, and crankshafts. Nickel has only a mild effect on hardenability but is outstanding in its ability to improve toughness, particularly at low temperatures.

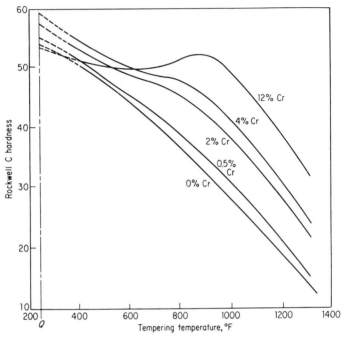

Fig. 9·5 The softening, with increasing tempering temperature, of quenched 0.35 per cent carbon steels as influenced by chromium content. (*From E. C. Bain and H. W. Paxton, "Alloying Elements in Steel," American Society for Metals, Metals Park, Ohio, 1961*)

9·8 Chromium steels. Chromium is a less expensive alloying element than nickel and forms simple carbides (Cr_7C_3, Cr_4C) or complex carbides [$(FeCr)_3C$]. These carbides have high hardness and good wear resistance. Chromium is soluble up to about 13 per cent in γ iron and has unlimited solubility in α ferrite. In low-carbon steels, chromium tends to go into solution, thus increasing the strength and toughness of the ferrite. When chromium is present in amounts in excess of 5 per cent, the high-temperature properties and corrosion resistance of the steel are greatly improved.

The plain-chromium alloy steels with low carbon are usually carburized. The presence of chromium increases the wear resistance of the case and the toughness of the core. With medium carbon, these steels are oil hardening and are used for springs, engine bolts, studs, axles, etc. A high-carbon (1 per cent) high-chromium (1.5 per cent) alloy steel is characterized by high hardness and wear resistance. This steel is used extensively for ball and roller bearings and for crushing machinery. A special type of chromium steel containing 1 per cent carbon and 2 to 4 per cent chromium has excellent magnetic properties and is used for permanent magnets.

The high-chromium steels containing over 10 per cent chromium are noted for their high resistance to corrosion and will be discussed in Sec. 9·15.

9.9 Nickel-chromium steels. In these steels the ratio of nickel to chromium is approximately $2\frac{1}{2}$ parts nickel to 1 part chromium. A combination of alloying elements usually imparts some of the characteristic properties of each one. The effect of nickel in increasing toughness and ductility is combined with the effect of chromium in improving hardenability and wear resistance. It is important to remember that the combined effect of two or more alloying elements on hardenability is usually greater than the sum of the effects of the same alloying elements used separately.

The low-carbon nickel-chromium alloy steels are carburized. The chromium supplies the wear resistance to the case while both alloying elements improve the toughness of the core. With 1.5 per cent nickel and 0.60 per cent chromium, they are used for worm gears, piston pins, etc. For heavy-duty applications, such as aircraft gears, shafts, and cams, the nickel content is increased to 3.5 per cent and the chromium content to 1.5 per cent. The medium-carbon nickel-chromium steels are used in the manufacture of automotive connecting rods and drive shafts.

The very high nickel-chromium alloy steels will be discussed in Sec. 9·15.

9·10 Manganese steels. Manganese is one of the least expensive alloying elements and is present in all steels as a deoxidizer. It is only when the manganese content exceeds about 1 per cent that the steel may be classed as alloy steel. Manganese contributes markedly to strength and hardness, but to a lesser degree than carbon, and is most effective in the higher-carbon steels. This element is a weak carbide former and has a moderate effect on hardenability. Like nickel, manganese lowers the critical range and decreases the carbon content of the eutectoid.

Fine-grained manganese steels attain unusual toughness and strength. These steels are often used for gears, spline shafts, axles, and rifle barrels. With a moderate amount of vanadium added, manganese steels are used for large forgings that must be air-cooled. After normalizing, this steel will yield properties equivalent to those obtained in a plain-carbon steel after a full hardening and tempering operation.

When the manganese content exceeds about 10 per cent, the steel will be austenitic after slow cooling. A special steel, known as *Hadfield manganese steel*, usually contains 12 per cent manganese. After a properly controlled heat treatment, this steel is characterized by high strength, high ductility, and excellent resistance to wear. It is an outstanding material for resisting severe service that combines abrasion and wear as found in power-shovel buckets and teeth, grinding and crushing machinery, and railway-track work. If this alloy is slow-cooled from 1750°F, the structure will consist of large brittle carbides surrounding austenite grains. This structure has low strength and ductility. In this condition the tensile strength is about 70,000 psi with elongation values down to 1 per cent. If the same alloy, after allowing the carbides to dissolve, is quenched from 1850°F, the structure will be fully austenitic with a tensile strength of about 120,000 psi, elongation of 45 per cent, and a BHN of 180. The alloy now has much greater strength and ductility as compared with the annealed condition. The steel is usually reheated below 500°F to reduce quenching stresses. In the austenitic condition following rapid cooling, the steel is not very hard; however, when it is placed in service and subjected to repeated impact, the hardness increases to about 550 BHN. This increase in hardness is due to the ability of manganese steels to work-harden rapidly and to the conversion of some austenite to martensite.

9·11 Molybdenum steels. Molybdenum is a relatively expensive alloying element, has a limited solubility in γ and α iron, and is a strong carbide former. Molybdenum has a strong effect on hardenability and, like chromium, increases the high-temperature hardness and strength of steels. Steels containing molybdenum are less susceptible to temper brittleness than other alloy steels. This element is most often used in combination with nickel or chromium or both nickel and chromium. For carburizing applications it improves the wear resistance of the case and the toughness of the core. The nickel-chromium-molybdenum steels with medium carbon content have very high hardenability and are used extensively in the aircraft industry for structural parts of the wing assembly, fuselage, and landing gear.

9·12 Tungsten steel. Tungsten has a marked effect on hardenability, is a strong carbide former, and retards the softening of martensite on tempering. In general, the effect of tungsten in steel is similar to that of molybdenum, although larger quantities are required. Approximately 2 to 3 per cent tungsten is equivalent to 1 per cent molybdenum. Since tungsten is relatively expensive and large quantities are necessary to obtain an appreciable effect, it is not used in general engineering steels. Tungsten is used primarily in tool steels.

9·13 Vanadium steels. Vanadium is the most expensive of the common alloying elements. It is a powerful deoxidizer and a strong carbide former which inhibits grain growth. Vanadium additions of about 0.05 per cent produce a sound, uniform, fine-grain casting. When dissolved, vanadium has a marked effect on hardenability, yielding high mechanical properties on air cooling. Therefore, carbon-vanadium steels are used for heavy locomotive and machinery forgings that are normalized.

The low-carbon chromium-vanadium steels are used in the case-hardened condition in the manufacture of pins and crankshafts. The medium-carbon chromium-vanadium steels have high toughness and strength and are used for axles and springs. The high-carbon grade with high hardness and wear resistance is used for bearings and tools.

9·14 Silicon steels. Silicon, like manganese, is present in all steels as a cheap deoxidizer. When a steel contains more than 0.60 per cent silicon, it is classed as a silicon steel. Like nickel, silicon is not a carbide former but rather dissolves in ferrite, increasing strength and toughness. A steel containing 1 to 2 per cent silicon known as *navy steel* is used for structural applications requiring a high yield point. *Hadfield silicon steel* with less than 0.1 per cent carbon and about 3 per cent silicon has excellent magnetic properties for use in the cores and poles of electrical machinery.

A properly balanced combination of manganese and silicon produces a steel with unusually high strength and with good ductility and toughness. This silicon-manganese steel is widely used for coil and leaf springs and also for chisels and punches.

9·15 Stainless steels. Stainless steels are used for both corrosion- and heat-resisting applications. A three-numeral numbering system is used to identify stainless steels. The last two numerals have no particular significance, but the first numeral indicates the group as follows:

Series Designation	*Groups*
2xx	Chromium-nickel-manganese; non-hardenable, austenitic, nonmagnetic
3xx	Chromium-nickel; nonhardenable, austenitic, nonmagnetic
4xx	Chromium; hardenable, martensitic, magnetic
4xx	Chromium; nonhardenable, ferritic, magnetic
5xx	Chromium; low chromium, heat-resisting

The corrosion-resisting property is due to a thin, adherent, stable chromium oxide or nickel oxide film that effectively protects the steel against many corroding media. This property is not evident in the low-chromium structural steels previously discussed and is apparent only when the chromium content exceeds about 10 per cent.

Since stainless steels contain relatively large amounts of chromium, the iron-chromium-carbon alloys belong to a ternary system. Figures

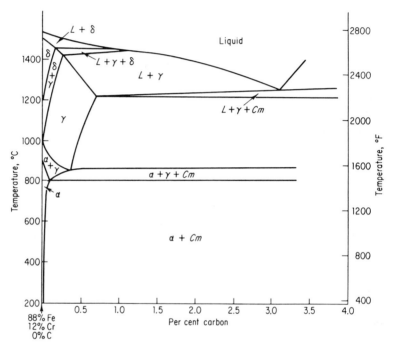

Fig. 9·6   Cross-section diagram for steels containing 12 per cent chromium.   (*From E. E. Thum, "Book of Stainless Steels," 2d ed., American Society for Metals, Metals Park, Ohio,* 1935)

9·6 and 9·8 represent plane sections through such a ternary system. While these plane figures are not true equilibrium diagrams, they are useful in a study of phase changes and in interpreting structures.

Figure 9·6 shows a diagram for steels with 12 per cent chromium and varying carbon. In comparison with the iron–iron carbide diagram, the presence of this amount of chromium has raised the critical temperatures and reduced the austenite area. However, with the proper amount of carbon, these steels may be heat-treated to a martensitic structure as were the plain-carbon steels.

The microstructure of a 12 per cent chromium steel in the annealed condition is shown in Fig. 9·7a. It consists of ferrite and small carbide particles. This same steel after quenching from 1850°F and tempering at 600°F consists of tempered martensite (Fig. 9·7b).

Figure 9·8 shows a diagram with 18 per cent chromium and varying carbon. Consideration of this diagram indicates that, if the carbon content of the steel is low, austenite will not be formed on heating. These steels are nonhardenable since subsequent quenching will only

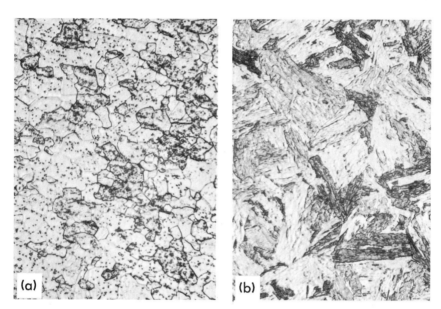

Fig. 9·7 Microstructure of a 12 per cent chromium steel. (a) Annealed; (b) quenched from 1850°F, tempered at 600°F. Etched in picric-hydrochloric acid, 500×. (*Research Laboratory, Universal-Cyclops Steel Corp.*)

form ferrite of low hardness. Figure 9·9a illustrates the ferritic microstructure obtained by quenching a 0.03 per cent carbon, 18 per cent chromium steel from the delta region. If the carbon content is increased so that on heating the steel will be in the δ plus γ field, some hardness will result on quenching because of the transformation of γ iron. This is illustrated in Fig. 9·9b for a 0.075 per cent carbon, 18 per cent chromium steel water-quenched from 1850°F. The microstructure consists of ferrite (light area) and transformation product (dark area). If the carbon is still further increased so that the steel is in the austenite $\gamma + Cm$ field on heating, subsequent quenching will produce full hardness. This is shown in Fig. 9·9c for a high-carbon, 18 per cent chromium steel water-quenched from 1850°F and tempered at 600°F. The microstructure consists of tempered martensite plus some undissolved carbides.

The addition of nickel to the chromium steel will produce further modifications in the diagram. Figure 9·10 indicates the trend in the changes of steel with 18 per cent chromium, 8 per cent nickel, and

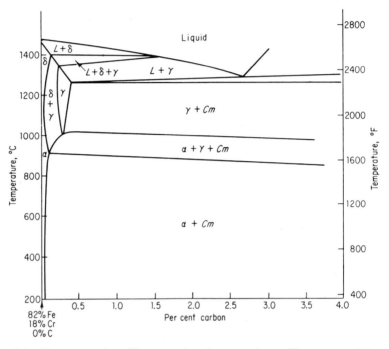

Fig. 9·8 Cross-section diagram for iron-carbon alloys containing 18 per cent chromium. (*From E. E. Thum, "Book of Stainless Steels," 2d ed., American Society for Metals, Metals Park, Ohio, 1935*)

varying carbon content. The austenite formed at the elevated temperature is a particularly stable phase reluctant to transform and tends to be retained after annealing. Figure 9·11a shows the fully austenitic microstructure of an 18 per cent chromium, 8 per cent nickel steel after annealing. The microstructure of this steel after cold working is shown in Fig. 9·11b.

The response of stainless and heat-resisting steels to heat treatment depends upon their composition. They are divided into three general groups.

Martensitic Stainless Steels. These steels are primarily straight chromium steels containing between 11.5 and 18 per cent chromium. Some examples of this group are types 403, 410, 416, 420, 440A, 501, and 502. Types 410 and 416 are probably the most commonly used alloys of this class. The martensitic types of stainless steel are magnetic, can be cold-worked without difficulty especially with low carbon

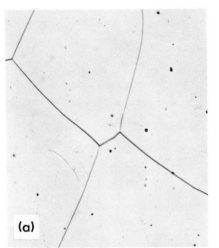

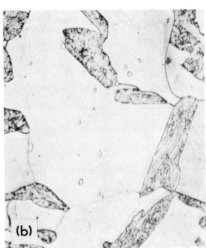

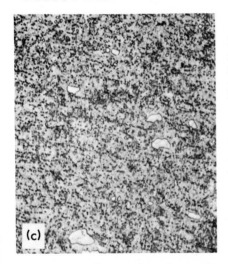

Fig. 9.9 Microstructures of an 18 per cent chromium steel with varying carbon content. (*a*) 0.03 per cent carbon, water-quenched from 2100°F, etched in 20 per cent HCl; (*b*) 0.075 per cent carbon, water-quenched from 1850°F and tempered at 1000°F, etched in picric-HCl; (*c*) 0.65 per cent carbon, water-quenched from 1850°F and tempered at 1000°F, etched in picric-HCl. All magnifications 500×. (*Research Laboratory, Universal-Cyclops Steel Corp.*)

content, can be machined satisfactorily, have good toughness, show good corrosion resistance to weather and to some chemicals, and are easily hot-worked. They attain the best corrosion resistance when hardened from the recommended temperature.

Ferritic Stainless Steels. This group includes types 405, 430, and 446. These straight chromium stainless steels are not hardenable by heat treatment. They are magnetic and can be cold-worked or

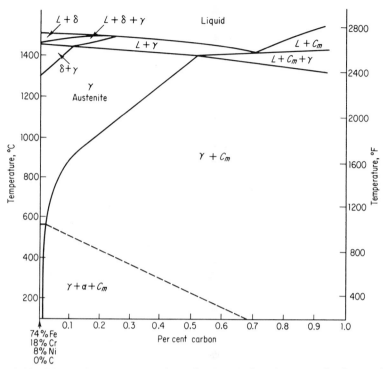

Fig. 9·10 Tentative cross-section diagram showing trend of reactions in steels alloyed with 18 per cent chromium and 8 per cent nickel. (*From E. E. Thum, "Book of Stainless Steels," 2d ed., American Society for Metals, Metals Park, Ohio, 1935*)

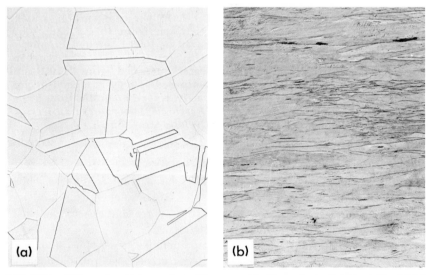

Fig. 9·11 Microstructures of an 18 per cent chromium, 8 per cent nickel steel. (*a*) After annealing; (*b*) after cold working. Etched in glyceregia, 100×. (*International Nickel Company*)

hot-worked but develop their maximum softness, ductility, and corrosion resistance in the annealed condition. These steels have lower strength at elevated temperatures than the martensitic type, but resistance to scaling and to corrosion is generally better.

Austenitic Stainless Steels. These are the chromium-nickel and chromium-nickel-manganese stainless steels. Some examples of this group are types 201, 202, 301, 302, 309, and 316. These types are austenitic, are essentially nonmagnetic in the annealed condition, and do not harden by heat treatment. The total content of nickel and chromium is at least 23 per cent. They can be hot-worked readily and can be cold-worked when proper allowance is made for their rapid work hardening. Cold working develops a wide range of mechanical properties, and the steel in this condition may become slightly magnetic. They are extremely shock-resistant and difficult to machine unless they contain sulfur and selenium. These steels have the best high-temperature strength and resistance to scaling of the stainless steels. The corrosion resistance of the austenitic stainless steels is usually better than that of the martensitic or ferritic steels.

The austenitic stainless steels are susceptible to intergranular corrosion at temperatures between 800 and 1600°F because of carbide precipitation in the grain boundaries. This loss of corrosion resistance may be avoided by using the proper type of stainless steel or by using a suitable heat treatment to "stabilize" the structure and prevent the presence of carbide at or near the grain boundaries.

The shortage of nickel in times of national emergency has presented a serious problem to stainless-steel producers and consumers. Started during World War II and continued through the Korean emergency, development work covering the substitution of manganese for nickel in stainless steel led to the production of types 201 and 202, the chromium-nickel-manganese stainless steels. Type 201 with a nominal composition of 17 per cent Cr, 4.5 per cent Ni, and 6.5 per cent Mn is a satisfactory substitute for type 301 (17 per cent Cr, 7 per cent Ni) where machinability and severe forming characteristics are not essential. Where those characteristics are essential, type 202 with a nominal composition of 18 per cent Cr, 5 per cent Ni, and 8 per cent Mn is more desirable because the higher manganese reduces the rate of work hardening. Although types 201 and 202 have somewhat less resistance to chemical corrosion than 301 and 302, their resistance to atmospheric corrosion is entirely comparable.

Table 9·3 gives the chemical composition and typical mechanical properties of some of the stainless steels.

Table 9·3   Chemical composition and typica

Group	Austenitic group					
Type number	201	202	301	302	309	316
Analysis, %:						
Chromium	16.0–18.0	17.0–19.0	16.0–18.0	17.0–19.0	22.0–24.0	16.0–18.0
Nickel	3.5–5.5	4.0–6.0	6.0–8.0	8.0–10.0	12.0–15.0	10.0–14.0
Other elements	N_2 0.25 max	N_2 0.25 max	...	...	...	Mo 2.0–3.0
Carbon	0.15 max	0.15 max	0.15 max	0.15 max	0.20 max	0.08 max
Manganese	5.5–7.5	7.5–10.0	2.0 max	2.0 max	2.0 max	2.0 max
Silicon	1.00 max	1.0 max	1.0 max	1.0 max	1.0 max	1.0 max
Temperature, °F:						
Forging—start	2300	2300	2200	2200	2150	2200
Annealing—ranges	1850–2000	1850–2000	1950–2050	1850–2050	2050–2150	1975–2150
Annealing—cooling†	WQ (AC)	WQ (AC)	WQ (AC)	WQ (AC)	WQ (AC)	WQ (AC)
Hardening—ranges	‡	‡	‡	‡	‡	‡
Quenching	...	...	...	...	...	...
Tempering—for intermediate hardness	...	...	...	...	...	...
Drawing—for relieving stresses	...	...	...	...	...	...
Mechanical properties—annealed:						
Structure annealed	A	A	A	A	A	A
Yield strength, 1,000 psi min	40	40	35	30	30	30
Ultimate strength, 1,000 psi min	115	100	100	80	75	75
Elongation, % in 2 in. min	40.0	40.0	50.0	50.0	40.0	40.0
Reduction in area, % min	...	...	60.0	60.0	50.0	50.0
Modulus of elasticity in tension, 10^6 psi	29.0	29.0	29.0	29.0	29.0	29.0
Hardness, Brinell	210 max	210 max	180 max	180 max	200 max	200 max
Hardness, Rockwell	B 95 max	B 95 max	B 90 max	B 90 max	B 95 max	B 95 max
Impact values, Izod, ft-lb	85 min	85 min	85 min	85 min	80 min	70 min
Mechanical properties, heat-treated:						
Yield strength, 1,000 psi	...	...	...	...	...	...
Ultimate strength, 1,000 psi	§	§	§	...	...	...
Elongation, % in 2 in.	...	...	...	...	...	...
Hardness, Brinell	...	...	...	...	...	...
Hardness, Rockwell	...	...	...	...	...	...

Abbreviations: AC = air cool, FC = furnace cool, SFC = slow furnace cool, WQ = water quench, O = oil quench, AC = air cool, F = ferrite, C = carbide, A = austenite.
* From "Stainless Steel Handbook," Allegheny Ludlum Steel Corp.
† Thin sections of 300 series, marked WQ (AC) are usually air-cooled, heavy sections water-quenched.
‡ Hardenable only by cold working.
§ Ultimate strengths up to 350,000 psi for wire and 250,000 psi for strip can be obtained by cold working.
¶ Generally used in the annealed condition only.

mechanical properties of some stainless steels*

	Martensitic group					Ferritic group		
410	416	420	440A	501	502	405	430	446
11.5–13.5	12.0–14.0	12.0–14.0	16.0–18.0	4.0–6.0	4.0–6.0	11.5–14.5	14.0–18.0	23.0–27.0
0.50 max	...	...	0.50 max	...	...	0.50 max	0.50 max	0.50 max
...	...	...	Mo 0.75 max	Mo 0.4–0.65	Mo 0.4–0.65	Al 0.10–0.30	...	N_2 0.25 max
0.15 max	0.15 max	0.15 max	0.60–0.75	0.10 min	0.10 max	0.08 max	0.12 max	0.20 max
1.0 max	1.25 max	1.0 max	1.0 max	1.0 max	1.0 max	1.0 max	1.0 max	1.5 max
1.0 max	1.0 max	1.0 max	1.0 max	1.0 max	1.0 max	1.0 max	1.0 max	1.0 max
2100	2150	2000	2100	2150	2150	2100	2100	2150
1500–1650	1500–1650	1550–1650	1550–1650	1525–1600	1525–1600	1350–1500	1400–1500	1450–1600
SFC	FC	FC	FC	FC	FC	AC	FC	WQ
1700–1850	1700–1850	1800–1900	1850–1900	1600–1700	¶	Nonhardenable		
O or A	O or A	O or A	O or A	O				
Over 1100	Up to 1200	Below 700	Over 1100	Over 1000				
Under 700	Below 700	Below 700	Under 700	Under 700				
F-C	F-C	F-C	F-C	F-C	F-C	F-C	F-C	F-C
32	40–50	50–60	55	30	25	32	35	45
60	60–80	90–100	95	70	65	60	60	75
20.0	30–20	25–20	20.0	28.0	30.0	20.0	20.0	20.0
50.0	60–50	50–40	40.0	65.0	75.0	50.0	40.0	40.0
29.0	29.0	29.0	30.0	29.0	29.0	29.0	29.0	29.0
200 max	145–185	200–230	240 max	160	150	180 max	200 max	200 max
B 95 max	B 79–90	B 93–98	B 100 max	...	B 75	B 90 max	B 95 max	B 95 max
85 min	50–30	...	Low	...	85 min	25 min	3–85	Low
35–180	60–130	120–220	55–240	90–135				
60–200	90–160	150–250	95–275	115–175				
25–2	20–10	12–2	20–2	20–15				
120–400	180–300	275–500	200–555	240–370				
B 70–C 45	B 88–107	C 30–52	B 95–C 55					

QUESTIONS

9·1   Explain how alloying elements that dissolve in ferrite increase its strength.

9·2   What effect would the addition of 1 per cent chromium have on the properties of a low-carbon steel?   A high-carbon steel?

9·3   What factors determine the wear-resisting properties of a steel?

9·4   Devise and explain a practical test to compare the wear resistance of different steels.

9·5   If the primary consideration is hardenability, which alloy steel should be selected?

9·6   Look up the chemical composition of 4340 steel (Table 7·2).   This steel is to be used as a structural member in an aircraft landing-gear assembly.   What mechanical properties would be desirable for this application?   Describe a heat treatment that would be applied to obtain these properties.

9·7   Same as Question 9·6 for 6150 steel to be used as a front coil spring in an automobile.

9·8   Look up the chemical composition of 4620 steel.   On the basis of chemical composition, what mechanical properties would you expect this steel to have? Specify a heat treatment for this steel and give some possible applications.

9·9   Why was manganese chosen as a substitute for nickel in the development of the 2xx series of stainless steels?

9·10   Which stainless steel is best suited for surgical instruments?   Explain.

9·11   Why do some pots and pans have a copper bottom and stainless steel inside?   What type of stainless steel is best for this application?   Why?

REFERENCES

Allegheny Ludlum Steel Corp.: "Stainless Steel Handbook," Pittsburgh, 1951.

American Society for Metals: "Metals Handbook," 7th ed., 1948, 1954 Supplement, and 8th ed., 1961, Metals Park, Ohio.

Archer, R. S., J. F. Briggs, and C. M. Loeb: "Molybdenum; Steels, Irons, Alloys," Climax Molybdenum Co., New York, 1948.

Bain, E. C., and H. W. Paxton: "Alloying Elements in Steel," 2d ed., American Society for Metals, Metals Park, Ohio, 1961.

Burnham, T. H.: "Special Steels," 2d ed., Sir Isaac Pitman & Sons, Ltd., London, 1933.

Hull, A. M.: "Nickel in Iron and Steel," John Wiley & Sons, Inc., New York, 1954.

International Nickel Co.: "Nickel Alloy Steels," 2d ed., New York, 1949.

Thum, E. E.: "Book of Stainless Steels," 2d ed., American Society for Metals, Metals Park, Ohio, 1935.

Zapffe, C. A.: "Stainless Steels," American Society for Metals, Metals Park, Ohio, 1949.

Chapter 10

TOOL STEELS

10·1 Classification of tool steels. Any steel used as a tool may be technically classed as a tool steel. However, the term is usually restricted to high-quality special steels used for cutting or forming purposes.

There are several methods of classifying tool steels. One method is according to the quenching media used, such as water-hardening steels, oil-hardening steels, and air-hardening steels. Alloy content is another means of classification, such as carbon tool steels, low-alloy tool steels, and medium-alloy tool steels. A final method of grouping is based on the application of the tool steel, such as hot-work steels, shock-resisting steels, high-speed steels, and cold-work steels.

The method of identification and type classification of tool steels adopted by the AISI (American Iron and Steel Institute) includes the method of quenching, applications, special characteristics, and steels for special industries. The commonly used tool steels have been grouped into six major headings, and each group or subgroup has been assigned an alphabetical letter as follows:

Group		Symbol and Type
Water-hardening	W	
Shock-resisting	S	
Cold-work	O	Oil-hardening
	A	Medium-alloy air-hardening
	D	High-carbon high-chromium
Hot-work	H	(H1–H19, incl., chromium-base; H20–H39, incl., tungsten-base; H40–H59, incl., molybdenum-base)
High-speed	T	Tungsten-base
	M	Molybdenum-base
Special-purpose	L	Low-alloy
	F	Carbon-tungsten
	P	Mold steels (P1–P19, incl., low-carbon; P20–P39, incl., other types)

The AISI identification and type classification of tool steels is given in Table 10·1.

285

Table 10·1 Identification and type classification of tool steels*

Type	Identifying elements, %									
	C	Mn	Si	Cr	Ni	V	W	Mo	Co	Cb

WATER-HARDENING TOOL STEELS
Symbol W

Type	C	Mn	Si	Cr	Ni	V	W	Mo	Co	Cb
W1	0.60/1.40†									
W2	0.60/1.40†	...	...	...	...	0.25				
W3	1.00	...	...	...	...	0.50				
W4	0.60/1.40†	...	...	0.25						
W5	1.10	...	...	0.50						
W6	1.00	...	...	0.25	...	0.25				
W7	1.00	...	...	0.50	...	0.20				

SHOCK-RESISTING TOOL STEELS
Symbol S

Type	C	Mn	Si	Cr	Ni	V	W	Mo	Co	Cb
S1	0.50	...	...	1.50	...	...	2.50			
S2	0.50	...	1.00	...	...	...	...	0.50		
S3	0.50	...	...	0.75	...	...	1.00			
S4	0.55	0.80	2.00							
S5	0.55	0.80	2.00	...	...	...	...	0.40		

COLD-WORK TOOL STEELS
Symbol O, Oil-hardening Types

Type	C	Mn	Si	Cr	Ni	V	W	Mo	Co	Cb
O1	0.90	1.00	...	0.50	...	...	0.50			
O2	0.90	1.60								
O7	1.20	...	...	0.75	...	...	1.75			

Symbol A, Medium-alloy Air-hardening Types

Type	C	Mn	Si	Cr	Ni	V	W	Mo	Co	Cb
A2	1.00	...	...	5.00	...	...	...	1.00		
A4	1.00	2.00	...	1.00	...	...	...	1.00		
A5	1.00	3.00	...	1.00	...	...	...	1.00		
A6	0.70	2.00	...	1.00	...	...	...	1.00		

Symbol D, High-carbon High-chromium Types

Type	C	Mn	Si	Cr	Ni	V	W	Mo	Co	Cb
D1	1.00	...	...	12.00	...	...	...	1.00		
D2	1.50	...	...	12.00	...	...	...	1.00		
D3	2.25	...	...	12.00						
D4	2.25	...	...	12.00				1.00		
D5	1.50	...	...	12.00	...	...	...	1.00	3.00	
D6	2.25	...	1.00	12.00	...	...	1.00			
D7	2.35	...	...	12.00	...	4.00	...	1.00		

Table 10·1 Identification and type classification of tool steels*
(Continued)

Type	Identifying elements, %									
	C	Mn	Si	Cr	Ni	V	W	Mo	Co	Cb

HOT-WORK TOOL STEELS
Symbol H
H1–H19, incl., Chromium-base Types (H1–H10 and H17–H19 Unassigned)

Type	C	Mn	Si	Cr	Ni	V	W	Mo	Co	Cb
H11	0.35	...	...	5.00	...	0.40	...	1.50		
H12	0.35	...	...	5.00	...	0.40	1.50	1.50		
H13	0.35	...	...	5.00	...	1.00	...	1.50		
H14	0.40	...	...	5.00	...	...	5.00			
H15	0.40	...	...	5.00	...	...	...	5.00		
H16	0.55	...	...	7.00	...	...	7.00			

H20–H39, incl., Tungsten-base Types (H27–H39 Unassigned)

Type	C	Mn	Si	Cr	Ni	V	W	Mo	Co	Cb
H20	0.35	...	...	2.00	...	...	9.00			
H21	0.35	...	...	3.50	...	...	9.00			
H22	0.35	...	...	2.00	...	...	11.00			
H23	0.30	...	...	12.00	...	...	12.00			
H24	0.45	...	...	3.00	...	...	15.00			
H25	0.25	...	...	4.00	...	...	15.00			
H26	0.50	...	...	4.00	...	1.00	18.00			

H40–H59, incl., Molybdenum-base Types (H40, H44–H59 Unassigned)

Type	C	Mn	Si	Cr	Ni	V	W	Mo	Co	Cb
H41	0.65	...	...	4.00	...	1.00	1.50	8.00		
H42	0.60	...	...	4.00	...	2.00	6.00	5.00		
H43	0.55	...	...	4.00	...	2.00	...	8.00		

HIGH-SPEED TOOL STEELS
Symbol T, Tungsten-base Types

Type	C	Mn	Si	Cr	Ni	V	W	Mo	Co	Cb
T1	0.70	...	...	4.00	...	1.00	18.00			
T2	0.80	...	...	4.00	...	2.00	18.00			
T3	1.05	...	...	4.00	...	3.00	18.00			
T4	0.75	...	...	4.00	...	1.00	18.00	...	5.00	
T5	0.80	...	...	4.00	...	2.00	18.00	...	8.00	
T6	0.80	...	...	4.50	...	1.50	20.00	...	12.00	
T7	0.75	...	...	4.00	...	2.00	14.00			
T8	0.75	...	...	4.00	...	2.00	14.00	...	5.00	
T9	1.20	...	...	4.00	...	4.00	18.00			
T15	1.50	...	...	4.00	...	5.00	12.00	...	5.00	

Table 10·1 Identification and type classification of tool steels*
(Continued)

Type	Identifying elements, %									
	C	Mn	Si	Cr	Ni	V	W	Mo	Co	Cb
Symbol M, Molybdenum-base Types										
M1	0.80	...	...	4.00	...	1.00	1.50	8.00		
M2	0.80	...	...	4.00	...	2.00	6.00	5.00		
M3	1.00	...	...	4.00	...	2.70	6.00	5.00		
M4	1.30	...	...	4.00	...	4.00	5.50	4.50		
M6	0.80	...	...	4.00	...	1.50	4.00	5.00	12.00	
M7	1.00	...	...	4.00	...	2.00	1.75	8.75		
M8	0.80	...	...	4.00	...	1.50	1.50	5.00	...	1.25
M10	0.85	...	...	4.00	...	2.00	...	8.00		
M15	1.50	...	...	4.00	...	5.00	6.50	3.50	5.00	
M30	0.80	...	...	4.00	...	1.25	2.00	8.00	5.00	
M34	0.90	...	...	4.00	...	2.00	2.00	8.00	8.00	
M35	0.80	...	...	4.00	...	2.00	6.00	5.00	5.00	
M36	0.80	...	...	4.00	...	2.00	6.00	5.00	8.00	
SPECIAL-PURPOSE TOOL STEELS Symbol L, Low-alloy Types										
L1	1.00	...	...	1.25						
L2	0.50/1.10†	...	...	1.00	...	0.20				
L3	1.00	...	...	1.50	...	0.20				
L4	1.00	0.60	...	1.50	...	0.25				
L5	1.00	1.00	...	1.00	...	...	...	0.25		
L6	0.70	...	...	0.75	1.50	...	...	0.25‡		
L7	1.00	0.35	...	1.40	...	...	...	0.40		
Symbol F, Carbon-Tungsten Types										
F1	1.00	...	...	...	...	...	1.25			
F2	1.25	...	...	...	...	...	3.50			
F3	1.25	...	...	0.75	...	...	3.50			
Symbol P, Mold Steels P1–P19, incl., Low-carbon Types (P7–P19 Unassigned)										
P1	0.10									
P2	0.07	...	...	2.00	0.50	...	...	0.20		
P3	0.10	...	...	0.60	1.25					
P4	0.07	...	...	5.00						
P5	0.10	...	...	2.25						
P6	0.10	...	...	1.50	3.50					
P20–P39, incl., Other Types (P21–P39 Unassigned)										
P20	0.30	...	...	0.75	...	...	...	0.25		

* From Steel Products Manual, "Tool Steels," American Iron and Steel Institute, 1955.

† Varying carbon contents may be available.

‡ At producer's option.

10·2 Selection of tool steels. The selection of a proper tool steel for a given application is a difficult task. The best approach is to correlate the metallurgical characteristics of tool steels with the requirements of the tool in operation.

In most cases, the choice of a tool steel is not limited to a single type or even to a particular family for a working solution to an individual tooling problem. Although many tool steels will perform on any given job, they will have to be judged on the basis of expected productivity, ease of fabrication, and cost. In the final analysis, it is the cost per unit part made by the tool that determines the proper selection.

Most tool-steel applications, with the exception of those to be made into machine parts, may be divided into types of operations: cutting, shearing, forming, drawing, extrusion, rolling, and battering. A cutting tool may have a single cutting edge which is in continuous contact with the work, such as a lathe or planer tool; or it may have two or more cutting edges which do continuous cutting, such as a drill or a tap; or it may have a number of cutting edges with each edge taking short cuts and functioning only part of the time, such as a milling cutter or hob. When cutting is the chief function of the tool steel, it should have high hardness as well as good heat and wear resistance.

Shearing tools for use in shears, punches, and blanking dies require high wear resistance and fair toughness. These characteristics must be properly balanced, depending on the tool design, thickness of the stock being sheared, and temperature of the shearing operation.

Forming tools are characterized by imparting their form to the part being made. This may be done by forcing the solid metal into the tool impression either hot or cold by using a hot-forging or cold-heading die. This group also includes dies for die casting where the molten or semimolten metal is forced under pressure into the form of the die. Forming tools must have high toughness and high strength, and many require high red hardness (resistance to heat softening).

Drawing and extrusion dies are characterized by substantial slippage between the metal being formed and the tool itself. Deep-drawing dies such as those used for the forming of cartridge cases generally require high strength and high wear resistance. Toughness to withstand outward pressures and wear resistance is most important for cold-extrusion dies, whereas dies for hot extrusion require, in addition, high red hardness.

Thread-rolling dies must be hard enough to withstand the forces in forming the thread and must have sufficient wear resistance and toughness to adjust to the stresses developed. Battering tools include chisels and all forms of tools involving heavy shock loads. The most important characteristic for these tools is high toughness.

From the above discussion, it is apparent that, for most applications, hardness, toughness, wear resistance, and red hardness are the most important selection factors in choosing tool steels. In individual applications, many other factors must be seriously considered. They include the amount of distortion which is permissible in the shape under consideration; the amount of surface decarburization which can be tolerated; hardenability or depth of hardness which can be obtained; resistance to heat checking; heat-treating requirements, including temperatures, atmospheres, and equipment; and finally, the machinability.

10·3 Comparative properties. The comparative properties of the most common tool steels are given in Table 10·2. Toughness, red hardness, wear resistance, nondeforming, machinability, safety in hardening, and resistance to decarburization have been qualitatively rated as Good, Fair, or Poor. Depth of hardening is rated as Shallow, Medium, or Deep. The steels have been rated relative to each other rather than within any one particular class. The hot-work steels have been rated as Good or Very Good in red hardness, but significant differences exist in "hot strength" of these steels, and a steel to be selected for hot die work requires careful study. Although the high-speed steels are rated Poor in toughness, there are differences in this property between the different high-speed steels which should be taken into account for a particular application.

10·4 Nondeforming properties. The tool steels in Table 10·2 have been rated on the basis of distortion obtained in hardening from the recommended hardening temperatures. Since steels expand and contract during heating and quenching, the extent to which dimensions change is most important for complex shapes. Intricately designed tools and dies must maintain their shape after hardening. Those steels rated Good or Best in nondeforming properties can be machined very close to size before heat treatment so that little grinding will be required after hardening. Parts that involve rather drastic section changes should not be made of steels which are subject to excessive warpage in heating or quenching, as this will generally lead to cracking during hardening. In general, air-hardening steels exhibit the least distortion; those quenched in oil show moderate distortion; and water-hardening steels show the greatest distortion. The distortion is associated with the temperature gradient and the resulting dimensional changes during heating and cooling, which were discussed in detail under Residual Stresses in Chap. 8.

10·5 Depth of hardening. This is related to the hardenability of the individual tool steels. The hardenability ratings in Table 10·2 are based on the use of the recommended quenching medium. The shallow-hardening steels such as the carbon tool steels (Group W), the tungsten finishing steels (Group F), and several of the carburizing grades in Group P are generally quenched in water. The hardenability increases with increasing alloy content. The only alloying element which decreases hardenability is cobalt. To develop high strength throughout a large section, it is important to select a high-alloy steel.

10·6   Toughness.   The term *toughness* as applied to tool steels may be thought of as the ability to resist breaking rather than the ability to absorb energy during deformation, as defined in Chap. 1. Most tools must be rigid articles, and usually even slight plastic deformation makes the tool unfit for use. As might be expected, this property is best in the medium- and low-carbon tool steels of Groups S and H, which form the basis of the shock-resisting tool steels. Shallow-hardening steels which end up with a relatively soft tough core are also rated Good in toughness. The cold-work tool steels which are high in carbon tend toward brittleness and low toughness.

10·7   Wear resistance.   All the tool steels have relatively good wear resistance, but several are outstanding in this property. Wear resistance may be defined as the resistance to abrasion or resistance to the loss of dimensional tolerances. Wear resistance might be required on a single cutting edge or over the total surface of the part. In general, a correlation exists between the hard, undissolved carbide particles and wear resistance.

10·8   Red hardness.   This property, also called *hot hardness*, is related to the resistance of the steel to the softening effect of heat. It is reflected to some extent in the resistance of the material to tempering, which is an important selective factor for high-speed and hot-work tools. A tool steel with good red hardness is essential when temperatures at which the tools must operate exceed 900°F. Alloying elements which form hard, stable carbides generally improve the resistance to softening at elevated temperature. Outstanding in this property are the tool steels that contain relatively large amounts of tungsten, chromium, and molybdenum.

10·9   Machinability.   This is the ability of the material to be cut freely and produce a good finish after being machined. The machinability ratings given in Table 10·2 merely show the relative difficulty which might be encountered in machining the steels in question during manufacture of tools and dies. The factors that affect machinability of tool steels are the hardness in the annealed condition, the microstructure of the steel, and the quantity of hard excess carbides.

When compared with the conventional alloy steels, tool steels are

Table 10·2   Comparative

Steel type	Hardening, °F	Quenching medium	Tempering range, °F	Approx hardness, Rockwell C†	Depth of hardening
W1	1400–1550	Brine or water	300–650	65–50	Shallow
W2	1400–1550	Brine or water	300–650	65–50	Shallow
S1	1650–1800	Oil	400–1200	58–40	Medium
S5	1600–1700	Oil	350–800	60–50	Medium
O1	1450–1500	Oil	300–500	62–57	Medium
A2	1700–1800	Air	350–1000	62–57	Deep
A4	1500–1600	Air	350–800	62–54	Deep
D2	1800–1975	Air	400–1000	61–54	Deep
D3	1700–1800	Oil	400–1000	61–54	Deep
D4	1775–1850	Air	400–1000	61–54	Deep
H11	1825–1875	Air	1000–1200	54–38	Deep
H16	2050–2150	Air or oil	1050–1250	60–45	Deep
H20	2000–2200	Air or oil	1100–1250	54–36	Deep
H23	2200–2350	Air or oil	1200–1500	47–30	Deep
H26	2150–2300	Salt, oil, or air	1050–1250	58–43	Deep
H41	2000–2175	Salt, oil, or air	1050–1200	60–50	Deep
T1	2300–2375	Oil, air, or salt	1000–1100	65–60	Deep
T3	2250–2325	Oil, air, or salt	1000–1100	65–60	Deep
T4	2300–2375	Oil, air, or salt	1000–1100	66–62	Deep
T6	2325–2400	Oil, air, or salt	1000–1100	65–60	Deep
M1	2150–2225	Oil, air, or salt	1000–1100	65–60	Deep
M2	2175–2250	Oil, air, or salt	1000–1100	65–60	Deep
M6	2150–2200	Oil, air, or salt	1000–1100	66–61	Deep
L1	1450–1500	Oil or water	300–600	64–56	Medium
L4	1475–1600	Oil or water	300–600	64–56	Medium
F2	1450–1600	Water or brine	300–500	66–62	Shallow
P1	1450–1475‡	Water or brine	300–500	64–58 §	Shallow
P2	1525–1550‡	Oil	300–500	64–58 §	Shallow

* Adapted from tables in Steel Products Manual, "Tool Steels," American Iron and Steel Institute, 1955.
† After tempering.
‡ After carburizing.
§ Carburized case hardness.

properties of some tool steels*

Nondeforming properties	Safety in hardening	Toughness	Red hardness	Wear resistance	Machinability	Resistance to decarburization
Poor	Fair	Good	Poor	Fair to good	Best	Best
Poor	Fair	Good	Poor	Fair to good	Best	Best
Fair	Good	Very good	Fair	Fair	Fair	Fair to good
Fair	Good	Best	Fair	Fair	Fair	Poor
Very good	Very good	Fair	Poor	Good	Good	Good
Best	Best	Fair	Fair	Very good	Fair	Fair
Best	Best	Fair	Fair	Good	Fair to poor	Good to fair
Best	Best	Poor	Good	Best	Poor	Fair
Very good	Good	Poor	Good	Best	Poor	Fair
Best	Best	Poor	Good	Best	Poor	Fair
Very good	Best	Good	Good	Fair	Fair	Fair
Good	Good	Good	Good	Fair	Fair	Fair
Air: good Oil: fair	Good	Good	Good	Fair to good	Fair	Fair
Air: good Oil: fair	Good	Fair	Very good	Fair to good	Fair	Fair
Salt, air: good Oil: fair	Good	Fair	Very good	Good	Fair	Fair
Salt, air: good Oil: fair	Fair	Poor	Very good	Good	Fair	Poor
Good	Good	Poor	Very good	Very good	Fair	Good
Good	Good	Poor	Very good	Very good	Fair	Good
Good	Fair	Poor	Best	Very good	Fair	Fair
Good	Fair	Poor	Best	Very good	Fair	Poor
Good	Fair	Poor	Very good	Very good	Fair	Poor
Good	Fair	Poor	Very good	Very good	Fair	Fair
Good	Fair	Poor	Very good	Very good	Fair	Poor
Water: poor Oil: fair	Water: poor Oil: fair	Fair	Poor	Good	Good	Good
Water: poor Oil: fair	Water: poor Oil: fair	Fair	Poor	Good	Good	Good
Poor	Poor	Poor	Poor	Very good	Fair	Good
Poor	Fair	Good	Poor	Good	Poor	Good
Good	Good	Good	Poor	Good	Good	Good

considerably more difficult to machine. The best machinable tool steel (W type) has a machinability rating of about 30 per cent that of B1112 screw stock. It is therefore usual to compare the machinability of tool steels with W1 at an arbitrary rating of 100. On this basis, the machinability for each of the different types of tool steel is rated in Table 10·3.

The machinability and general workability of tool steels decrease with increasing carbon and alloy content. Low annealed hardnesses

Table 10·3 Machinability ratings of tool steels
Water-hardening grades rated at 100

Tool-steel Group	Machinability Rating
W	100
S	85
O	90
A	85
D	40–50
H (Cr)	75
H (W or Mo)	50–60
T	40–55
M	45–60
L	90
F	75
P	75–100

* From "Metals Handbook," 8th ed., American Society for Metals, Metals Park, Ohio, 1961.

are usually more difficult to attain as the carbon and alloy content increases. The presence of carbon in combination with strong carbide-forming elements such as vanadium, tungsten, chromium, and molybdenum reduces machinability by the formation of a large number of hard carbide particles which are out of solution after annealing.

10·10 Resistance to decarburization. This is an important factor in the selection of tool steels since it influences the type of heat-treating equipment selected and the amount of material to be removed from the surface after hardening. Decarburization usually occurs when steels are heated above 1300°F, and unless some method is used to protect the steel such as heating in a protective atmosphere, they are likely to lose some of their surface carbon. Decarburization will result in a soft rather than a hard surface after hardening. Tools that are intricately designed and cannot be ground after hardening must not show any decarburization.

The straight carbon tool steels are least subject to decarburization. The shock-resisting tool steels are poor in this property; the hot-work tool steels are considered fair; and the majority of the other tool steels have good resistance to decarburization.

10·11   Brand names. For many years, a manufacturer requiring a tool steel for a particular application would indicate the nature of this application to a tool-steel producer and would receive a recommended tool steel. This practice has led to the use of brand names which the tool-steel producer gave to each of his different types of steel. Tool-steel producers made every effort to maintain the quality and thus the reputation of their brand names.

With the rapid growth of industry, many tool-steel consumers had more than one source of supply and had to issue specifications covering chemical composition and some physical properties of the steel. At the same time, many tool-steel manufacturers published information regarding the chemical composition and physical properties of their various brands of tool steel. Although the AISI has standardized the chemical composition of tool steels (Table 10·1), the use of trade names has persisted to the present day. Table 10·4 lists approximate comparable tool-steel brand names of various manufacturers.

10·12   Water-hardening tool steels (Group W). These are essentially plain-carbon tool steels, although some of the higher-carbon-content steels have small amounts of chromium and vanadium added to improve hardenability and wear resistance. The carbon content varies between 0.60 and 1.40 per cent, and the steels may be roughly placed into three subdivisions according to carbon content.

0.60 to 0.75 per cent carbon—for applications where toughness is the primary consideration, such as hammers, concrete breakers, rivet sets, and heading dies for short runs.

0.75 to 0.95 per cent carbon—for applications where toughness and hardness are equally important, such as punches, chisels, dies, and shear blades.

0.95 to 1.40 per cent carbon—for applications where increased wear resistance and retention of cutting edge are important. They are used for woodworking tools, drills, taps, reamers, and turning tools.

In general, the straight carbon tool steels are less expensive than the alloy tool steels, and with proper heat treatment they yield a hard martensitic surface with a tough core. These steels must be water-quenched for high hardness and are therefore subject to considerable distortion. They have the best machinability ratings of all the tool steels and are the best in respect to decarburization, but their resistance to heat is poor. Because of this low red hardness, carbon steels cannot be used as cutting tools under conditions where an appreciable amount of heat is generated at the cutting edge. Their use as cutting tools is limited to conditions involving low speeds and

Table 10·4   Comparabl

General classification	AISI No.	Allegheny-Ludlum	Bethlehem	Braeburn	Carpenter	Columbia
Water-hardening tool steels:						
Standard quality	W1	Pompton	XCL	Standard	No. 11 Comet	Standard
Extra quality	W1	Pompton Extra	XX	Extra	No. 11 Extra	Extra
Extra quality	W2	Python	Superior	. . .	No. 11 Extra Vanadium	Vanadium Extra
Shock-resisting tool steels	S1	Seminole	67 Chisel	Vibro	. . .	Buster
	S5	AL 609	Omega	. . .	No. 481	CEC Smooth
Cold-work tool steels:						
Oil-hardening types	O1	Saratoga	BTR	Kiski	. . .	EXL-Die
	O2	Deward	. . .	S.O.D.	Stentor	. . .
Medium-alloy air-hardening	A2	Sagamore	A-H5	Airque	No. 484	EZ-Die Smoothcut
High-carbon high-chromium	D2	Ontario	Lehigh H	Superior 3	No. 610	Atmodie
	D3	Huron	Lehigh S	Superior 1	Hampden	. . .
Hot-work tool steels, chromium base	H12	Potomac	Cromo-W Cromo-WV	Pressurdie No. 2	No. 345	Alco Die
	H13	Potomac M	Cromo-High V	Pressurdie No. 3	No. 883	Vanadium Fire Die
Plastic-mold steels:						
Straight iron	P1	. . .	Duramold C	. . .	Mirromold	. . .
5% chromium air-hardening	P4	. . .	Duramold A	. . .	Super Samson	. . .

light cuts on relatively soft materials, such as wood, brass, aluminum, and unhardened low-carbon steels.

10·13   Shock-resisting tool steels (Group S).   These steels were developed for those applications where toughness and the ability to withstand repeated shock are paramount.   They are generally low in carbon content, the carbon varying between 0.45 and 0.65 per cent. The principal alloying elements in these steels are silicon, chromium, tungsten, and sometimes molybdenum or nickel.   Silicon and nickel strengthen the ferrite, while chromium increases hardenability and contributes slightly to wear resistance.   Molybdenum aids in increasing hardenability, while tungsten imparts some red hardness to these steels.   Most of these steels are oil-hardening, although some have to be water-quenched to develop full hardness.

The high silicon content tends to accelerate decarburization, and

l-steel brand names

ucible	Firth-Sterling	Jessop	Latrobe	Uddeholm	Universal Cyclops	Vanadium-Alloys	Vulcan Crucible
Black iamond	Sterling	Lion	Standard Carbon	UHB	Standard	Red Star Tool	Fort Pitt
abelle Extra	F-S Extra	Lion Extra	Extra Carbon	UHB Extra	Extra	Extra L	Extra
Alva Extra	Extra V	Lion extra Vanadium	...	UHB-VA	Extra Draco	Elvandi	
ha Pneu	J-S Punch	Top Notch	XL Chisel	UHB-711	Alco M, Alco S	Par Exc	Q.A.
Labelle icon No. 2	Chimo	No. 259	...	UHB Resisto	Cyclops 67	Mosil	487D
Ketos	Invaro No. 1	Truform	Badger	UHB-46	Wando	Non-shrinkable Colonial No. 6	Oil hardening
aragon	Invaro No. 2	Special oil hardening	Mangano	...	...	...	Non-shrinkable
Airkool	Airvan	Windsor	Select B	UHB-151	Sparta	Air Hard	Vuldie
irdi 150	Chromovan	CNS-1	Olympic	TRI-Mo	Ultradie No. 2 and 3	Ohio Die	Alidie
HYCC	Triple Die	CNS-2	GSN	TRI-Van	Ultradie No. 1	...	Hi Pro
hro-Mow	HWD-1	DICA B	LPD	UHB Special	Thermold B	Hot Form No. 1 and 2	TCM
Nudie V	HWD-3	DICA B Vanadium	V.D.C.	UHB Orvar	Thermold Av	Hot Form 5	Vulcast
usca cold ubbing	...	...	...	UHB Forma	...	...	Plastic Die
rmold	...	...	...	UHB Premo			

suitable precautions should be taken in heat treatment to minimize this. They are classed as fair in regard to red hardness, wear resistance, and machinability, and hardness is usually kept below Rockwell C 60. The steels in this group are used in the manufacture of forming tools, punches, chisels, pneumatic tools, and shear blades.

10·14 Cold-work tool steels. This is considered to be the most important group of tool steels since the majority of tool applications can be served by one or more of the steels in this classification.

The oil-hardening low-alloy type (Group O) contains manganese and smaller amounts of chromium and tungsten. They have very good nondeforming properties and are less likely to bend, sag, twist, distort, or crack during heat treatment than are the water-hardening steels. They have good wear resistance, good machinability, and good resistance to decarburization; toughness is only fair, and their red hardness is as poor as the straight carbon tool steels. These steels are used for taps, solid threading dies, form tools, and expansion reamers.

The medium-alloy type (Group A) with 1 per cent carbon contains up to 3 per cent manganese, up to 5 per cent chromium, and 1 per cent molybdenum. The increased alloy content, particularly manganese and molybdenum, confers marked air-hardening properties and increased hardenability. This group has excellent nondeforming properties, good wear resistance, fair toughness, red hardness, and resistance to decarburization, but only fair to poor machinability. These steels are used for blanking, forming, trimming, and thread-rolling dies.

The high-carbon high-chromium types (Group D) contain up to 2.35 per cent carbon and 12 per cent chromium. They may also contain molybdenum, tungsten, vanadium, and cobalt. The combination of high carbon and high chromium gives excellent wear resistance and nondeforming properties. They have good abrasion resistance, and minimum dimensional change in hardening makes these steels popular for blanking and piercing dies; drawing dies for wire, bars, and tubes; thread-rolling dies; and master gauges.

10·15   Hot-work tool steels (Group H). In many applications the tool is subjected to excessive heat because the material is being worked as in hot forging and extruding, die casting, and plastic molding. Tool steels developed for these applications are known as *hot-work tool steels* and have good red hardness.

The alloying elements noted for red hardness are chromium, molybdenum, and tungsten. However, the sum of these elements must be at least 5 per cent before the property of red hardness becomes appreciable.

The hot-work tool steels may be subdivided into three groups:

Hot-work chromium-base (H11 to H16) containing a minimum of 5 per cent chromium and smaller amounts of vanadium, tungsten, and molybdenum.

Hot-work tungsten-base (H20 to H26) containing at least 9 per cent tungsten and 2 to 12 per cent chromium.

Hot-work molybdenum-base (H41 to H43) containing 8 per cent molybdenum, 4 per cent chromium, and smaller amounts of tungsten and vanadium.

In general, they have good toughness because of low carbon content, good to excellent red hardness, and fair wear resistance and machinability. They are only fair to poor in resistance to decarburization but are air-hardening with little or no distortion from heat treating.

These steels are used for die blocks; die inserts; tools in hot-forging machines; tools for hot extrusion of aluminum, magnesium, brass, and steel; hot shears; plastic molds; and die-casting dies.

10·16 High-speed tool steels. These steels are among the most highly alloyed of the tool steels and usually contain large amounts of tungsten or molybdenum along with chromium, vanadium, and sometimes cobalt. The carbon content varies between 0.70 and 1 per cent, although some types contain as much as 1.5 per cent carbon.

The major application of high-speed steels is for cutting tools, but they are also used for making extrusion dies, burnishing tools, and blanking punches and dies.

Compositions of the high-speed steels are designed to provide excellent red hardness and reasonably good shock resistance. They have good nondeforming properties and may be quenched in oil, air, or molten salts. They are rated as deep-hardening, have good wear resistance, fair machinability, and fair to poor resistance to decarburization.

The high-speed steels are subdivided into two groups: molybdenum-base (Group M) and tungsten-base (Group T). The most widely used tungsten-base type is known as 18-4-1, denoting the content, respectively, of tungsten, chromium, and vanadium in percentages. From the standpoint of fabrication and tool performance, there is little difference between the molybdenum and tungsten grades. The important properties of red hardness, wear resistance, and toughness are about the same. Since there are adequate domestic supplies of molybdenum and since most of the tungsten must be imported, the molybdenum steels are lower in price, and over 80 per cent of all the high-speed steel produced is of the molybdenum type.

When better than average red hardness is required, steels containing cobalt are recommended. Higher vanadium content is desirable when the material being cut is highly abrasive. In steels T15 and M15, a combination of cobalt plus high vanadium provides superiority in both red hardness and abrasion resistance. The use of high-cobalt steels requires careful protection against decarburization during heat treatment, and since these steels are more brittle, they must be protected against excessive shock or vibration in service.

10·17 Special-purpose tool steels. Many tool steels do not fall into the usual categories and are therefore designated as special-purpose tool steels. They have been developed to handle the peculiar requirements of one certain application and are more expensive for many applications than would be the more standard steels.

The carbon-tungsten type (Group F) has very good wear resistance and is used for burnishing tools, wire-drawing dies, forming dies, and cold-extruding dies.

The low-alloy types (Group L), especially those containing nickel, are outstanding in toughness. They are used for many tools and parts that are subjected to heavy shock, such as shearing dies, thread-roller dies, clutch parts, pawls, and indexing fingers.

The plastic-mold types (Group P) are used for molds that are shaped by hubbing or a combination of hubbing and machining. In hubbing, a master hub is forced into a soft blank. The soft die is then carburized and hardened to a surface hardness of Rockwell C 58 to 64.

10·18   Heat treatment of tool steels.   Proper heat treatment of tool steels is one of the most important factors in determining how they will perform in service. Although the emphasis in heat treatment is usually on the cooling rate, it should be realized that as much damage may be done to the steel on heating as on cooling.

Tool steels should not be heated so rapidly as to introduce large temperature gradients in the piece. This may be avoided by slow heating or by preheating the steel at a lower temperature before placing it in the high-heat furnace. Some heat treaters prefer placing the tool-steel parts into a cold furnace and then bringing both the work and the furnace up to temperature together. It is also important that the tool steel be allowed to remain at the proper temperature for a sufficient time to make certain that the entire section has been heated uniformly.

To avoid overheating, tool steels should not be heated to too high a temperature or kept at heat too long. Quenching from excessive temperature may result in cracking. Overheating causes excessive grain growth and consequent loss in toughness.

It is essential that some means be used to protect the surface of the tool steel from excessive scaling or decarburization during heating. This has been discussed in Sec. 8·18. Any decarburized areas must be removed from tool-steel surfaces to provide satisfactory hardnesses.

The manner and media of quenching vary according to the steel being quenched and the speed required in quenching. The usual quenching media are water, brine, oil, and air. Carbon and low-alloy tool steels are quenched in brine or water; high-alloy tool steels are quenched in oil, air, or molten salts. While still air, fan cooling, and compressed-air blasts are used for air cooling, still air is the preferred method, for it is more likely to provide uniform cooling. Interrupted quenching is also used for tool steels. By this method, the steel is quenched in a liquid bath of salt or lead between 900 and 1200°F, then cooled in air to about 150°F.

It is recommended procedure to temper tool steels immediately after quenching and before they have cooled to room temperature to minimize the danger of cracking due to strains introduced by quenching. The tempering, or drawing, operation relieves the stresses developed during hardening and provides more toughness. Preferred practice is to utilize long draws at comparatively low temperatures rather than short draws at high temperatures.

Carbon and low-alloy tool steels are generally tempered at temperatures between 300 and 500°F, while for high-alloy tool steels the range 300 to 500°F is used for hardness and 900 to 1200°F for toughness. The high-speed tool steels are tempered between 950 and 1100°F, and the use of a double draw which repeats the original cycle is common practice.

10·19 Tool failures. The analysis to determine the probable cause for premature tool failure is often complex. Thorough investigation, however, will generally reveal good reasons behind every tool failure. It is the purpose of this section to discuss briefly five fundamental factors that contribute to tool failure.

Faulty Tool Design. This may lead to failure either in heat treatment or during service. When a tool is to be liquid-quenched, the use of heavy sections next to light sections should be avoided. During quenching, the light sections will cool rapidly and harden before the heavy sections. This will set up quenching stresses that often result in cracking. Figure 10·1 shows a failed die made of carbon tool steel, while Fig. 10·2 shows a cracked die made of manganese oil-hardening tool steel. In each case, cracking occurred during quenching because of excessive stresses set up by the drastic change in section. This type of failure may usually be avoided by making the tool as a two-piece assembly. The use of square holes is another prime source of tool failure due to faulty design. If it is essential to use adjacent heavy and light sections or sharp corners, the use of an air-hardening steel is recommended.

Faulty Steel. Despite the careful control used in the manufacture and inspection of tool steels, occasionally there is some defect in the steel. There may be porous areas resulting from shrinkage during solidification of the ingot which are known as *voids* or *pipe*. There may be *streaks* or *laps* due to segregation or nonmetallic inclusions, which usually run longitudinally with respect to the original bar stock. Other defects are *tears*, which are transverse surface defects resulting from working the steel under conditions where it does not have sufficient ductility; internal-cooling cracks known as *flakes*; and surface-cooling cracks as a result of cooling too rapidly after the last forging or rolling operation.

Tools made from large bar stock (over 4 in. diameter) of high-chromium steels generally show a brittle carbide network due to insufficient hot work (Fig. 10·4a). The use of disks of small bar stock which are upset-forged provides additional hot work, which breaks up the brittle carbide network and ensures a more uniform carbide distribution.   Figure 10·3 shows an 8-in.-diameter milling cutter which

Fig. 10·1   Die made of carbon tool steel.   Cracking occurred in quench because of excessive stresses set up between the thin rim and the body. (At top) Longitudinal section through die.   Numbers are Rockwell C hardness values.   (*Bethlehem Steel Company*)

failed in service, and subsequent microstudy showed the presence of a brittle carbide network.   This milling cutter was made of bar stock and did not undergo sufficient reduction by hot working to remove the remnants of the as-cast carbide network.   The normal microstructure, with good carbide distribution resulting from a properly hot-worked high-speed steel after quenching and tempering, is illustrated in Fig. 10·4*b*.

Faulty Heat Treatment. This factor is the cause of the large majority of tool failures. Tools should be properly handled during and after the quench. They should be removed from the quench while still warm and transferred immediately to a tempering furnace. As was pointed out in the previous section on heat treatment, tools should be quenched from the recommended hardening temperature. The use of excessively high hardening temperature causes grain coarsening,

Fig. 10·2 Die made of manganese oil-hardening tool steel. Cracking occurred because of excessive quenching stress set up between the heavy body and the small protruding section. (*Bethlehem Steel Company*)

which is evident on a fractured surface. Evidence of overheating may usually be found by microexamination. Figure 10·5 shows a manganese oil-hardening tool-steel cam which cracked in hardening. The microstructure revealed coarse, acicular martensite typical of overheated steel, instead of the normal microstructure of fine tempered martensite and spheroidal carbides. It is estimated that this steel was heated to 1800°F instead of the proper temperature of 1475°F.

Improper Grinding. Very high surface stresses may be set up in a hardened tool because of the grinding operation. These stresses may be high enough to cause cracks. Light grinding cracks tend to appear at 90° from the direction of grinding while heavy grinding cracks

Fig. 10·3 Failed milling cutters made of M2 high-speed steel. Note chipped teeth. Failure occurred because of poor carbide distribution resulting from insufficient reduction by hot working in the steel plant. (*Bethlehem Steel Company*)

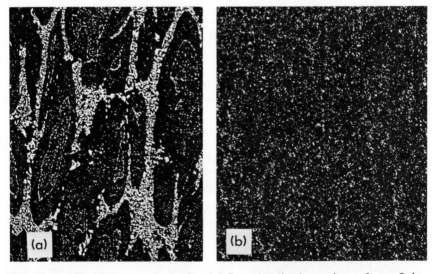

Fig. 10·4 M2 high-speed steel. (*a*) Longitudinal section of an 8-in. bar showing a carbide network due to insufficient hot working. (*b*) Longitudinal section of a 1-in. bar upset-forged showing normal spheroidal carbide distribution after sufficient hot working. Etched in 4 per cent nital, 100×. (*Latrobe Steel Company*)

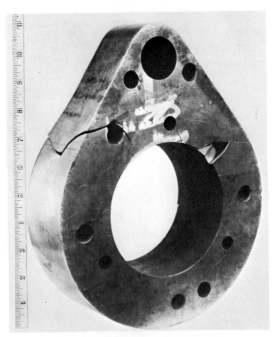

Fig. 10·5 Cam made of manganese oil-hardening tool steel which cracked in hardening because it was quenched from an excessively high temperature. (*Bethlehem Steel Company*)

Fig. 10·6 (Right) Failed reamer made of M2 high-speed steel. (Left) Bushing on which failure occurred. (*Bethlehem Steel Company*)

present a characteristic network pattern (see Fig. 1·25d).   The presence of grinding cracks is best revealed by magnetic-particle testing.

Mechanical Overload and Operational Factors.   Mechanical factors that cause tool failures due to overload may be accidental or are the

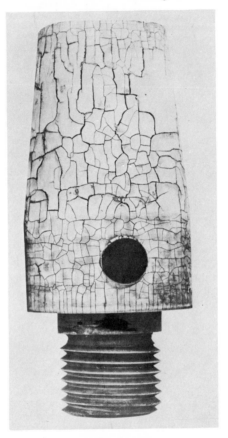

Fig. 10·7   Punch tip, 3¾ in. diameter by 8¾ in., made of H12 hot-work steel.   This tool became stuck in hot forgings several times and was heated to a much higher temperature than it was designed to withstand. Heat checks resulted.   (*Bethlehem Steel Company*)

result of excessive stress concentration or improper clearances and alignment.   This type of tool failure is often difficult to determine, since thorough investigation of the failed tool will not reveal any cause for the short life.   Figure 10·6 shows a failed reamer made of M2 high-speed steel.   The bushing on the left was drilled to an undersize hole, and when this reamer attempted to take an excessively heavy cut, breakage resulted.

A common method of failure due to operational factors occurs in tools used for hot-work operations. These tools are subjected to repeated thermal stresses because of alternate heating and cooling of the tools. This leads to a network of very fine hairline cracks known as *heat checks*. Figure 10·7 shows heat checks developed on the surface of a punch tip made of H12 hot-work tool steel. It should be realized that, under these severe operating conditions, eventual failure of the tool is to be expected and that there is no simple solution to the problem of avoiding failure due to heat checking.

SPECIAL CUTTING MATERIALS

10·20 Stellites. These are essentially cobalt-chromium-tungsten alloys. They contain from 25 to 35 per cent chromium, 4 to 25 per cent tungsten, 1 to 3 per cent carbon, and the remainder cobalt. The hardness of stellite varies from Rockwell C 40 to 60 depending upon the tungsten and carbon content. Microscopically, the alloys consist mainly of tungstides and carbides. Their outstanding properties are high hardness, high resistance to wear and corrosion, and excellent red hardness. This combination of properties makes them very suitable for cutting applications.

Stellite metal-cutting tools are widely used for machining steel, cast iron, cast steel, stainless steel, brass, and most machinable materials. They may be operated at higher speeds than those used with high-speed-steel tools. Stellite alloys are usually cast to the desired shape and size and are therefore not so tough as high-speed steels. They are also appreciably weaker and more brittle than high-speed steels, so that a careful analysis of specific machining operations is necessary in selecting the proper tool. Stellite cutting tools are used as single-point lathe tools, milling cutter blades for large inserted tooth cutters, spot facers, reamers, form tools, and burnishing rollers. Stellite is also used as a hard-facing material for trimming dies and gauge blocks, on plowshares and cultivators for farm use, on the wearing parts of crushing and grinding machinery, and on bucket teeth for excavating and dredging equipment.

10·21 Cemented carbides. These materials are made of very finely divided carbide particles of the refractory metals, cemented together by a metal or alloy of the iron group, forming a body of very high hardness and high compressive strength. Cemented carbides are manufactured by powder-metallurgy techniques. The process consists essentially in preparing the powder carbides of tungsten, titanium, or tantalum; mixing one or more of these powders with a binder, usually cobalt powder; pressing the blended powder into compacts of the desired shape; and sintering the pressed shapes to achieve consolidation.

The blended powders are formed into desired shapes by cold pressing, followed by sintering or by hot pressing, during which pressing and sintering are done at the same time. Pressures used in cold pressing vary between 5 and 30 tons per sq in., depending upon the size and shape of the compact. Sintering is carried out at temperatures between 2500 and 2700°F for 30 to 60 min. At these elevated temperatures, the cobalt forms a eutectic with the carbides, and this eutectic becomes the cementing material. After cooling, the sintered compact has its final properties, since it does not respond to any known heat treatment.

Cemented carbides are very hard (over Rockwell C 70), have very high compressive strength (over 700,000 psi), and possess unusual red hardness.

Since cemented carbides have low toughness and tensile strength, usual practice is to braze a small piece of carbide material to a steel shank, which provides rigid support under the cutting edge. These tools are ground or sharpened by using a silicon carbide or diamond-impregnated grinding wheel.

Planers, drills, reamers, boring and facing tools, etc., for the machining of both metals and nonmetals are made with carbides. Cutting speed and feeds employed with carbide tools are generally higher than those used with high-speed-steel tools or with stellite.

Cemented-carbide dies are used for the hot drawing of tungsten, molybdenum, and high-speed-steel wire. Carbide dies are also used for the cold drawing of wire, bar, and tubing made of steel, copper, aluminum, and other materials.

QUESTIONS

10·1   List the properties most important for tool steels and give one industrial application where each property would be required.

10·2   What would be the influence of each of the following alloying elements on the properties of a tool steel: chromium, tungsten, molybdenum, vanadium, silicon, manganese, and cobalt?

10·3   Describe the basis for selection of a tool steel to be used as a thread-rolling die on AISI 1020 steel.

10·4   Describe the heat treatment you would apply to the tool steel selected in Question 10·3 and the reasons for this heat treatment.

10·5   Same as Questions 10·3 and 10·4 for a die to be used to cold-head AISI 1020 bearing rollers.

10·6   Using the equation given below, plot a graph showing the dimensional change, inches per inches, when spheroidite changes to austenite as the carbon content varies from 0 to 1.40 per cent.

Dimensional change, in. per in. $= -0.0155 + 0.0075$ (per cent C)

10·7 Same as Question 10·6 for the change from austenite to martensite with varying carbon, using the following formula:

Dimensional change, in. per in. $= 0.0155 - 0.0018$ (per cent C)

10·8 Plot the net dimensional change for the reaction spheroidite → austenite → martensite as the carbon content varies from 0 to 1.40 per cent. (Hint: Use the equations given in Questions 10·6 and 10·7 to determine an equation for the net dimensional change.)

REFERENCES

Allegheny Ludlum Steel Corporation: "Tool Steel Handbook," Pittsburgh, 1951.

American Society for Metals: "Metals Handbook," 7th ed., 1948: 8th ed., 1961, Metals Park, Ohio.

American Society of Tool and Manufacturing Engineers: "Tool Engineers Handbook," 2d ed., McGraw-Hill Book Company, Inc., New York, 1959.

Bethlehem Steel Company: "The Tool Steel Trouble Shooter Handbook 322," Bethlehem, Pa., 1952.

Palmer, F. R.: "Tool Steel Simplified," Carpenter Steel Co., Reading, Pa., 1937.

Roberts, G. A., J. C. Hamaker, and A. R. Johnson: "Tool Steels," American Society for Metals, Metals Park, Ohio, 1962.

Seabright, L. H.: "The Selection and Hardening of Tool Steels," McGraw-Hill Book Company, Inc., New York, 1950.

Chapter 11

WROUGHT IRON AND CAST IRON

11·1 Manufacture of wrought iron. Wrought iron is essentially a two-component metal consisting of high-purity iron and slag. The slag is composed mainly of iron silicate. The small and uniformly distributed particles of slag exist physically separate in the iron. There is no fusion or chemical relationship between the slag and the iron.

Wrought iron was originally produced by the hand-puddling process, later by mechanical puddling, and since 1930 by the Byers or Aston process. Regardless of the process, there are three essential steps in the manufacture of wrought iron: first, to melt and refine the base metal; second, to produce and keep molten a proper slag; and third, to granulate, or disintegrate, the base metal and mechanically incorporate with it the desired amount of slag.

In the Byers process each step is separated and carried out in individual pieces of equipment. The raw materials of pig iron, iron oxide, and silica are melted in cupolas. The pig iron is purified to a highly refined state in a bessemer converter and then transferred to the ladle of the processing machine. An exact iron silicate slag made by melting together iron oxide and certain siliceous materials in an open-hearth furnace is poured into a ladle and moved directly below the processing machine.

The next step is the key operation of the process—that of base-metal disintegration and slag incorporation. The liquid refined iron at a temperature of about 2800°F is poured at a predetermined rate into the ladle containing the molten slag, which is at about 2300°F (Fig. 11·1). To ensure a uniform distribution of the refined metal into the slag, the processing machine automatically oscillates as well as moves forward and backward. Since the slag is maintained at a temperature considerably lower than the freezing point of the iron, the iron is continuously and rapidly solidified. The liquid iron contains large

310

quantities of gases in solution, but when the metal solidifies, the gases are no longer soluble in it. This rapid solidification liberates the gases in the form of many small explosions of sufficient force to shatter the metal into small fragments which settle to the bottom of the slag ladle. Because of the noise of the explosions, this operation is called *shotting*. Since the iron is at a welding temperature, and because of the

Fig. 11·1   The key operation in the manufacture of wrought iron.   (*A. M. Byers Company*)

fluxing action of the siliceous slag, these fragments stick together to form a spongelike ball of iron globules coated with silicate slag.

The excess slag is poured off and the sponge ball, weighing between 6,000 and 8,000 lb, is placed in a press. The press squeezes out the surplus slag and welds the cellular mass of slag-coated particles of plastic iron into a bloom. The bloom is reduced in cross section to a billet, which is reheated and rolled into plate, bars, rods, tubing, etc.

11·2   Properties and applications of wrought iron.   Quality wrought iron is distinguished by its low carbon and manganese contents. The carbon content is generally below 0.08 per cent and the manganese content below 0.06 per cent. The phosphorus content is usually higher than that of steel and ordinarily ranges from 0.10 to 0.15 per cent.

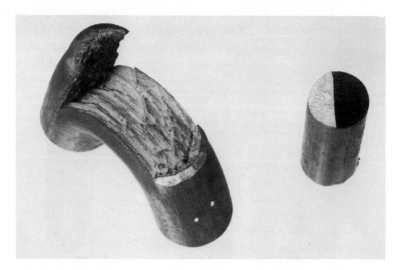

Fig. 11·2   (Left) Fibrous fracture of wrought iron; (right) crystalline fracture of steel.

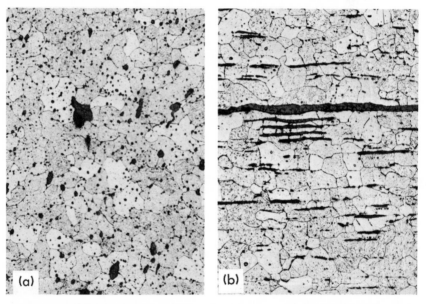

Fig. 11·3   The microstructure of wrought iron.   Slag in a ferrite matrix. (*a*) Transverse section; (*b*) longitudinal section.   Etched in 2 per cent nital, 100×.

The sulfur content is kept low, and the silicon content of between 0.10 and 0.20 per cent is concentrated almost entirely in the slag. The slag content usually varies from about 1 to 3 per cent by weight. A typical chemical analysis of wrought iron is as follows:

	Per Cent
Carbon	0.08
Manganese	0.015
Silicon	0.158
Phosphorus	0.062
Sulfur	0.010
Slag, by weight	1.20

Since wrought iron is a composite material, there are many methods of distinguishing between wrought iron and steel. Figure 11·2 shows the typical fibrous fracture of wrought iron whereas steel shows a crystalline or granular break.

The uniform distribution of the slag throughout the ferrite matrix is clearly shown by microscopic examination of a transverse section (Fig. 11·3a). The threadlike appearance of the slag is evident from microscopic examination of a longitudinal section, that is, a section parallel to the direction of rolling (Fig. 11·3b).

The mechanical properties of wrought iron are largely those of pure iron. Because of the nature of the slag distribution, however, the tensile strength and ductility are greater in the longitudinal or rolling direction than in the direction transverse to rolling. Typical mechanical properties of wrought iron in the longitudinal and transverse directions are given in Table 11·1. Improvement of rolling procedure

Table 11·1   Tensile properties of wrought iron

Property	Longitudinal	Transverse
Tensile strength, psi	48,000–50,000	36,000–38,000
Yield point, psi	27,000–30,000	27,000–30,000
Elongation, % in 8 in.	18–25	2–5
Reduction in area, %	35–45	3–6

has made possible the equalization of the tensile strength and ductility in both directions.

It is possible to improve the strength of wrought iron by alloying. The most popular alloy wrought irons are those containing between 1.5 and 3.5 per cent nickel. The comparative mechanical properties of unalloyed and nickel wrought iron are given in Table 11·2.

Charpy impact tests reveal that nickel-alloy wrought iron retains its impact strength to a high degree at subzero temperatures.

One of the principal virtues of wrought iron is its ability to resist corrosion. When exposed to corrosive media, it is quickly coated with an oxide film. As corrosion continues, the slag fibers begin to function as rust resistors. The dense, uniform, initial oxide film is securely fastened to the surface of the metal by the pinning effect of the slag fibers and protects the surfaces from further oxidation.

Table 11·2   Tensile properties of unalloyed and nickel wrought iron

Property	Unalloyed wrought iron	Nickel wrought iron
Tensile strength, psi	48,000	60,000
Yield point, psi	30,000	45,000
Elongation, % in 8 in.	25	22
Reduction in area, %	45	40

Wrought iron is used for standard pipe, nails, barbed wire, rivets, and welding fittings. It is available in plates, sheets, tubular forms and structural shapes. Wrought iron has many applications in the railroad, shipbuilding, and oil industries, as well as for architectural purposes and for farm implements.

CAST IRON

11·3   Introduction.   Cast irons, like steels, are basically alloys of iron and carbon. In relation to the iron–iron carbide diagram, cast irons contain a greater amount of carbon than that necessary to saturate austenite at the eutectic temperature. Therefore, cast irons contain between 2 and 6.67 per cent carbon. Since high carbon content tends to make the cast iron very brittle, most commercially manufactured types are in the range of 2.5 to 4 per cent carbon.

The ductility of cast iron is very low, and it cannot be rolled, drawn, or worked at room temperature. Most of the cast irons are not malleable at any temperature. However, they melt readily and can be cast into complicated shapes which are usually machined to final dimensions. Since casting is the only suitable process applied to these alloys, they are known as *cast irons*.

Although the common cast irons are brittle and have lower strength properties than most steels, they are cheap, can be cast more readily than steel, and have other useful properties. In addition, by proper alloying, good foundry control, and appropriate heat treatment, the properties of any type of cast iron may be varied over a wide range. Significant developments in foundry control have led to the production of large tonnages of cast irons whose properties are generally consistent.

11·4 Types of cast iron. The best method of classifying cast iron is according to metallographic structure. There are four variables to be considered which lead to the different types of cast iron, namely the carbon content, the alloy and impurity content, the cooling rate during and after freezing, and the heat treatment after casting. These variables control the condition of the carbon and also its physical form. The carbon may be combined as iron carbide in cementite, or it may exist as free carbon in graphite. The shape and distribution of the free carbon particles will greatly influence the physical properties of the cast iron. The types of cast iron are as follows:

White cast irons, in which all the carbon is in the combined form as cementite.

Malleable cast irons, in which most or all of the carbon is uncombined in the form of irregular round particles known as *temper carbon*. This is obtained by heat treatment of white cast iron.

Gray cast irons, in which most or all of the carbon is uncombined in the form of graphite flakes.

Chilled cast irons, in which a white cast-iron layer at the surface is combined with a gray-iron interior.

Nodular cast irons, in which, by special alloy additions, the carbon is largely uncombined in the form of compact spheroids. This structure differs from malleable iron in that it is obtained directly from solidification and the round carbon particles are more regular in shape.

Alloy cast irons, in which the properties or the structure of any of the above types are modified by the addition of alloying elements.

11·5 White cast iron. The changes that take place in white cast iron during solidification and subsequent cooling are determined by the iron–iron carbide diagram discussed in Chap. 7. All white cast irons are hypoeutectic alloys, and the cooling of a 2.50 per cent carbon alloy will now be described.

This alloy, at x_1 in Fig. 11·4, exists as a uniform liquid solution of carbon dissolved in liquid iron. It remains in this condition as cooling takes place until the liquidus line is crossed at x_2. Solidification now begins by the formation of austenite crystals containing about 1 per cent carbon. As the temperature falls, primary austenite continues to solidify, its composition moving down and to the right along the solidus line toward point C. The liquid in the meantime is becoming richer in carbon, its composition also moving down and to the right along the liquidus line toward point E. At the eutectic temperature,

2065°F, the alloy consists of austenite dendrites containing 2 per cent carbon and a liquid solution containing 4.3 per cent carbon. The liquid accounts for $(2.5 - 2.0)/(4.3 - 2.0)$, or 22 per cent of the alloy by weight. This liquid now undergoes the eutectic reaction isothermally to form the eutectic mixture of austenite and cementite known as

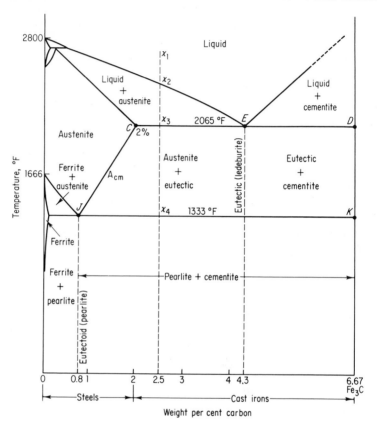

Fig. 11·4   The iron–iron carbide phase diagram.

ledeburite. Since the reaction takes place at a relatively high temperature, ledeburite tends to appear as a coarse mixture rather than the fine mixture typical of many eutectics. It is not unusual for ledeburite to be separated completely, with the eutectic austenite added to the primary austenite dendrites, leaving behind layers of massive, free cementite.

As the temperature falls, between x_3 and x_4, the solubility of carbon in austenite decreases, as indicated by the A_{cm} line CJ. This causes precipitation of proeutectoid cementite, most of which is deposited upon the cementite already present. At the eutectoid temperature, 1333°F, the remaining austenite containing 0.8 per cent carbon and constituting $(6.67 - 2.5)/(6.67 - 0.8)$, or 70 per cent of the alloy, undergoes the eutectoid reaction isothermally to form pearlite. During subsequent cooling to room temperature, the structure remains essentially unchanged.

The typical microstructure of white cast iron, consisting of dendrites of transformed austenite (pearlite) in a white matrix of cementite, is

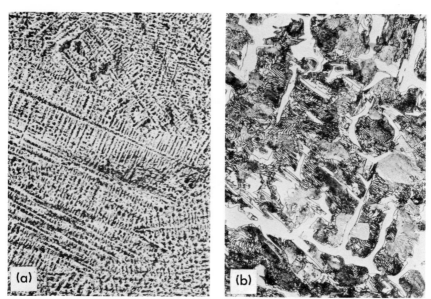

Fig. 11·5   The microstructure of white cast iron.   (*a*) Dark areas are primary dendrites of transformed austenite (pearlite) in a white cementite matrix, 20×.   (*b*) Same sample at 250× showing pearlite and cementite.   Etched in 2 per cent nital.

illustrated in Fig. 11·5*a*. Higher magnification of the same sample (Fig. 11·5*b*) reveals that the dark areas are pearlite.

It was pointed out in Chap. 7 that cementite is a hard, brittle interstitial compound. Since white cast iron contains a relatively large amount of cementite as a continuous interdendritic network, it makes the cast iron hard and wear-resistant but extremely brittle and difficult to machine. "Completely white" cast irons are limited in engineering applications because of this brittleness and lack of machinability. They are used where resistance to wear is most important and the service does not require ductility, such as liners for cement mixers, ball mills, certain types of drawing dies, and extrusion nozzles. A large tonnage of white cast iron is used as a starting material for the manufacture of malleable cast iron.

11·6   Malleable cast iron.   It was pointed out in Sec. 7·2 that cementite (iron carbide) is actually a metastable phase.   There is a tendency for cementite to decompose into iron and carbon, but under normal conditions, it tends to persist indefinitely in its original form.

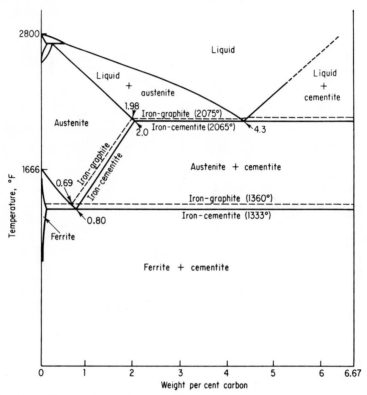

Fig. 11·6   The stable iron-graphite system (dotted lines) superimposed on the metastable iron–iron carbide system.

Up to this point, cementite has been treated as a stable phase; however, this tendency to form free carbon is the basis for the manufacture of malleable cast iron.

The reaction $Fe_3C \rightleftharpoons 3Fe + C$ is favored by elevated temperatures, the existence of solid nonmetallic impurities, higher carbon contents, and the presence of elements that the aid decomposition of Fe_3C.

On the iron–iron carbide equilibrium diagram for the metastable system, shown in Fig. 11·6, are superimposed the phase boundaries of the stable iron-carbon (graphite) system as dotted lines.

The purpose of malleabilization is to convert all the combined carbon in white iron into irregular nodules of temper carbon (graphite) and ferrite. Commercially, this process is carried out in two steps known as the *first* and *second stages of the anneal.*

White irons suitable for conversion to malleable iron are of the following range of composition:

	Per Cent
Carbon	2.00–2.65
Silicon	0.90–1.40
Manganese	0.25–0.55
Phosphorus	Less than 0.18
Sulfur	0.05–0.18

In the first-stage annealing, the white-iron casting is slowly reheated to a temperature between 1550 and 1800°F. During heating, the pearlite is converted to austenite at the lower critical line. The austenite thus formed dissolves some additional cementite as it is heated to the annealing temperature.

Figure 11·6 shows that the austenite of the metastable system can dissolve more carbon than can austenite of the stable system. Therefore, a driving force exists for the carbon to precipitate out of the austenite as free graphite. This graphitization starts at the malleableizing temperature. The initial precipitation of a graphite nucleus depletes the austenite of carbon, and so more is dissolved from the adjacent cementite, leading to further carbon deposition on the original graphite nucleus. The graphite nuclei grow at approximately equal rates in all directions and ultimately appear as irregular nodules or spheroids usually called *temper carbon* (Fig. 11·7a). The white-iron casting is held at the first-stage annealing temperature until all massive carbides have been decomposed. Since graphitization is a relatively slow process, the casting must be soaked at temperature for at least 20 hr, and large loads may require as much as 72 hr. The structure at completion of first-stage graphitization consists of temper-carbon nodules distributed throughout the matrix of saturated austenite.

As the temperature is lowered slowly, more carbon is precipitated out from austenite because of the decrease in solubility of carbon in austenite.

Second-stage annealing consists of a very slow cool through the critical range at which the eutectoid reaction takes place. This allows the decomposition of austenite into the stable phases of ferrite and graphite. Once graphitization is complete, no further structural changes take place during cooling to room temperature, and the structure consists of temper-carbon nodules in a ferrite matrix (Fig. 11·7b). This type is known as *standard* or *ferritic malleable iron.*

In the form of compact nodules, the temper carbon does not break up the continuity of the tough ferritic matrix.   This results in a higher strength and ductility than exhibited by gray cast iron.   The graphite nodules also serve to lubricate cutting tools, which accounts for the very high machinability of malleable iron.   Ferritic malleable iron has been widely used for automotive, agricultural, and railroad equipment; expansion joints and railing casting on bridges; chain-hoist assemblies,

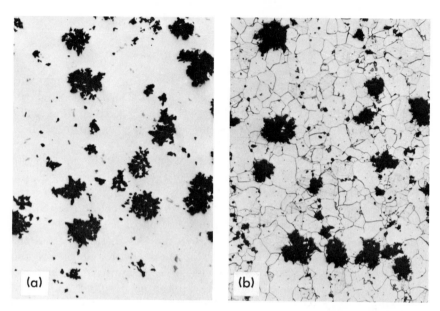

Fig. 11·7   (*a*) Malleable iron, unetched.   Irregular nodules of graphite called *temper carbon*, 100×.   (*b*) Ferritic malleable iron.   Etched in 5 per cent nital, 100×.

industrial casters; pipe fittings; and many applications in general hardware.

Alloyed malleable irons are those whose properties result from the addition of alloying elements not normally present in significant quantities in ferritic malleable iron.   Since those alloyed malleable irons are completely malleableized, their influence is largely on the ferritic matrix.   The two principal kinds are copper-alloyed malleable iron and copper-molybdenum-alloyed malleable iron.   The effect of copper is to increase corrosion resistance, tensile strength, and yield point at very slight reduction in ductility.   Hardness is also increased, as shown in Fig. 11·8.   The addition of copper and molybdenum in combination produces a malleable iron of superior corrosion resistance and mechanical properties.   The mechanical properties of a copper-molybdenum-alloyed malleable iron are as follows:

Tensile strength, psi	58,000–65,000
Yield point, psi	40,000–45,000
Elongation, % in 2 in.	15–20
BHN	135–155

Compare these properties with those given for ferritic malleable iron in Table 11·3.

11·7   Pearlitic malleable iron.   If a controlled quantity of carbon, in the order of 0.3 to 0.9 per cent, is retained as finely distributed iron carbide, an entirely different set of mechanical properties

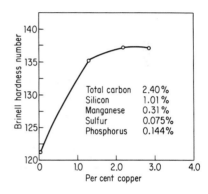

Fig. 11·8   Relationship between copper content and hardness for a malleable iron of the composition shown. (*Malleable Founders Society*)

Total carbon	2.40%
Silicon	1.01%
Manganese	0.31%
Sulfur	0.075%
Phosphorus	0.144%

results.   The strength and hardness of the castings will be increased over those of ferritic malleable iron by an amount which is roughly proportional to the quantity of combined carbon remaining in the finished product.

First-stage graphitization is a necessary prerequisite for all methods of manufacturing malleable-iron castings.   If manganese is added, the regular cycle can be maintained to retain combined carbon throughout the matrix, or the second-stage annealing of the normal process may be replaced by a quench, usually air, which cools the castings through the eutectoid range fast enough to retain combined carbon throughout the matrix.   The amount of pearlite formed depends upon the temperature at which the quench starts and the rate of cooling.   High quench temperatures and fast cooling rates (air blast) result in greater amounts of retained carbon or pearlite.   If the air quench produces a fast enough cooling rate through the eutectoid range, the matrix will be completely pearlitic (Fig. 11·9).

If the cooling rate through the critical range is not quite fast enough to retain all the combined carbon, the areas surrounding the temper-carbon nodules will be completely graphitized while those at greater distances from the nodules will be pearlitic (Fig. 11·10).   Because of its general appearance, this is referred to as a *bull's-eye* structure.

A fully ferritic malleable iron may be converted into pearlitic malleable iron by reheating above the lower critical temperature, followed by rapid cooling.   The higher the temperature, the more carbon will be

Fig. 11·9   Pearlitic malleable iron. (*Malleable Founders Society*)

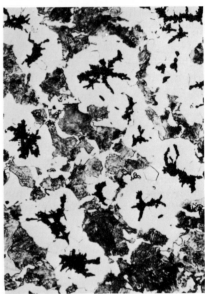

Fig. 11·10   Typical appearance of a "bull's-eye" structure. Temper-carbon nodules surrounded by ferritic areas, with lamellar pearlite located between the bull's eyes. Nital etch, 100×. (*Malleable Founders Society*)

dissolved from the graphite nodules.   Subsequent quenching will retain the combined carbon and develop the desired properties.

Oil quenching is widely used to obtain quenching speeds faster than those obtainable by an air quench alone.   At these relatively rapid quenching speeds, the austenite will transform to martensite. The amount of martensite formed will depend upon the quenching speed of the particular oil used, the temperature from which the work is quenched, the time at that temperature, the thickness of the casting, and the chemistry of the iron.   Liquid quenching will produce a pearlitic malleable iron of high strength and hardness which responds rapidly to tempering.

It is common practice to temper the malleable irons after quenching. Those having coarse pearlitic structures are tempered at relatively high temperatures (between 1200 and 1320°F) to spheroidize the pearlite (Fig. 11·11). The martensitic malleable irons may be tempered at any temperature from 450 to 1320°F. Depending upon the temperature used, the matrix will be tempered martensite or spheroidite.

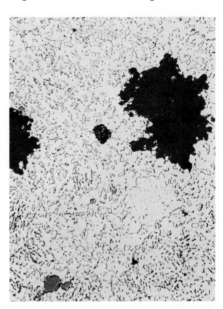

Fig. 11·11 Microstructure of a pearlitic malleable iron tempered to obtain a spheroidite matrix. Nital etch, 500×. (*Malleable Founders Society*)

The tensile properties of ferritic and pearlitic malleable iron are given in Table 11·3.

Alloyed pearlitic malleable castings are made from white irons that contain one or more alloying elements so that the regular malleableizing anneal will not result in a ferritic matrix. The alloy additions usually do not affect first-stage graphitization but serve as carbide stabilizers during the eutectoid range or subeutectoid tempering treatments. Many of the alloying elements also increase hardenability and strengthen the matrix. Manganese and sulfur may be added in quantities not normally found in standard malleable iron. Copper may be added to

Table 11·3 Tensile properties of malleable cast iron

Type	Tensile strength, 1,000 psi	Yield strength, 1,000 psi	Elongation, % in 2 in.	BHN
Ferritic	50–60	32–39	20–10	110–156
Pearlitic	65–120	45–100	16–2	163–269

improve strength, corrosion resistance, and graphite distribution. Suitably alloyed pearlitic malleable iron may be fully martensitic in sections as heavy as 2 in. after air quenching from 1600°F.

Some of the industrial applications of pearlitic malleable iron are for axle and differential housings, camshafts and crankshafts in automobiles; for gears, chain links, sprockets, and elevator brackets in conveyor equipment; for rolls, pumps, nozzles, cams, and rocker arms as machine parts; for gun mounts, tank parts, and pistol parts in

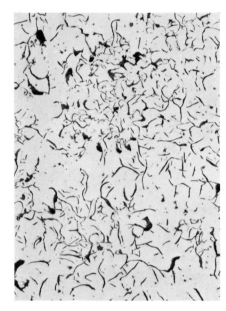

Fig. 11·12 Graphite flakes in gray cast iron. Unetched, 100×.

ordinance; and finally for a variety of small tools such as wrenches, hammers, clamps, and shears.

11·8 Gray cast iron. This group is one of the most widely used alloys of iron. In the manufacture of gray cast irons, the tendency of cementite to separate into graphite and austenite or ferrite is favored by controlling alloy composition and cooling rates. Most gray cast irons are hypoeutectic alloys containing between 2.5 and 4 per cent carbon.

These alloys solidify by first forming primary austenite. The initial appearance of combined carbon is in the cementite resulting from the eutectic reaction at 2065°F. The graphitization process is aided by high carbon content, high temperature, and the proper amount of graphitizing elements, notably silicon.

There is experimental evidence that, with proper control of the above factors, the alloy will follow the stable iron-graphite equilibrium diagram (Fig. 11·6), forming austenite and graphite at the eutectic temperature of 2075°F.   At any rate, any cementite which is formed will graphitize rapidly.   The graphite appears as many irregular, generally elongated and curved plates which give gray cast iron its characteristic grayish or blackish fracture (Fig. 11·12).

During continued cooling, there is additional precipitation of carbon because of the decrease in solubility of carbon in austenite.   This carbon is precipitated as graphite or as proeutectoid cementite which promptly graphitizes.

Fig. 11·13 Microstructure of gray cast iron. Graphite flakes in a pearlitic matrix with a small amount of ferrite (white areas). Etched in 2 per cent nital: (*a*)100×; (*b*)500×.

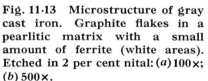

The strength of gray cast iron depends almost entirely on the matrix in which the graphite is embedded.   This matrix is largely determined by the condition of the eutectoid cementite.   If the composition and cooling rate are such that the eutectoid cementite also graphitizes, then the matrix will be entirely ferritic.   On the other hand, if graphitization of the eutectoid cementite is prevented, the matrix will be entirely pearlitic.   The constitution of the matrix may be varied from pearlite, through mixtures of pearlite and ferrite in different proportions, down to practically pure ferrite.   The graphite-ferrite mixture is the softest and weakest gray iron; the strength and hardness increase with the increase in combined carbon, reaching a maximum with the pearlitic gray iron.   Figure 11·13 shows the microstructure of gray cast iron with the matrix almost entirely pearlitic.

11·9 Silicon in cast iron. Silicon is a very important element in the metallurgy of gray iron.   It increases fluidity and influences the solidification of the molten alloy. The eutectic composition is shifted to the left approximately 0.30 per cent carbon for each 1 per cent silicon, which effectively depresses the temperature at which the alloy begins to solidify. As the silicon content is increased, the austenite field decreases in area, the eutectoid carbon content is lowered, and the eutectoid transformation occurs over a broadening range.

Silicon is a graphitizer, and if not counterbalanced by carbide-promoting elements, it favors solidification according to the stable iron-graphite system. Therefore, during solidification in the presence of silicon, carbon is precipitated as primary graphite in the form of flakes. Once primary graphite has formed, its shape cannot be altered by any method. It is these weak graphite flakes that break up the continuity of the matrix and the notch effect at the end of these flakes that accounts for the low strength and low ductility of gray iron.

Careful control of the silicon content and cooling rate is required to graphitize the eutectic and proeutectoid cementite but not the eutectoid cementite in order to end up with a pearlitic gray iron.

11·10   Sulfur in cast iron. Most commercial gray irons contain between 0.06 and 0.12 per cent sulfur. The effect of sulfur on the form of carbon is the reverse of silicon. The higher the sulfur content, the greater will be the amount of combined carbon, thus tending to produce a hard, brittle white iron.

Aside from producing combined carbon, sulfur tends to react with iron to form iron sulfide (FeS). This low-melting compound, present as thin interdendritic layers, increases the possibility of cracking at elevated temperatures (*red-short*). High sulfur tends to reduce fluidity and often is responsible for the presence of blowholes (trapped air) in castings.

Fortunately, manganese has a greater affinity for sulfur than iron, forming manganese sulfide (MnS). The manganese sulfide particles appear as small, widely dispersed inclusions which do not impair the properties of the casting. It is common commercial practice to use a manganese content of two to three times the sulfur content.

11·11   Manganese in cast iron. Manganese is a carbide stabilizer, tending to increase the amount of combined carbon, but it is much less potent than sulfur. If manganese is present in the correct amount to form manganese sulfide, its effect is to reduce the proportion of combined carbon by removing the effect of sulfur. Excess manganese has little effect on solidification and only weakly retards primary graphitization. On eutectoid graphitization, however, manganese is strongly carbide-stabilizing.

11·12   Phosphorus in cast iron. Most gray irons contain between 0.10 and 0.90 per cent phosphorus originating from the iron ore.

Most of the phosphorus combines with the iron to form iron phosphide (Fe$_3$P).   This iron phosphide forms a ternary eutectic with cementite and austenite (pearlite at room temperature).   The ternary eutectic is known as *steadite* and is a normal feature in the microstructure of cast irons (Fig. 11·14).   Steadite is relatively brittle, and with high phosphorus content, the steadite areas tend to form a continuous network outlining the primary austenite dendrites.   The condition reduces toughness and makes the cast iron brittle, so that the phosphorus

Fig. 11·14 Gray iron showing steadite areas (arrow).   Etched in 2 per cent nital, 500×.   (*The International Nickel Company*)

content must be carefully controlled to obtain optimum mechanical properties.

Phosphorus increases fluidity and extends the range of eutectic freezing, thus increasing primary graphitization when the silicon content is high and phosphorus content is low.   It is therefore useful in very thin castings where a less fluid iron may not take a perfect impression of the mold.

If the silicon, sulfur, manganese, and phosphorus contents are controlled at proper levels, the only remaining variable affecting the strength of a pearlitic gray iron is the graphite flakes.   Since graphite is extremely soft and weak, its size, shape, and distribution will determine the mechanical properties of the cast iron.   It is the reduction of the size of the graphite flakes and the increase in their distribution that have accounted for the improvement in the quality of gray cast iron.

11·13   Size of distribution of graphite flakes.   Large graphite flakes seriously interrupt the continuity of the pearlitic matrix, thereby reducing the strength and ductility of the gray iron.   Small graphite flakes are less damaging and are therefore generally preferred.

Graphite-flake sizes are usually determined by comparison with standard sizes prepared jointly by the AFS (American Foundrymen's Society) and the ASTM (American Society for Testing Materials). The procedure for preparation and measurement of flake size is given in ASTM Designation A247-47, 1961 Book of ASTM Standards, Part 3. The measurement is made of the lengths of the largest graphite flakes

Table 11·4   Graphite flake sizes

AFS-ASTM Flake Size Number	Length of Longest Flakes at 100×, in.
1	4 or more
2	2–4
3	1–2
4	½–1
5	¼–½
6	⅛–¼
7	¹⁄₁₆–⅛
8	¹⁄₁₆ or less

in an unetched section of the gray iron at 100×.   Numbers are assigned as indicated in Table 11·4.

The flake lengths are illustrated in Fig. 11·15 by typical fields showing as nearly as possible the various sizes.

Slow cooling of hypoeutectic irons to favor graphitization also produces large crystals of primary austenite.   This restricts the eutectic mixture or graphite to the grain boundaries and results in graphite flakes that are relatively few in number and coarse.

Increasing the carbon content to increase the amount of eutectic also increases the amount of graphite formed.   This may weaken the cast iron more than a smaller flake size can strengthen it.

Increasing the silicon content increases the amount of eutectic formed, thus reducing flake size.   However, since high silicon content has such a strong graphitizing influence, the matrix will probably be ferritic, resulting in a weak casting.

The best method of reducing the size and improving the distribution of the graphite flakes seems to be by the addition of a small amount of material known as an *inoculant*.   Inoculating agents that have been used successfully are metallic calcium, aluminum, titanium, zirconium, silicon carbide, calcium silicide, or combinations of these.   The exact mechanism by which they operate is not clearly understood.   They probably promote the nucleation of primary austenite, resulting in small grains, which reduces the size and improves the distribution of the graphite flakes.

The way in which the graphite flakes are arranged in the microstructure of gray cast iron is usually indicated as one or more types that have been jointly prepared by the AFS and the ASTM. The five flake types are shown in Fig. 11·16.

Type D and Type E flake patterns usually result from the graphitization of a normal eutectic structure. These types appear in irons of very high purity or in commercial irons that have been cooled rather rapidly during solidification. Although the graphitic flake size is small, the interdendritic pattern and high graphite content weakens the material. Therefore, Types D and E flake patterns are undesirable in gray irons. When the cooling rate is slower, most commercial gray irons show complete divorcement of the eutectic, so that Types D and E flake patterns do not occur.

The most desirable flake pattern in gray iron is represented by the uniform distribution and random orientation of Type A. This results from a completely divorced eutectic structure. As was mentioned earlier, the size of the individual graphite flakes is determined by the size of the austenite crystals around which they form.

The rosette pattern of Type B graphite flakes is common only in the intermediate region of a chilled cast iron. This region is known as the *mottled* region and consists of a mixture of gray and white cast iron (Fig. 11·17). The cooling rate in this region is the maximum that would permit graphitization.

The few large, straight graphite flakes present in Type C always indicate that the iron is hypereutectic in carbon content. Silicon and several other alloying elements reduce the carbon content of the eutectic, and if they are present in sufficient amounts the eutectic composition may be reduced to below 3.5 per cent carbon.

11·14 Mechanical properties and applications of gray cast iron. The most important classification of gray irons, from an engineering standpoint, is that employed in the ASTM Specification A48. The gray-iron castings are classed in seven classes (Nos. 20, 25, 30, 35, 40, 50, 60) which give the minimum tensile strength of test bars in 1,000 psi. For example, class 20 gray iron would have a minimum tensile strength of 20,000 psi; class 30, 30,000 psi; and so on. Table 11·5 gives typical mechanical properties of standard gray-iron test bars, as cast.

Tensile strength is important in selecting a gray iron for parts that are subjected to static loads in indirect tension or bending. Such parts include pressure vessels, housings, valves, fittings, and levers.

Size 1   Longest flakes 4 in. or more in length.   Size 2   Longest flakes 2 to 4 in. in length.

Size 3   Longest flakes 1 to 2 in. in length.   Size 4   Longest flakes ½ to 1 in. in length.

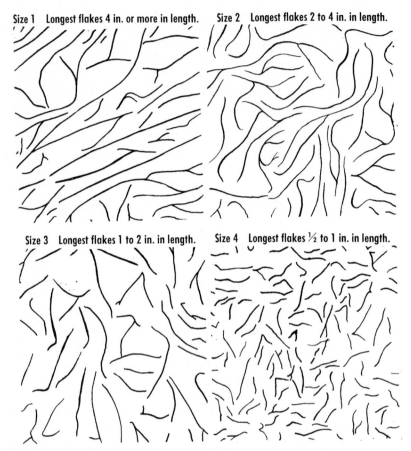

Fig. 11·15   Graphite-flake size chart illustrated by typical fields showing *and AFS*)

Irons above 40,000 psi in tensile strength are usually considered *high-strength irons* and are somewhat more expensive to produce and more difficult to machine. Gray irons do not exhibit a well-defined yield point as do most mild steels. The stress-strain curve does not show a straight-line portion; thus a definite modulus of elasticity cannot be determined. Usual methods are to determine the "relative" modulus at 25 per cent of the expected tensile strength, or the "tangent" modulus by drawing a tangent at some given stress value. The per cent elongation is small for all cast irons, rarely exceeding 3 to 4 per cent, and the reduction of area is too slight to be appreciable.

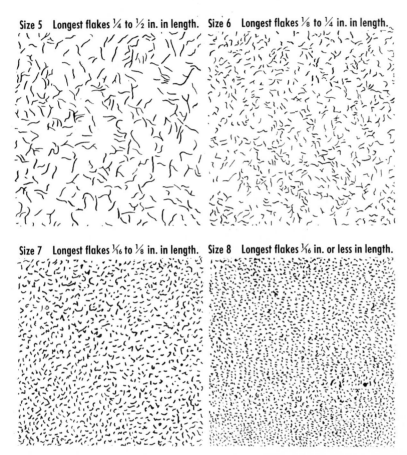

Size 5   Longest flakes ¼ to ½ in. in length.   Size 6   Longest flakes ⅛ to ¼ in. in length.

Size 7   Longest flakes ¹⁄₁₆ to ⅛ in. in length.   Size 8   Longest flakes ¹⁄₁₆ in. or less in length.

as nearly as possible the sizes represented.   (*Prepared jointly by ASTM*

Compressive strength is important when the gray iron is used for structure and machinery foundations or supports. Like all brittle materials, the compressive strength of gray iron is much greater than its tensile strength and is largely a function of the shearing strength. Failure in compression usually occurs along an oblique plane unless the specimen is long enough to allow failure by buckling.

Many grades of gray iron have higher torsional shear strength than some grades of steel. This characteristic along with low notch sensitivity makes gray iron a suitable material for various types of shafting.

The hardness of gray iron is an average result of the soft graphite in the iron and the metallic matrix. Variation in graphite size and

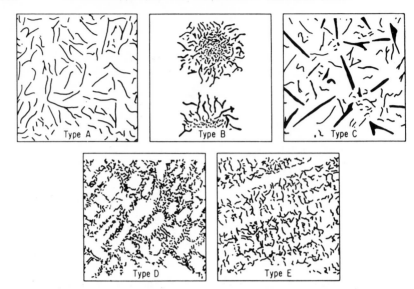

Fig. 11·16   Graphite-flake types. Type A—uniform distribution, random orientation; Type B—rosette groupings, random orientation; Type C—superimposed flake sizes, random orientation; Type D—interdendritic segregation, random orientation; Type E—interdendritic segregation, preferred orientation. (*Prepared jointly by ASTM and AFS*)

distribution will cause wide variations in hardness (particularly Rockwell hardness).   The Brinell tester, covering a larger area, tends to give a more accurate hardness value than the Rockwell tester.

11·15   Chilled cast iron.   Chilled-iron castings are made by casting the molten metal against a metal chiller, resulting in a surface of white cast iron.   This hard, abrasion-resistant white-iron surface or

Table 11·5   Typical mechanical properties of standard gray-iron test bars, as cast*

ASTM class	Tensile strength, psi	Compressive strength, psi	Torsional shear strength, psi	Modulus of elasticity, million psi		Reversed bending fatigue limit, psi	Transverse strength of 1.2-in.-diam bar 18-in. span, lb	BHN
				Tension	Torsion			
20	22,000	83,000	26,000	9.6–14.0	3.9–5.6	10,000	1,850	156
25	26,000	97,000	32,000	11.5–14.8	4.6–6.0	11,500	2,175	174
30	31,000	109,000	40,000	13.0–16.4	5.2–6.6	14,000	2,525	201
35	36,500	124,000	48,500	14.5–17.2	5.8–6.9	16,000	2,850	212
40	42,500	140,000	57,000	16.0–20.0	6.4–7.8	18,500	3,175	235
50	52,500	164,000	73,000	18.8–22.8	7.2–8.0	21,500	3,600	262
60	62,500	187,500	88,500	20.4–23.5	7.8–8.5	24,500	3,700	302

* By permission from "Metals Handbook," 8th ed., American Society for Metals, Metals Park, Ohio, 1961.

case is backed up by a softer gray-iron core. This case-core structure is obtained by careful control of the overall alloy composition and adjustment of the cooling rate.

Freezing starts first, and the cooling rate is most rapid where the molten metal is in contact with the mold walls. The cooling rate decreases as the center of the casting is approached. A chilled-iron casting may be produced by adjusting the composition of the iron so that the normal cooling rate at the surface is just fast enough to produce white iron while the slower cooling rate below the surface will produce mottled or gray iron (Fig. 11·17).

If only selected surfaces are to be white iron, it is common practice to use a composition which would normally solidify as gray iron and employ metal liners (chills) to accelerate the cooling rate of the selected areas. The depth of the white-iron layer is controlled by using thin metal plates whenever a thin white-iron layer is desired and heavier metal plates where a deeper chill is necessary.

The depth of chill decreases and the hardness of the chilled zone increases with increasing carbon content. Since silicon is a graphitizer, the depth of chill is decreased with increasing silicon content.

The addition of manganese decreases the depth of chill until the sulfur has been neutralized by formation of manganese sulfide. Above this amount, manganese increases chill depth and hardness.

Phosphorus decreases the depth of chill. With carbon and silicon

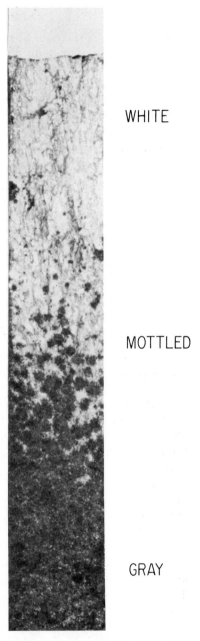

WHITE

MOTTLED

GRAY

Fig. 11·17 Fracture of a chilled-iron casting showing the white, mottled, and gray portions, 3×.

constant, an increase of 0.1 per cent phosphorus will decrease the depth of chill about 0.1 in.

Nickel reduces the chill depth, and its influence is about one-fourth that of silicon. The reduction in chill depth is accompanied by a gradual increase in hardness until the nickel content reaches about 5 per cent. Nickel also refines the carbide structure of the chill and the gray-iron structure below the chill.

Chromium is used in small amounts to control chill depth; 0.01 per cent chromium will neutralize about 0.015 per cent silicon. Because of the formation of chromium carbides, chromium is used in amounts of 1 to 4 per cent in chilled irons to increase hardness and improve

Table 11·6 Composition and hardness of typical chilled-iron castings*

Application	C	Si	Mn	Hardness
Car wheels	3.35	0.50	0.55	62 scleroscope
Plowshares	3.40	1.35	0.60	514 Brinell
Mold boards	3.50	1.00	0.60	534 Brinell
Sprockets	3.30	1.80	0.65	477 Brinell

* By permission from "Metals Handbook," 8th ed., American Society for Metals, Metals Park, Ohio, 1961.

abrasion resistance. It also stabilizes carbide and suppresses the formation of graphite in heavy sections. When added in amounts of 12 to 35 per cent, chromium will impart resistance to corrosion and oxidation at elevated temperatures.

Copper, in additions of less than 4 per cent, decreases the depth of chill, but in excess of this amount the chill depth and hardness increase. Copper also reduces the ratio of the mottled portion to the white-iron portion.

Molybdenum is only about one-third as effective as chromium in increasing the chill depth; however, it improves the resistance of the chilled face to spalling, pitting, chipping, and heat checking.

A constant chill depth may be obtained by using a combination of alloying elements that have opposite effects. Since nickel reduces chill depth, it is common practice to add chromium, which increases chill depth, to neutralize the nickel and result in a constant chill depth. The normal ratio employed for this purpose is 3 parts of nickel to 1 of chromium.

Chilled-iron casting is used for railway-car wheels, crushing rolls, stamp shoes and dies, sprockets, plowshares, and many other heavy-duty machinery parts. Table 11·6 gives the composition and hardness of typical chilled-iron castings.

11·16   Nodular cast iron.   Nodular cast iron, also known as *ductile iron, spheroidal graphite iron,* and *spherulitic iron,* is cast iron in which the graphite is present as tiny balls or spheroids.   The compact spheroids interrupt the continuity of the matrix much less than graphite flakes; this results in higher strength and toughness compared with a similar structure of gray iron.   Nodular cast iron differs

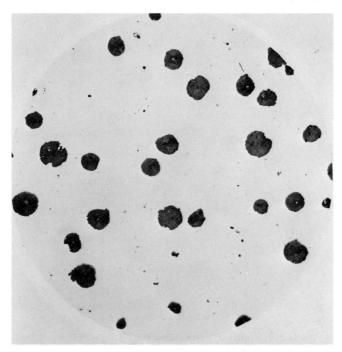

Fig. 11·18   Nodular iron, unetched, 125×.   (*The International Nickel Company*)

from malleable iron in that it is usually obtained as a result of solidification and does not require heat treatment.   The spheroids are more rounded than the irregular aggregates of temper carbon found in malleable iron (Fig. 11·18).

The total carbon content of nodular iron is the same as in gray cast iron.   Spheroidal graphite particles form during solidification because of the presence of a small amount of certain alloying elements.   The nodule-forming addition, usually magnesium or cerium, is made to the ladle just before casting.   Since these elements have a strong affinity for sulfur, the base iron-alloy sulfur content must be below 0.015 per cent for the treatment to be effective.

The amount of ferrite in the as-cast matrix depends on composition and rate of cooling. Nodular irons with a matrix having a maximum of 10 per cent pearlite are known as *ferritic irons* (Fig. 11·19). This structure gives maximum ductility, toughness, and machinability.

A matrix structure which is largely pearlite can be produced as cast or by normalizing. Normalizing is carried out by air cooling from a temperature of 1600 to 1650°F. Pearlitic irons (Fig. 11·20)

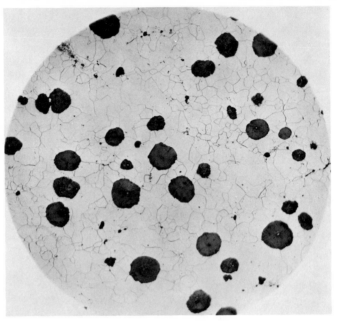

Fig. 11·19   Ferritic nodular iron.   Etched in 2 per cent nital, 125×. (*The International Nickel Company*)

are stronger but less ductile than ferrite irons. A martensitic matrix may be obtained by quenching in oil or water from 1600 to 1700°F. The quenched structures are usually tempered, after hardening, to the desired strength and hardness levels.

Austenitic irons are highly alloyed types which retain their austenitic structure down to at least −75°F. These irons are of interest because of their relatively high corrosion resistance and good creep properties at elevated temperatures.

The tensile mechanical properties of basic types of nodular iron are given in Table 11·7.

Some typical applications of nodular iron are agricultural—tractor and implement parts; automotive and diesel—crankshafts, pistons, and cylinder heads; electrical fittings, switch boxes, motor frames, and

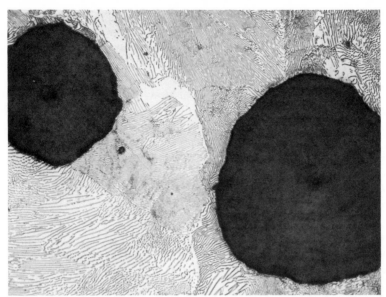

Fig. 11·20 Pearlitic nodular iron. Etched in 2 per cent nital, 500×. (*The International Nickel Company*)

circuit-breaker parts; mining—hoist drums, drive pulleys, flywheels, and elevator buckets; steel mill—work rolls, furnace doors, table rolls, and bearings; tool and die—wrenches, levers, handles, clamp frames, chuck bodies, and miscellaneous dies for shaping steel, aluminum, brass, bronze, and titanium.

Table 11·7 Mechanical properties of basic types of nodular iron*

Type	Alloy content	Tensile strength, psi	Yield strength, psi	Elongation, % in 2 in.	BHN
Ferritic	Low	55,000	35,000	25	130
	High	90,000	70,000	12	210
Pearlitic	Low	80,000	60,000	10	200
	Low†	130,000	90,000	7	275
	High	130,000	110,000	2	275
Quenched	. . .	100,000	80,000	10	215
		150,000	130,000	2	320
Austenitic	‡	60,000	30,000	40	130
	§	60,000	40,000	10	160

* By permission from "Metals Handbook," 1954 Supplement, American Society for Metals, Metals Park, Ohio.
† Normalized.
‡ 3.00 per cent C, 2.50 per cent Si, 20.0 per cent Ni, 2.0 per cent Mn.
§ 3.00 per cent C, 2.0 per cent Si, 20 per cent Ni, 1 per cent Mn, 1.5 per cent Cr.

11·17   Alloy cast irons.   An alloy cast iron is one which contains a specially added element or elements in sufficient amount to produce a measurable modification in the physical or mechanical properties. Elements normally obtained from raw materials, such as silicon, manganese, sulfur, and phosphorus, are not considered alloy additions.

Alloying elements are added to cast iron for special properties such as resistance to corrosion, heat, or wear, and to improve mechanical properties.   Most alloying elements in cast iron will accelerate or retard graphitization, and this is one of the important reasons for alloying. The most common alloying elements are chromium, copper, molybdenum, nickel, and vanadium.

Chromium increases combined carbon by forming complex iron-chromium carbides that are more stable than iron carbide.   Small amounts of chromium increase strength, hardness, depth of chill, and resistance to wear and heat but decrease machinability.   The strong carbide-forming tendency of chromium is illustrated by the following effects on the microstructure of a soft gray iron as the chromium content is increased:

Per Cent Chromium	*Structure*
0	Ferrite and coarse graphite
0.3	Less ferrite, some pearlite, and finer graphite
0.6	Fine graphite and pearlite
1.0	Fine graphite, pearlite, and small carbide
3.0	Disappearance of graphite
5.0	Much massive carbide
10–30	Fine carbide

Chromium additions of less than 1 per cent give a general improvement in mechanical properties.   For resistance to corrosion or for use at high temperatures, as much as 35 per cent chromium has been added to cast irons.   Most often, chromium is used in combination with other alloying elements.

Copper is a graphitizer but is only about one-fifth as potent as silicon in this respect.   For general engineering applications the copper content is between 0.25 and 2.5 per cent.   Copper tends to break up massive cementite and strengthen the matrix.

Molybdenum improves mechanical properties and is a mild stabilizer of carbides.   Molybdenum is added in quantities from 0.25 to 1.25 per cent, and its effect is similar to that in steel.   Fatigue strength, tensile strength, transverse strength, heat resistance, and hardness of the cast iron are all improved.   Molybdenum also retards the transformation of austenite, thus increasing hardenability and freedom from cracking and distortion.   Molybdenum is always used in combination with other alloying elements.

Vanadium is a very powerful carbide former, stabilizes cementite, and reduces graphitization. Vanadium additions, between 0.10 and 0.25 per cent, increase tensile strength, transverse strength, and hardness.

Nickel is a graphitizer but only about one-half as effective as silicon in this respect. The purpose of nickel (0.5 to 6.0 per cent) in the engineering gray irons is to control the structure by retarding austenite

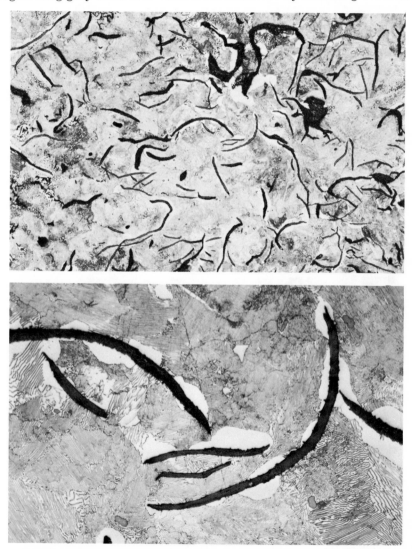

Fig. 11·21   Low-nickel cast iron.   As cast, graphite, pearlite, and a small amount of ferrite.   Etched in 2 per cent nital.   Top 100×, bottom 500×.   (*The International Nickel Company*)

transformation, stabilizing pearlite, and maintaining combined carbon at the eutectoid quantity. Thus the microstructure of a low-nickel cast iron shows graphite, pearlite, and very little ferrite (Fig. 11·21). In combination with about 1 per cent molybdenum, the matrix tends to be bainitic (Fig. 11·22). This structure has a hardness of about 385 BHN.

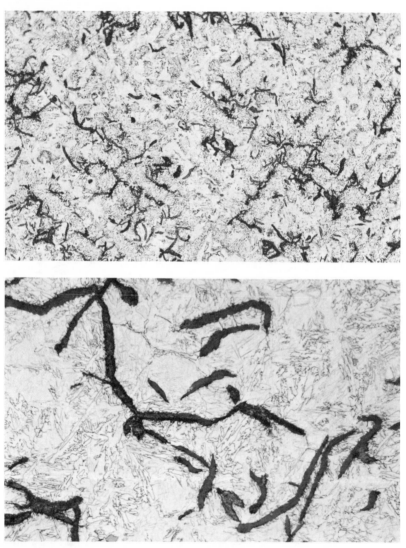

Fig. 11·22   Nickel-molybdenum cast iron (1.50 per cent Ni, 1.62 per cent Mo).   As cast, graphite in bainitic matrix.   Etched in 2 per cent nital. Top 100×, bottom 500×.   (*The International Nickel Company*)

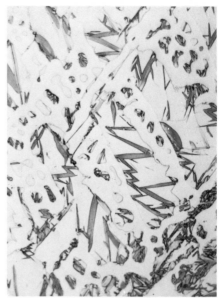

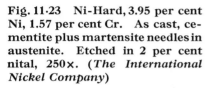

Fig. 11·23 Ni-Hard, 3.95 per cent Ni, 1.57 per cent Cr. As cast, cementite plus martensite needles in austenite. Etched in 2 per cent nital, 250×. (*The International Nickel Company*)

For excellent abrasion resistance, about 4 per cent nickel in combination with about 1.50 per cent chromium is added to white cast iron. The structure is shown in Fig. 11·23. The primary dendrites, originally austenite, have been partially transformed to martensite. The combination of iron carbides in a martensitic matrix results in high hardness (600 to 750 BHN) along with good strength and toughness.

The addition of 14 to 38 per cent nickel to gray irons results in high

Table 11·8 Typical low-alloy cast irons*

Silicon, %	2.25	2.09	2.23	2.12	2.11	2.57
Total carbon, %	3.53	3.33	3.38	3.44	3.41	2.81
Combined carbon, %	0.57	0.89	0.64	0.74	0.72	0.73
Sulfur, %	0.08	0.06	0.06	0.06	0.06	0.06
Phosphorus, %	0.14	0.16	0.14	0.16	0.16	0.16
Manganese, %	0.59	0.62	0.60	0.60	0.60	0.60
Nickel, %	0.71	1.77	1.46	1.00	2.00	2.00
Chromium, %	0.25	0.74	0.15	0.25	0.20	0.20
Molybdenum, %	. . .	. . .	. . .	0.60	0.90	0.90
Transverse strength, lb	2,400	2,625	26.5	3,000	3,300	3,700
Tensile strength, psi	28,000	36,000	30,000	39,000	44,000	66,000
BHN	180	214	187	212	250	300

* By permission from A. W. Grosvenor, "Basic Metallurgy," vol. 1, American Society for Metals, Metals Park, Ohio, 1954.

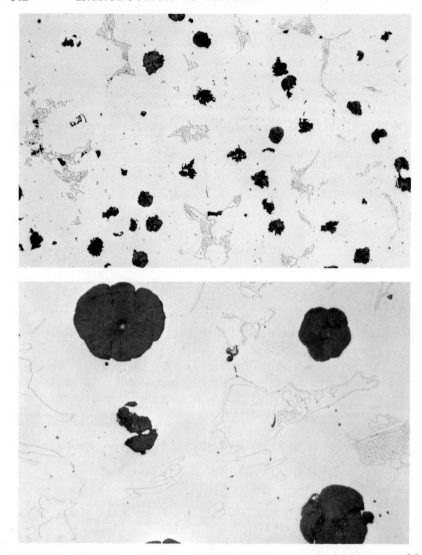

Fig. 11·24   Ni-Resist, 21.06 per cent Ni, 2.20 per cent Cr, 0.06 per cent Mg. As cast, nodular graphite and carbides in austenitic matrix.   Etched in 2 per cent nital.   Top, 100×, bottom 500×.   (*The International Nickel Company*)

heat resistance, high corrosion resistance, and low expansivity.   Because of the large amount of nickel, the matrix will be austenitic (Fig. 11·24).

The composition and mechanical properties of some low-alloy cast irons are given in Table 11·8.

QUESTIONS

11·1 Explain the difference in longitudinal and transverse tensile strength of wrought iron.

11·2 Differentiate between free and combined carbon.

11·3 Discuss the effect of the amount of free carbon on the properties of gray cast iron.

11·4 How may the properties of gray cast iron be varied?

11·5 Differentiate, in microstructure, gray cast iron, malleable iron, and nodular iron.

11·6 Why are graphite flakes in gray iron very often surrounded by ferrite areas?

11·7 Why should the iron–iron carbide diagram not be used to determine the structures in gray iron?

11·8 Why is malleable iron made only from hypoeutectic white iron?

11·9 Is it possible to make nodular iron by heat treatment? Explain.

11·10 Why should the sulfur content be low in the manufacture of nodular iron?

11·11 In the manufacture of nodular iron, why are inoculants added only just before casting?

11·12 Why is welding of chilled cast irons not recommended?

REFERENCES

American Foundrymen's Association: "Cast Metals Handbook," Chicago, 1944.

American Society for Metals: "Metals Handbook," 7th ed., 1948; 8th ed., 1961, Metals Park, Ohio.

Bolton, John W.: "Gray Cast Iron," Penton Publishing Company, Cleveland, 1937.

Boyles, A.: "The Structure of Cast Iron," American Society for Metals, Metals Park, Ohio, 1947.

Gray Iron Founders' Society: "Gray Iron Castings Handbook," Cleveland, 1958.

Malleable Founders Society: "Malleable Iron Castings," Cleveland, 1960.

Sisco, F. T.: "The Alloys of Iron and Carbon," McGraw-Hill Book Company, Inc., New York, 1937.

Chapter 12

NONFERROUS METALS AND ALLOYS

12·1 Introduction. Metallic materials, when considered in a broad sense, may be divided into two large groups, ferrous and nonferrous. The ferrous materials are iron-based and the nonferrous materials have some element other than iron as the principal constituent. The bulk of the nonferrous materials is made up of the alloys of copper, aluminum, magnesium, nickel, tin, lead, and zinc. Other nonferrous metals and alloys that are used to a lesser extent include cadmium, molybdenum, cobalt, zirconium, beryllium, tantalum, and the precious metals gold, silver, and the platinum group.

This chapter will be concerned with the more important nonferrous metals and alloys.

COPPER AND COPPER ALLOYS

12·2 Copper. The properties of copper that are most important are high electrical and thermal conductivity, good corrosion resistance, machinability, strength, and ease of fabrication. In addition, copper is nonmagnetic, has a pleasing color, can be welded, brazed, and soldered, and is easily finished by plating or lacquering. Certain of these basic properties may be improved by suitable alloying. Most of the copper that is used for electrical conductors contains over 99.9 per cent copper and is identified as electrolytic tough-pitch copper (ETP) or oxygen-free high-conductivity copper (OFHC). Electrolytic tough-pitch copper is also used for roofing, gutters, downspouts, automobile radiators and gaskets, kettles, vats, pressure vessels, and distillery and other process equipment. Electrolytic tough-pitch copper contains from 0.02 to 0.05 per cent oxygen, which is combined with copper as the compound cuprous oxide (Cu_2O). As cast, copper oxide and copper form an interdendritic eutectic mixture (Fig. 12·1). After working and annealing, the interdendritic network is destroyed (Fig. 12·2)

344

and the strength is improved.   Oxygen-free copper is used in electronic tubes or similar applications because it makes a perfect seal to glass.

Arsenical copper containing about 0.3 per cent arsenic has improved resistance to special corrosive conditions and is used for certain condenser and heat-exchanger applications.

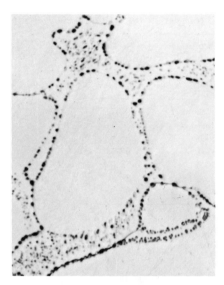 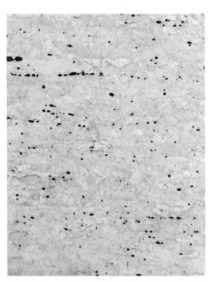

Fig. 12·1 Copper–copper oxide eutectic in cast tough-pitch copper. Lightly etched with sodium dichromate, 500×. (*Revere Copper and Brass Co.*)

Fig. 12·2 Particles of copper oxide in wrought tough-pitch copper. Lightly etched in ammonium hydroxide and hydrogen peroxide, 250×. (*Revere Copper and Brass Co.*)

Free-cutting copper with about 0.6 per cent tellurium has excellent machining properties and is used for bolts, studs, welding tips, and electrical parts such as contact pins, switch gears, relays, and precision electrical equipment.

Silver-bearing copper has a silver content of 7 to 30 oz per ton. Silver raises the recrystallization temperature of copper, thus preventing softening during soldering of commutators.   It is preferred in the manufacture of electric motors for railroad and aircraft use.

12·3 Temper designation of copper and copper alloys. Since copper and most copper alloys are homogeneous single phases, they are not susceptible to heat treatment and their strength may be altered only by cold working.   There are two general classes of temper for non-heat-treatable wrought-copper alloys: cold-worked and soft or annealed.

The different cold-worked tempers shown in Table 12·1 are obtained by cold-working the annealed material a definite amount. The percentage reduction for strip is based on thickness difference and for wire on area difference.

Table 12·1   Cold-worked temper designations*

Description	Approximate % reduction by cold working	
	Strip	Wire
Quarter hard	10.9	20.7
Half hard	20.7	37.1
Three-quarter hard	29.4	50.0
Hard	37.1	60.5
Extra hard	50.0	75.0
Spring	60.5	84.4
Extra spring	68.7	90.2

* From "Metals Handbook," 1961 edition, p. 1006, American Society for Metals, Metals Park, Ohio.

Table 12·2   Commonly used grain sizes

Grain Size, mm	Recommended for
0.015	Slight forming operations; best polishing
0.025	Easy drawing, good polishing such as hubcaps
0.035	Good drawing and polishing as for headlight reflectors
0.050	Heavy drawing and spinning; more difficult to polish
0.100	Severe draws on heavy material

Annealed tempers are used for forming at room temperature and are described by range of grain size or nominal grain size, expressed as average grain diameter in millimeters. Measurement of grain size is standardized by ASTM E79, Estimating the Average Grain Size of Wrought Copper and Copper-base Alloys. The grain size best suited for a particular application depends upon the thickness of the metal, the depth of draw, and the type of surface required after the draw. Commonly used grain sizes are shown in Table 12·2.

12·4 Copper alloys. The most important commercial copper alloys may be classified as follows:

I. Brasses—alloys of copper and zinc
    A. Alpha brasses—alloys containing up to 36 per cent zinc
        1. Yellow alpha brasses—20 to 36 per cent zinc
        2. Red brasses—5 to 20 per cent zinc
    B. Alpha plus beta brasses—54 to 62 per cent copper
II. Bronzes—up to 12 per cent of alloying element
    A. Tin bronzes
    B. Silicon bronzes
    C. Aluminum bronzes
    D. Beryllium bronzes
III. Cupronickels—alloys of copper and nickel
IV. Nickel silvers—alloys of copper, nickel, and zinc

12·5 Brasses—general. Brasses are essentially alloys of copper and zinc. Some of these alloys have small amounts of other elements such as lead, tin, or aluminum. Variations in composition will result in desired color, strength, ductility, machinability, corrosion resistance, or a combination of such properties.

The portion of the binary copper-zinc phase diagram which is applicable to commercial alloys is shown in Fig. 12·3. The solubility

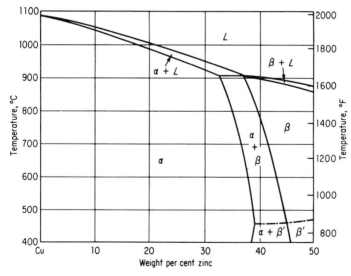

Fig. 12·3 Cu-rich portion of the Cu-Zn phase diagram. (*From "Metals Handbook,"* 1948 *edition, p.* 1206, *American Society for Metals, Metals Park, Ohio*)

of zinc in the alpha (α) solid solution increases from 32.5 per cent at 1657°F to about 39 per cent at 850°F. Since copper is f.c.c. (face-centered cubic), the α solid solution is f.c.c. The beta (β) phase is a b.c.c. (body-centered cubic) electron compound and undergoes ordering, indicated by a dot-dash line, in the region of 850 to 875°F. On cooling in this temperature range the b.c.c. β phase, with copper and zinc atoms randomly dispersed at lattice points, changes continuously to the ordered structure β′, which is still b.c.c. but with the copper atoms at the corners and zinc atoms at the centers of the unit cubes. The

Table 12·3   Effect of zinc on properties of copper alloys*

Zn,%	Tensile strength, psi	Elongation, % in 2 in.	BHN, 10 mm, 500 kg
0	32,000	46	38
5	36,000	49	49
10	41,000	52	54
15	42,000	56	58
20	43,000	59	56
25	45,000	62	54
30	46,000	65	55
35	46,000	60	55
40 (+β′)	54,000	45	75

* Data from Chase Brass & Copper Co. for commercial alloys of moderate grain size.

ordering reaction is so rapid that it cannot be retarded or prevented by quenching.

The effect of zinc on the tensile properties of annealed copper alloys is shown in Table 12·3.

In most cases, the addition of solid-solution elements tends to decrease ductility as strength increases. The addition of zinc, as shown in Table 12·3, increases ductility along with strength. The best combination of strength and ductility is obtained in 70Cu-30Zn brass.

The commercial brasses may be divided into two groups, brasses for cold working (α brasses) and brasses for hot working (α plus β brasses).

12·6 Alpha brasses. Alpha brasses containing up to 36 per cent zinc possess relatively good corrosion resistance and good working properties. The color of α brasses varies according to copper content from red for high-copper alloys to yellow at about 62 per cent copper. The α brasses may be divided into two groups, yellow α brasses and red brasses.

YELLOW α BRASSES. These contain 20 to 36 per cent zinc, combine good strength with high ductility and are therefore suited for drastic cold-working operations. It is common practice to stress-relief anneal these brasses after severe cold working to prevent *season cracking*. Season cracking or stress-corrosion cracking is due to the high residual stresses left in the brass as a result of cold working.

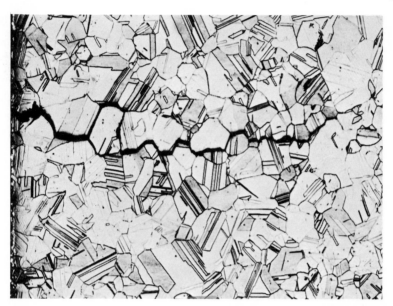

Fig. 12·4 Stress-corrosion cracking in α brass, 150x. (*Revere Copper and Brass Co.*)

These stresses make the brass more susceptible to intergranular corrosion, particularly in ammonia atmospheres (Fig. 12·4). Stress relieving in the recovery range (up to about 500°F) or the substitution of a less susceptible copper alloy will minimize the danger of stress-corrosion cracking.

Yellow α brasses are also subject to a pitting corrosion called *dezincification*. This type of corrosion usually occurs when brass is in contact with sea water or with fresh waters that have a high content of oxygen and carbon dioxide. Dezincification involves dissolution of the alloy and a subsequent deposition of porous nonadherent copper. Action of this kind, unless stopped, will eventually penetrate the cross section of the metal and lead to leakage through the porous copper layer. If it occurs in a localized area it is known as *plug-type dezincification* (Fig. 12·5). Small amounts of tin or antimony minimize dezincification in yellow brasses.

The most widely used yellow α brasses are *cartridge brass* (70Cu-30Zn) and *yellow brass* (65Cu-35Zn). Typical applications include automotive—radiator cores, tanks, headlight reflectors; electrical—flashlight shells, lamp fixtures, socket shells, screw shells; hardware—eyelets, fasteners, grommets, rivets, springs; plumbing accessories; and ammunition components.

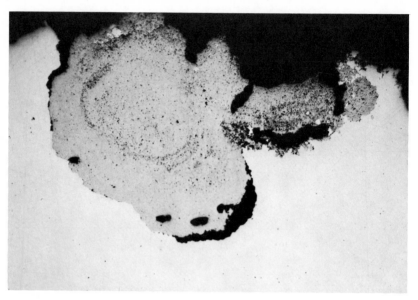

Fig. 12·5 Plug-type dezincification in brass, unetched, 50×. (*Revere Copper and Brass Co.*)

The addition of 0.5 to 3 per cent lead improves machinability so that leaded brass is used for screw-machine parts, engraving plates, keys, lock parts, tumblers, gears, and watch parts.

Two variations of yellow α brasses have been developed for special applications. *Admiralty metal* (71Cu-28Zn-1Sn), with the addition of 1 per cent tin for improved strength and corrosion resistance, is used for condenser and heat-exchanger tubes in steam-power-plant equipment. Better corrosion resistance is obtained in *aluminum brass* (76Cu-22Zn-2Al). This alloy forms a tenacious, self-healing film which protects the tube against high cooling-water velocities in marine and land power stations.

RED BRASSES. These contain between 5 and 20 per cent zinc. They generally have better corrosion resistance than yellow brasses and are not susceptible to season cracking or dezincification. The most common low-zinc brasses are gilding metal (95Cu-5Zn), commercial bronze (90Cu-10Zn), red brass (85Cu-15Zn), and low brass (80Cu-20Zn).

Gilding metal has higher strength than copper and is used for coins, medals, tokens, fuse caps, primers, emblems, plaques, and as a base for articles to be gold-plated or highly polished.

Commercial bronze has excellent cold-working and hot-working properties and is used for costume jewelry, compacts, lipstick cases, marine hardware, forgings, rivets, and screws. Leaded commercial bronze (1.75 per cent Pb) is used for screws and other parts for automatic screw-machine work.

Red brass is used for electrical conduit, screw shells, sockets, hardware, condenser and heat-exchanger tubes, plumbing pipe, lipstick cases, compacts, nameplates, tags, and radiator cores.

Low brass is used for ornamental metalwork, medallions, thermostat bellows, musical instruments, flexible hose, and other deep-drawn articles.

12·7 Alpha plus beta brasses. These contain from 54 to 62 per cent copper. Consideration of Fig. 12·3 shows that these alloys will consist of two phases, α and β'. The β' phase is harder and more brittle at room temperature than α; therefore, these alloys are more difficult to cold-work than the α brasses. At elevated temperatures the β phase becomes very plastic, and since most of these alloys may be heated into the single-phase β region, they have excellent hot-working properties.

The most widely used $\alpha + \beta'$ brass is *muntz metal* (60Cu-40Zn), which has high strength and excellent hot-working properties. The two-phase structure of muntz metal is shown in Fig. 12·6. Rapid cooling from the β region may suppress the precipitation of most of the α phase. Figure 12·7 shows the microstructure of muntz metal after water quenching from 1515°F. The quench preserved most of the β, but some α has formed, particularly at the grain boundaries. Subsequent reheating to a low temperature will allow more of the α to come out of the supersaturated solution; thus it is possible to heat-treat this alloy. Muntz metal is used in sheet form for ship sheathing, condenser heads, perforated metal, and architectural work. It is also used for valve stems, brazing rods, and condenser tubes. Leaded muntz metal containing 0.40 to 0.80 per cent lead has improved machinability.

Free-cutting brass (61.5Cu-35.5Zn-3Pb) has the best machinability of any brass combined with good mechanical and corrosion-resistant properties.

Forging brass (60Cu-38Zn-2Pb) has the best hot-working properties of any brass and is used for hot forgings, hardware, and plumbing parts.

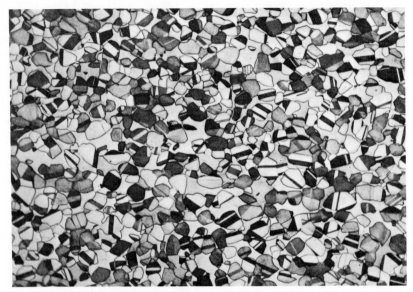

Fig. 12·6 Two-phase structure of annealed muntz metal. β **appears light surrounding the** α **grains. Etched in ammonium hydroxide and hydrogen peroxide, 150×. (Revere Copper and Brass Co.)**

Architectural bronze (57Cu-40Zn-3Pb) has excellent forging and free machining properties. Typical applications are handrails, decorative moldings, grilles, storefronts, hinges, lock bodies, and industrial forgings.

Naval brass (60Cu-39.25Zn-0.75Sn), also known as *tobin bronze*, has increased resistance to salt-water corrosion and is used for condenser plates, welding rod, propeller shafts, piston rods, and valve stems.

Fig. 12·7 Muntz metal water-quenched from 1515°F. Etched in ammonium hydroxide and hydrogen peroxide, 50×. (By permission from R. M. Brick and A. Phillips, "Structure and Properties of Alloys," 2d ed., McGraw-Hill Book Company, Inc., New York, 1949)

Leaded naval brass with the addition of 1.75 Pb for improved machinability is used for marine hardware.

Manganese bronze (58.5Cu-39Zn-1.4Fe-1Sn-0.1Mn), really a high-zinc brass, has high strength combined with excellent wear resistance and is used for clutch disks, extruded shapes, forgings, pump rods, shafting rod, valve stems, and welding rod.

12·8 Cast brasses. The previous discussion was concerned primarily with wrought brasses, which are mainly binary alloys of copper and zinc. The cast brasses are similar in name to the wrought brasses but usually contain appreciable amounts of other alloying elements. Tin may be present from 1 to 6 per cent, lead from 1 to 10 per cent, and some alloys may contain iron, manganese, nickel, and aluminum.

An example of a casting brass is *leaded red brass* (85Cu-5Sn-5Pb-5Zn), which is used for general castings requiring fair strength, soundness, and good machining properties, such as low-pressure valves, pipe fittings, small gears, and small pump castings.

12·9 Bronzes—general. The term *bronze* was originally applied to the copper-tin alloys; however, the term is now used for any copper alloy, with the exception of copper-zinc alloys, that contains up to approximately 12 per cent of the principal alloying element. Bronze, as a name, conveys the idea of a higher-class alloy than brass, and as indicated in the preceding sections, it has been incorrectly applied to some alloys that are really special brasses. Commercial bronzes are primarily alloys of copper and tin, aluminum, silicon, or beryllium. In addition, they may contain phosphorus, lead, zinc, or nickel.

12·10 Tin bronzes. These are generally referred to as *phosphor bronzes* since phosphorus is always present as a deoxidizer in casting. The usual range of phosphorus content is between 0.01 and 0.5 per cent, and of tin between 1 and 11 per cent.

The copper-rich portion of the copper-tin alloy system is shown in Fig. 12·8. The β phase forms as the result of a peritectic reaction at 1468°F. At 1087°F, the β phase undergoes a eutectoid reaction to form the eutectoid mixture ($\alpha + \gamma$). At 968°F, gamma (γ) also undergoes a eutectoid transformation to ($\alpha + \delta$). The diagram also indicates the decomposition of the delta (δ) phase. This takes place by a eutectoid reaction at 662°F forming ($\alpha + \epsilon$). This reaction is so sluggish that in commercial alloys, the epsilon (ϵ) phase is nonexistent. The slope of the solvus line below 968°F shows a considerable decrease in the solubility of tin in the α phase. The precipitation of the δ or ϵ phase due to this change in solubility is so slow that, for practical purposes, the solvus line is as indicated by the vertical dotted line below 968°F. For this reason, slow-cooled cast tin bronzes containing below 7 per cent tin generally show only a single phase, the α solid solution. There is some of the δ phase in most castings containing over 7 per cent tin. The structure of a rapidly cooled cast 10 per cent phosphor bronze (Fig. 12·9a) shows small particles of the δ phase in a fine dendritic α matrix. Detail of the δ phase is shown in Fig. 12·9b.

The phosphor bronzes are characterized by high strength, toughness, high corrosion resistance, low coefficient of friction, and freedom from

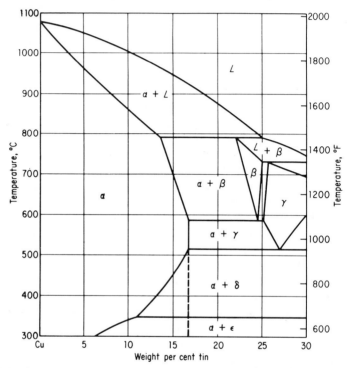

Fig. 12·8 Copper-rich portion of the copper-tin phase diagram. (*From "Metals Handbook," 1948 edition, p. 1204, American Society for Metals, Metals Park, Ohio*)

season cracking. They are used extensively for diaphragms, bellows, lock washers, cotter pins, bushings, clutch disks, and springs.

Zinc is sometimes used to replace part of the tin. The result is an improvement in the casting properties and toughness with little effect on wear resistance.

Lead is often added to tin bronze to improve machinability and wear resistance. High-lead tin bronze may contain as much as 25 per cent lead. The leaded alloys are used for bushing and bearings under moderate or light loads.

12·11 Silicon bronzes. The copper-rich portion of the copper-silicon alloy system is shown in Fig. 12·10. The solubility of silicon

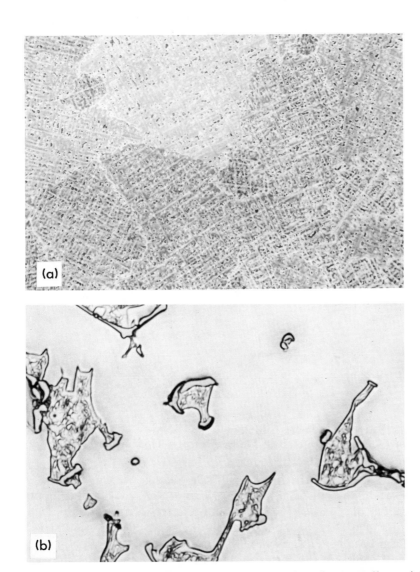

Fig. 12·9   Structure of a cast 10 per cent phosphor-bronze alloy.   (*a*)
Rapidly cooled, particles of δ in a dendritic α matrix, 75×; (*b*) detail of
the δ phase, 1,000×.   (*American Brass Company*)

in the α phase is 5.3 per cent at 1565°F and decreases with temperature. The eutectoid reaction at 1030°F is very sluggish, so that commercial silicon bronzes, which generally contain less than 5 per cent silicon, are single-phase alloys.

Silicon bronzes are the strongest of the work-hardenable copper alloys. They have mechanical properties comparable to those of mild steel and corrosion resistance comparable to that of copper. They are used for tanks, pressure vessels, marine construction, and hydraulic pressure lines.

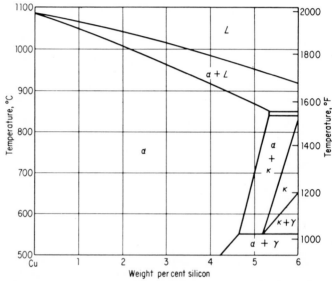

Fig. 12·10 Copper-rich portion of the copper-silicon alloy system. (*From "Metals Handbook," 1948 edition, p. 1203, American Society for Metals, Metals Park, Ohio*)

12·12 Aluminum bronzes. The copper-rich portion of the copper-aluminum alloy system is shown in Fig. 12·11. The maximum solubility of aluminum in the α solid solution is approximately 9.5 per cent at 1050°F. The β phase undergoes a eutectoid reaction at 1050°F to form the (α + γ_2) mixture.

Most commercial aluminum bronzes contain between 4 and 11 per cent aluminum. Those alloys containing up to 7.5 per cent aluminum are generally single-phase alloys, while those containing between 7.5 and 11 per cent aluminum are two-phase alloys. Other elements such as iron, nickel, manganese, and silicon are frequently added to aluminum bronzes. Iron (0.5 to 5.0 per cent) increases strength and hardness and refines the grain; nickel (up to 5 per cent) has the same effect as iron but is not so effective; silicon (up to 2 per cent) improves machinability; manganese promotes soundness in castings by combining with gases and also improves strength.

The single-phase aluminum bronzes show good cold-working properties and good strength combined with corrosion resistance to atmospheric and water attack. They are used for condenser tubes,

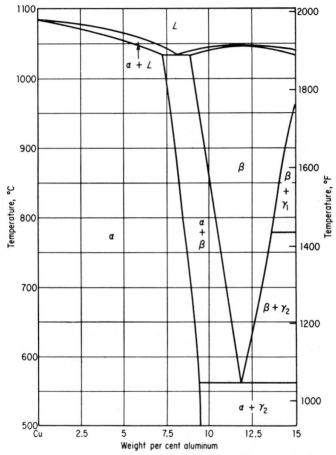

Fig. 12·11   Copper-rich portion of the copper-aluminum alloy system. (*From "Metals Handbook,"* 1948 *edition, p.* 1160, *American Society for Metals, Metals Park, Ohio*)

cold-work forms, corrosion-resistant vessels, nuts, bolts, and for protective sheathing in marine applications.

The $\alpha + \beta$ aluminum bronzes are interesting because they can be heat-treated to obtain structures similar to those in steel. Figure 12·12a shows the structure of primary α and granular eutectoid, representative of an as-cast 10 per cent aluminum bronze. On furnace cooling from above the eutectoid temperature, a lamellar structure resembling pearlite is formed (Fig. 12·12b). If the two-phase alloy is quenched from 1500 to 1600°F, a needlelike structure resembling

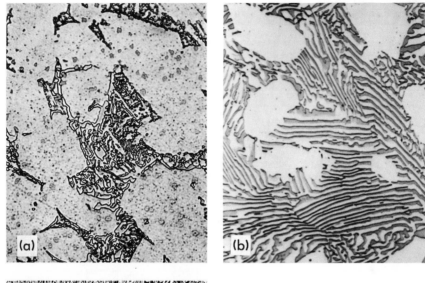

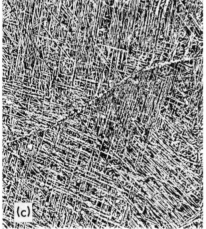

Fig. 12·12 Structures of aluminum bronze. All samples etched with ferric nitrate. (a) As-cast 10 per cent aluminum bronze showing primary α and granular eutectoid, 750×; (b) furnace-cooled aluminum bronze showing lamellar eutectoid, 500×; (c) quenched 10.7 per cent aluminum bronze showing a martensitic β structure, 100×. (*Ampco Metal, Inc.*)

martensite is formed (Fig. 12·12c). The quenched alloys are tempered between 700 and 1100°F to increase strength and hardness. Heat-treated aluminum bronzes are used for gears, propeller hubs, blades, pump parts, bearings, bushings, nonsparking tools, and drawing and forming dies.

12·13 Beryllium bronzes. The copper-rich portion of the copper-beryllium alloy system is shown in Fig. 12·13. The solubility of beryllium in the α solid solution decreases from 2·1 per cent at 1590°F to less than 0.25 per cent at room temperature.   This change in solubility is always indicative of age-hardening possibilities.

The theory of age hardening is discussed in Sec. 6·14.   The optimum mechanical properties are obtained in an alloy containing approximately 2 per cent beryllium.   A typical heat-treating cycle for this

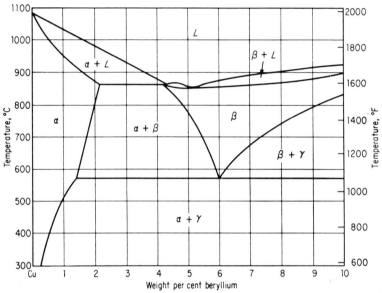

Fig. 12·13   Copper-rich portion of the copper-beryllium alloy system. (From "Metals Handbook," 1948 edition, p. 1176, American Society for Metals, Metals Park, Ohio)

alloy would be: solution-anneal at 1450°F, water-quench, cold-work, and finally age at 600°F.

Figure 12·14 shows the microstructures of a beryllium bronze containing a nominal 1.92 per cent beryllium and 0.20 to 0.30 per cent cobalt.   Figure 12·14a shows the structure after a slow cool has allowed precipitation of the dark-etching γ phase primarily at the grain boundaries.   Water quenching from the proper annealing temperature will result in a single-phase structure, and subsequent aging will allow precipitation of the γ phase as very fine particles throughout the α matrix (Fig. 12·14b).   The use of too high an aging temperature causes grain-boundary coarsening typical of overaging (Fig. 12·4c).   Under certain conditions, the β phase comes out of solution during solidification of the ingot.   This primary β usually persists during subsequent processing and appears as densely populated bands known as β *stringers*

(Fig. 12·4d).   The mechanical properties of two beryllium-bronze alloys are shown in Table 6·3.

Beryllium bronzes are used for parts requiring a combination of excellent formability in the soft condition with high yield strength,

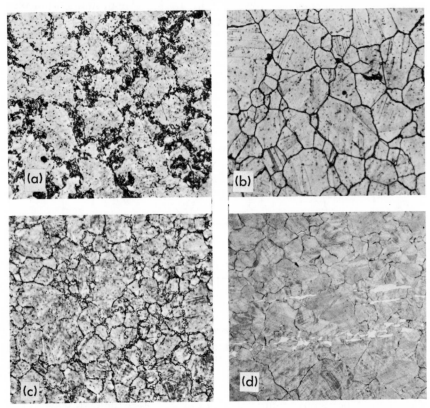

Fig. 12·14   Microstructures of beryllium bronze.   Etched with aqueous solution of ammonium persulfate and ammonium hydroxide, 300×. (a) Slow-cooled and aged for 3 hr at 600°F.   γ phase (dark) mainly at α grain boundaries.   (b) Solution-treated and aged for 3 hr at 600°F.   Fine particles of γ in an α matrix.   (c) Solution-treated and aged for 2 hr at 700°F.   Grain-boundary coarsening typical of an overaged structure. (d) β "stringers" shown as densely populated bands.   The β phase, originating in the cooling of the ingot, is not attacked by the etchant and appears white against a darkened matrix.   (The Beryllium Corporation)

high fatigue strength, and creep resistance in the hardened condition (many springs); parts requiring corrosion resistance, high strength, and relatively high electrical conductivity (diaphragms, contact bridges, surgical instruments, bolts, and screws); hard parts that will wear well against hardened steel (firing pins, dies, nonsparking tools).

12·14 Cupronickels. These are copper-nickel alloys that contain up to 30 per cent nickel. The copper-nickel binary phase diagram (Fig. 6·9) shows complete solubility, so that all cupronickels are single-phase alloys. They are not susceptible to heat treatment and may have their properties altered only by cold working.

The cupronickel alloys have high resistance to corrosion fatigue and also high resistance to the corrosive and erosive action of rapidly moving sea water. They are widely used for condenser, distiller, evaporator, and heat-exchanger tubes for naval vessels and coastal power plants.

12·15 Nickel silvers. These are essentially ternary alloys of copper, nickel, and zinc. Commercial alloys are produced with the following range of composition: copper 50 to 70 per cent, nickel 5 to 30 per cent, zinc 5 to 40 per cent.

The nickel silvers containing over 60 per cent copper are single-phase alloys that show only fair hot-working properties but are ductile and easily worked at room temperature. The addition of nickel to the copper-zinc alloy gives it a pleasing silver-blue white color and good corrosion resistance to food chemicals, water, and atmosphere. These alloys make excellent base metals for plating with chromium, nickel, or silver. They are used for rivets, screws, table flatware, zippers, costume jewelry, nameplates, and radio dials.

The nickel silvers containing between 50 and 60 per cent copper are two-phase $\alpha + \beta$ alloys. They have a relatively high modulus of elasticity and like the $\alpha + \beta$ brasses are readily hot-worked. Nickel silvers are less susceptible to stress corrosion than binary copper-zinc alloys of the same zinc content.

Typical applications of the $\alpha + \beta$ nickel silvers include springs and contacts in telephone equipment, resistance wire, hardware, and surgical and dental equipment.

The composition and typical mechanical properties of copper and some copper alloys are summarized in Table 12·4.

ALUMINUM AND ALUMINUM ALLOYS

12·16 Aluminum. The best-known characteristic of aluminum is its light weight, the density being about one-third that of steel or copper alloys. Certain aluminum alloys have a better strength-to-weight ratio than that of high-strength steels. Aluminum has good malleability and formability, high corrosion resistance, and high electrical and thermal conductivity. An ultrapure form of aluminum is used for photographic reflectors to take advantage of its high light reflectivity and nontarnishing characteristics.

Table 12·4 Chemical composition and typical mechanical properties of copper and some copper alloys*

Wrought Alloys

Material	Form	Composition, %				Tensile strength, 1,000 psi		Yield strength 0.5% offset 1,000 psi		Elongation, % in 2 in.		Hardness, Rockwell B	
		Cu	Zn	Sn	Others	Hard	Soft	Hard	Soft	Hard	Soft	Hard	Soft
Copper	Sheet	99.9+	...	...	...	55	32	48	...	4	50	58	...
Gilding metal	Sheet	95.0	5.0	...	...	55	35	45	11	5	38	68	7
Commercial bronze	Sheet	90.0	10.0	...	...	67	37	53	11	3	40	75	10
Red brass	Sheet	85.0	15.0	...	...	80	45	55	15	4	43	85	10
Low brass	Sheet	80.0	20.0	...	...	85	43	65	15	4	50	86	11
	Rod	80.0	20.0	...	...	80	45	60	15	5	50	...	...
Spring brass	Sheet	75.0	25.0	...	...	80	47	60	15	5	45	87	15
Brass	Sheet	70.0	30.0	...	...	86	45	65	15	4	50	87	...
Cartridge brass	Sheet	69.0	31.0	...	...	85	46	65	15	4	58	87	22
Yellow brass	Sheet	65.0	35.0	...	...	90	45	70	15	5	60	85	30
Muntz metal	Sheet	60.0	40.0	...	...	80	57	60	15	9	48	87	42
Phosphor bronze	Sheet	96.0	...	4.0	0.25 P	90	45	75	18	4	50	90	30
	Sheet	92.0	...	8.0	+P	110	60	85	25	3	55	99	45
Aluminum brass	Tube	76.0	22.0	...	2 Al	83	62	75	16	17	52	86	33
Aluminum bronze	...	92.0	...	...	8 Al	134	76	100	30	13	55	99	69
Manganese bronze	Rod	68.0	29.0	...	1 Al, 1 Mn, 1 Fe	85	60	50	25	20	45	90	25
Admiralty metal	Tube	71.0	21.0	1.0	...	100	53	98	18	3	60	95	...
Naval brass	Rod	60.0	39.0	0.75	0.25 Pb	62	54	39	15	30	40	55	13
Silicon brass	...	78.0	20.0	...	2.0 Si	110	55	83	12	4	60	...	...
Tin brass	...	88.0	10.0	2.0	...	85	...	...	...	3	...	86	...

Casting Alloys

Material	Composition, %				Tensile strength, 1,000 psi	Yield strength, 1,000 psi	Elongation, %	BHN, 500 kg, 10 mm
	Cu	Zn	Sn	Others				
Cond. copper	99.85	...	...	...	30	17	45	40
Brass	70.0	30.0	...	...	28	16	22	65
Tin brass	63.0	36.0	1.0	...	30	18	18	75
Silicon brass	81.0	15.0	...	4 Si	90	45	16	120
Aluminum brass	63.0	32.5	...	2.5 Al	62	35	18	70
Bronze	88.0	...	12.0	+P	40	22	11	135
	81.0	...	19.0	+P	35	25	12	75
Gear bronze	88.0	4.0	5.5	2.5 Ni	42	17	32	60
Leaded red brass	85.0	5.0	5.0	5 Pb	34	17	25	65
	80.0	...	10.0	10 Pb	35	17	20	
Silicon bronze	95.0	1.0	...	4 Si	55	22	35	90
	93.0	4.0	...	2.5 Si, 0.5 Fe	50	18	20	
Aluminum bronze	89.0	...	...	10 Al, 1 Fe	67	32	15	140
	88.0	...	...	9 Al, 3 Fe	80	35	25	140
Manganese bronze	68.0	20.0	...	4 Mn, 5 Al, 2.5 Fe	110	70	15	210
	64.0	24.0	...	4 Mn, 5 Al, 3 Fe	115	70	15	
Nickel silver	60.0	20.0	...	20 Ni	45	20	35	55
Cupronickel	70.0	...	...	30 Ni	64	33	35	120

* From S. L. Hoyt, "Metal Data," Reinhold Publishing Corporation, New York, 1952.

Aluminum is nontoxic, nonmagnetic, and nonsparking. The nonmagnetic characteristic makes aluminum useful for electrical shielding purposes such as bus-bar housings or enclosures for other electrical equipment.

Although the electrical conductivity of electric-conductor (EC) grade of aluminum is about 62 per cent that of copper, its light weight makes it more suitable as an electrical conductor for many industrial applications.

Pure aluminum has a tensile strength of about 13,000 psi. However, substantial increases in strength are obtained by cold working or alloying. Some alloys, properly heat-treated, approach tensile strengths of 100,000 psi.

One of the most important characteristics of aluminum is its machinability and workability. It can be cast by any known method, rolled to any desired thickness, stamped, drawn, spun, hammered, forged, and extruded to almost any conceivable shape.

12·17   Alloy designation system.   The designation of wrought aluminum and wrought aluminum alloys was standardized by The Aluminum Association in 1954. It follows a four-digit numbering system. The first digit indicates the alloy group (Table 12·5). The second digit

Table 12·5   Designation for alloy groups*

Aluminum Association No.

Aluminum, 99.00% and greater, major alloying element	1xxx
Copper	2xxx
Manganese	3xxx
Silicon	4xxx
Magnesium	5xxx
Magnesium and silicon	6xxx
Zinc	7xxx
Other element	8xxx
Unused series	9xxx

* The Aluminum Association.

indicates modification of the original alloy or impurity limits; zero is used for the original alloy, and integers 1 through 9 indicate alloy modifications. In the 1xxx group for minimum aluminum purities of 99.00 per cent and greater, the last two digits are the same as the two digits to the right of the decimal point in the minimum aluminum percentage when it is expressed to the nearest 0.01 per cent. Thus 1060 indicates a material of 99.60 minimum per cent aluminum purity and no special control on individual impurities.

In the 2xxx through 8xxx alloy groups, the last two digits serve only to identify the different aluminum alloys in the group.

12·18   Temper designation. The temper designation follows the alloy designation and is separated from it by a dash. The Aluminum Association Temper Designation System, adopted in 1948, is used for wrought and cast aluminum and aluminum alloys. It is based on the sequences of basic treatments used to produce the various tempers.

The standard temper-designation system consists of a letter, indicating the basic temper. Except for the annealed and as-fabricated tempers, it is more specifically defined by the addition of one or more digits. There are four basic tempers: F as fabricated, O annealed, H strain-hardened, and T heat-treated.

-F: *As Fabricated.* Applied to products which acquire some temper as the result of normal manufacturing operations. There is no guarantee of mechanical properties.

-O: *Annealed, Recrystallized.* This is the softest temper of wrought alloy products.

-H: *Strain-hardened.* This applies to products which have their mechanical properties increased by cold working only. The -H is always followed by two or more digits. The first digit indicates the specific combination of basic operations as follows:

-H1: *Strain-hardened Only.* The second digit designates the amount of cold work performed, with the numeral 8 representing the full-hard condition. Therefore, half hard is -H14, quarter hard is -H12, etc. Extra hard tempers are designated by numeral 9. A third digit is often used to indicate the degree of control of temper or to identify a special set of mechanical properties.

-H2: *Strain-hardened and Then Partially Annealed.* Applied to products that are cold-worked to a harder temper and then have their strength reduced to the desired level by partial annealing. The residual amount of cold work is designated by the same method as the -H1 series.

-H3: *Strain-hardened and Then Stabilized.* Applied only to alloys containing magnesium which are given a low-temperature heating to stabilize their properties. The degree of strain hardening remaining after the stabilizing treatment is indicated in the usual way by one or more digits.

-W: *Solution Heat-treated.* An unstable temper applicable only to alloys which spontaneously age at room temperature after solution heat treatment. This designation, because of natural aging, is specific only when the period of aging is indicated: for example, 2024-W ($\frac{1}{2}$ hr).

-T: *Thermally Treated.* Applies to products thermally treated, with or without supplementary strain hardening, to produce stable tempers.

The -T is followed by the numerals 2 through 10, inclusive, designating a specific combination of basic operations. Deliberate variations of the conditions, resulting in significantly different characteristics for the product, are indicated by adding one or more digits to the basic designation.

-T2: Annealed (cast products only)

-T3: Solution heat-treated and then cold-worked

-T4: Solution heat-treated and naturally aged to a substantially stable condition

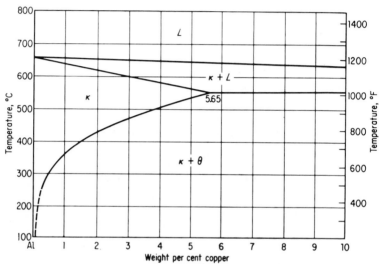

Fig. 12·15 Aluminum-rich portion of the copper-aluminum alloy system. (*From "Metals Handbook," 1948 edition, p. 1160, American Society for Metals, Metals Park, Ohio*)

-T5: Artificially aged only. Applies to products which are artificially aged after an elevated-temperature rapid-cool fabrication process, such as casting or extrusion

-T6: Solution heat-treated and then artificially aged

-T7: Solution heat-treated and then stabilized: applies to products where the temperature and time conditions for stabilizing are such that the alloy is carried beyond the point of maximum hardness, providing control of growth and/or residual stress

-T8: Solution heat-treated, cold-worked, and then artificially aged

-T9: Solution heat-treated, artificially aged, and then cold-worked

-T10: Artificially aged and then cold-worked, the same as -T5 but followed by cold working to improve strength

12·19 Aluminum-copper alloys. The aluminum-rich end of the aluminum-copper equilibrium diagram is shown in Fig. 12·15.

The maximum solubility of copper in aluminum is 5.65 per cent at 1018°F, and the solubility decreases to 0.45 per cent at 572°F. Therefore, alloys containing between 2.5 and 5 per cent copper will respond to heat treatment by age hardening. The theta (θ) phase is an intermediate alloy phase whose composition corresponds closely to the compound $CuAl_2$. Solution treatment is carried out by heating the alloy into the kappa (κ) single-phase region followed by rapid cooling. Subsequent aging, either natural or artificial, will allow precipitation of the θ phase, thus increasing the strength of the alloy. These alloys may contain smaller amounts of silicon, iron, magnesium, manganese, chromium, and zinc.

The three most widely used wrought aluminum-copper alloys are 2014, 2017, and 2024. The oldest of all the heat-treatable aluminum alloys is duralumin (2017) containing 4 per cent copper. This alloy is widely used for rivets in aircraft construction. Since this is a natural-aging alloy, after solution treatment it is refrigerated to prevent aging. As a single phase, in the solution-treated condition, it has good ductility so that the rivethead may be easily formed. Subsequent return of the material to room temperature causes precipitation of the θ phase as small submicroscopic particles, increasing the hardness and strength.

Alloy 2014 has higher copper and manganese content than 2017 and is susceptible to artificial aging. In the artificially aged temper, 2014 has a higher tensile strength, much higher yield strength, and lower elongation than 2017. This alloy is used for heavy-duty forgings, aircraft fittings, and truck frames. Alloy 2024, containing 4.5 per cent copper and 1.5 per cent magnesium, develops the highest strengths of any naturally aged aluminum-copper type of alloy. The higher magnesium content, compared with 2017, makes it more difficult to fabricate. A combination of strain hardening and aging will develop the maximum yield strength attainable in high-strength alloy sheet. Typical uses of 2024 alloy are aircraft structures, rivets, hardware, truck wheels, and screw-machine products. An aluminum-copper alloy containing 2 per cent nickel (2218) has been developed for applications involving elevated temperatures such as forged cylinder heads and pistons.

The only binary aluminum-copper casting alloy is 195, containing 4 per cent copper. When properly heat-treated, this alloy has an excellent combination of strength and ductility. Alloy 195 sand-cast is used for flywheel and rear-axle housings, bus wheels, aircraft wheels, and crankcases.

Several casting alloys are produced that contain approximately 8 per cent copper. These alloys, 112, 113, and 212, may contain substantial controlled additions of silicon, as well as iron and zinc. The presence of silicon increases fluidity, so that alloys 113 and 212 are preferred for thin-sectioned castings such as housings, cover plates, and hydraulic brake pistons.

A series of casting alloys such as 85, 108, 319, and 380, classed as aluminum-copper-silicon alloys, have been developed containing less than 5 per cent copper, and silicon from 3 to 8 per cent. The copper provides higher strength and better machining properties than the

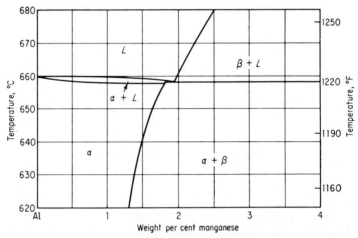

Fig. 12·16   Aluminum-rich portion of the aluminum-manganese alloy system. (*From "Metals Handbook," 1948 edition, p.* 1163, *American Society for Metals, Metals Park, Ohio*)

straight aluminum-silicon alloys, while the silicon provides better casting and pressuretightness properties than the aluminum-copper alloys. Typical applications include brackets, typewriter frames, manifolds, valve bodies, oil pans, gasoline, and oil tanks.

12·20   Aluminum-manganese alloy.   The aluminum-rich portion of the aluminum-manganese alloy system is shown in Fig. 12·16. The maximum solubility of manganese in the α solid solution is 1.82 at the eutectic temperature of 1216°F. Although the solubility decreases with decreasing temperature, alloys in this group are generally not age-hardenable. Because of the limited solubility, manganese is not used as a major alloying element in any casting alloys and is used in only a few wrought alloys. One of the alloys in this group is the popular 3003 alloy, which has good formability, very good resistance to corrosion, and good meldability. Typical applications are utensils, food and chemical handling and storage equipment, gasoline and oil tanks, pressure vessels, and piping.

12·21   Aluminum-silicon alloys.   The aluminum-rich portion of the aluminum-silicon alloy system is shown in Fig. 12·17. The maximum solubility of silicon in the α solid solution is 1.65 per cent at the eutectic temperature of 1071°F. Although the solvus line shows lower solubility at lower temperatures, these alloys are generally not heat-treatable. Wrought alloy 4032, containing 12.5 per cent silicon, has good forgeability and low coefficient of thermal expansion. It is used for forged automotive pistons.

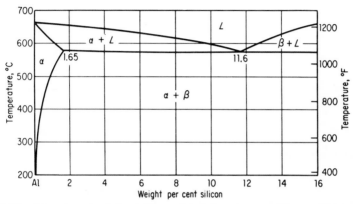

Fig. 12·17   Aluminum-rich portion of the aluminum-silicon alloy system.
(*From "Metals Handbook," 1948 edition, p. 1166, American Society for Metals, Metals Park, Ohio*)

Aluminum-silicon casting alloys have excellent castability and resistance to corrosion. Alloy 13 (12 per cent silicon) and alloy 43 (5 per cent silicon) are used for intricate castings, food-handling equipment, and marine fittings.

12·22   Aluminum-magnesium alloys.   The aluminum-rich portion of the aluminum-magnesium system is shown in Fig. 12·18. Although the solvus line shows a considerable drop in the solubility of magnesium in aluminum with decreasing temperature, most commercial wrought alloys in this group contain less than 5 per cent magnesium, and with low silicon content, they are not heat-treatable.

The wrought alloys constitute the 5000 series and are characterized by good weldability, good corrosion resistance, and moderate strength. Alloy 5005 (0.8 per cent magnesium) is used for architectural extrusions; alloy 5050 (1.2 per cent magnesium) for tubing and automotive gas and oil lines; alloy 5052 (2.5 per cent magnesium) for aircraft fuel and oil lines; alloy 5083 (4.5 per cent magnesium) for marine and welded structural applications; and alloy 5056 (5.2 per cent magnesium) for insect screens, cable sheathing, and rivets for use with magnesium alloys.

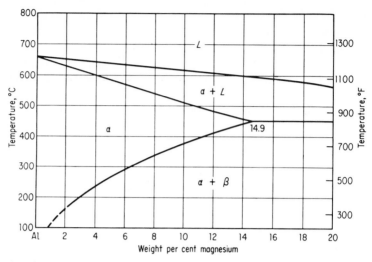

Fig. 12·18   Aluminum-rich portion of the aluminum-magnesium alloy system. (*From "Metals Handbook,"* 1948 *edition, p.* 1163, *American Society for Metals, Metals Park, Ohio*)

The aluminum-magnesium casting alloys include alloy 214 (3.8 per cent magnesium), alloy 218 (8 per cent magnesium), and alloy 220 (10 per cent magnesium).   The first two alloys are used for dairy and food handling equipment, fittings for chemical and sewage use, fittings for marine use, and aircraft brake shoes.   Alloy 220 is the only one in this group which is age-hardenable, resulting in the highest mechanical properties of any of the aluminum casting alloys.   The casting

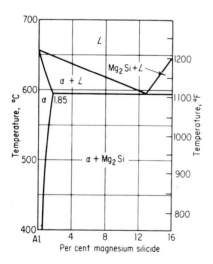

Fig. 12·19   Aluminum-rich portion of the aluminum-magnesium silicide system. (*From "Metals Handbook,"* 1948 *edition, p.* 1246, *American Society for Metals, Metals Park, Ohio*)

properties of alloys in this group are poor, and they require careful foundry practice.

12·23 Aluminum-silicon-magnesium alloys. Magnesium and silicon combine to form a compound magnesium silicide (Mg_2Si), which in turn forms a simple eutectic system with aluminum. The aluminum-rich portion of the Al-Mg_2Si system is shown in Fig. 12·19. It is precipitation of the Mg_2Si after artificial aging (temper T6) which allows these alloys to reach their full strength. The wrought alloys include 6053, 6061, and 6063. Magnesium and silicon are usually present in the ratio to form magnesium silicide. These alloys are

Fig. 12·20 Aluminum-rich portion of the aluminum-zinc alloy system. (*From "Metals Handbook," 1948 edition, p. 1167, American Society for Metals, Metals Park, Ohio*)

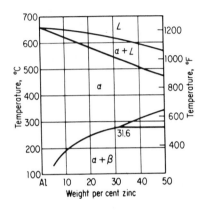

characterized by excellent corrosion resistance and are more workable than other heat-treatable alloys. Typical applications include aircraft landing mats, canoes, furniture, vacuum-cleaner tubing, bridge railings, and architectural applications.

The aluminum-silicon-magnesium casting alloys 355, 356, and 360 provide a desirable combination of castability, pressuretightness, strength, and corrosion resistance. In the heat-treated condition their mechanical properties approach those of the aluminum-copper alloys. They are widely used in aircraft applications, machine-tool parts, and general-purpose castings.

12·24 Aluminum-zinc alloys. The aluminum-rich portion of the aluminum-zinc alloy system is shown in Fig. 12·20. The solubility of zinc in aluminum is 31.6 per cent at 527°F, decreasing to 5.6 per cent at 257°F. Commercial wrought alloys contain zinc, magnesium, and copper with smaller additions of manganese and chromium. Alloy 7075 (5.5 per cent zinc, 2.5 per cent magnesium, 1.5 per cent copper), alloy 7079 (4.3 per cent zinc, 3.3 per cent magnesium, 0.6 per cent copper), and alloy 7178 (6.8 per cent zinc, 2.7 per cent magnesium, 2.0 per cent copper) develop the highest tensile strengths obtainable

in aluminum alloys.   The susceptibility of these alloys to stress corrosion has been minimized by the addition of chromium and by proper
heat treatment.   They are used in applications requiring high strength
and good corrosion resistance such as aircraft structural parts.

The aluminum-zinc casting alloy known as 40E, containing 5.5 per

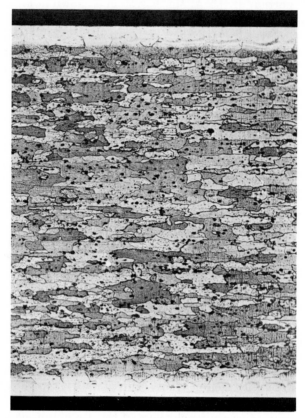

**Fig. 12·21   Full cross section of Alclad 2024-T4 sheet, 125×.   (*Research
Laboratory, Aluminum Company of America*)**

cent zinc, 0.6 per cent magnesium, 0.5 per cent chromium, and 0.2 per
cent titanium, provides high mechanical properties without solution
treatment.   This alloy also has fair casting characteristics, good corrosion resistance, and very good machinability.   It is used for aircraft
fittings, turret housings, and radio equipment.

**12·25   Corrosion resistance of aluminum and aluminum
alloys.**   The high corrosion resistance of aluminum is due to the
self-protecting, thin, invisible oxide film that forms immediately on
exposing surfaces to the atmosphere.   This film protects the metal

from further corrosion. If the oxide film is removed, in many environments, a new film will form immediately and the metal remains fully protected.

In certain strongly acid or alkaline solutions, or in contact with moist corrosive materials that prevent access of oxygen to the aluminum surface, the protective film does not form readily. Therefore, the aluminum should be adequately protected, or not used at all.

A relatively thick oxide coating on aluminum and aluminum alloys may be produced by placing the metal into an aqueous solution containing 15 to 25 per cent sulfuric acid. This process, known as *anodizing*, produces a clear, transparent coating containing submicroscopic pores that are usually sealed before use to prevent absorption and staining. Sealing may be accomplished by suitable heating in hot water.

The corrosion resistance of aluminum-copper alloys and aluminum-zinc alloys is satisfactory for most applications but is generally lower than that of the other aluminum alloys. Under certain corrosive conditions they are subject to intergranular corrosion. Therefore, these alloys in the form of sheet are usually clad with a high-purity alloy such as commercial aluminum (1100) or a magnesium-silicon alloy of the 6000 series. The coating slabs are mechanically attached to the alloy core ingot and the bonding is accomplished by hot rolling. The nominal cladding thickness per side is usually 1½ or 2½ per cent of the thickness of the base material. Figure 12·21 shows the full cross section of Alclad 2024 sheet. The clear white cladding layer is visible at the edges of the sheet. Alclad alloys are extensively used for aircraft applications because of the excellent combination of high strength and high resistance to corrosion.

The nominal chemical composition and typical mechanical properties of some wrought- and cast-aluminum alloys are given in Tables 12·6 and 12·7.

MAGNESIUM AND MAGNESIUM ALLOYS

12·26 Magnesium. The chief advantages of magnesium are its light weight, ease of machinability, and the high strength-to-weight ratio obtainable with its alloys.

On the basis of equal volumes, aluminum weighs 1½ times more, iron and steel weigh 4 times more, and copper and nickel alloys weigh 5 times more than magnesium.

Magnesium has a c.p.h. (close-packed hexagonal) crystal structure, and plastic deformation takes place at room temperature by slip along the basal planes. The ductility of magnesium is lower than that of f.c.c. metals since there are fewer slip systems available for plastic

Table 12·6 Nominal composition and typical mechanical properties of some wrought-aluminum alloys*

Alloy and temper	Nominal composition, %							Typical mechanical properties			
	Si	Cu	Mn	Mg	Cr	Zn	Ni	Tensile strength, 1,000 psi	Yield strength, 1,000 psi	Elongation, % in 2 in., ½-in.-diam specimen	BHN
EC	(99.45 + % aluminum)										
-O								12	4		
-H14								16	14		
1100	(99.0 + % aluminum)										
-O								13	5	45	23
-H14								18	17	20	105
-H18								24	22	15	44
2014	0.8	4.4	0.8	0.4							
-O	...	...	...	...	...	...	...	27	14	18	45
-T4	...	...	...	...	...	...	...	62	42	20	105
-T6	...	...	...	...	...	...	...	70	60	13	135
2017	0.8	4.0	0.5	0.5	0.1						
-O	...	...	...	...	...	...	...	26	10	22	45
-T4	...	...	...	...	...	...	...	62	40	22	105
2024	0.5	4.5	0.6	1.5	0.1						
-O	...	...	...	...	...	...	...	27	11	22	47
-T4	...	...	...	...	...	...	...	68	47	19	120
2218	0.2	4.0	...	1.5	...	...	2.0				
-T61	...	...	...	...	...	...	...	59	44	13	
3003	0.6	...	1.2								
-O	...	...	...	...	...	...	...	16	6	40	28
-H14	...	...	...	...	...	...	...	22	21	16	40
4032	12.5	0.9	...	1.0	...	...	0.9				
-T6	...	...	...	...	...	...	...	55	46	9	120
5005	0.4	...	...	0.8							
-O	...	...	...	...	...	...	...	18	6	30†	28
-H34	...	...	...	...	...	...	...	23	20	8†	41
5050	0.4	...	...	1.2							
-O	...	...	...	...	...	...	...	21	8	24†	36
-H34	...	...	...	...	...	...	...	28	24	8†	53
5052	...	...	...	2.5	0.25						
-O	...	...	...	...	...	...	...	28	13	30	47
-H34	...	...	...	...	...	...	...	38	31	14	68
5056	...	...	0.1	5.2	0.1						
-O	...	...	...	...	...	...	...	42	22	35	65
-H18	...	...	...	...	...	...	...	63	59	10	105
5083	...	...	0.7	4.5							
-O	...	...	...	...	...	...	...	42	21	22	
6061	0.6	0.25	...	1.0	0.25						
-O	...	...	...	...	...	...	...	18	8	30	30
-T6	...	...	...	...	...	...	...	45	40	17	95
6063	0.4	0.1	0.1	0.7	0.1	0.1					
-O	...	...	...	...	...	...	...	13	7	...	25
-T6	...	...	...	...	...	...	...	35	31	12†	73
7075	0.5	1.5	...	2.5	0.3	5.5					
-O	...	...	...	...	...	...	...	33	15	16	60
-T6	...	...	...	...	...	...	...	83	73	11	150
7178	0.5	2.0	...	2.7	0.3	6.8					
-O	...	...	...	...	...	...	...	33	15	16	
-T6	...	...	...	...	...	...	...	88	78	11	

* Compiled from information in "Metals Handbook," 1961 edition, American Society for Metals, Metals Park, Ohio.

† Sheet specimens 1⁄16 in. thick.

Table 12·7 Nominal composition and typical mechanical properties of some cast-aluminum alloys*

Alloy and temper†	Method of casting‡	Nominal composition, %					Typical mechanical properties			
		Si	Cu	Mg	Zn	Ni	Tensile strength, 1,000 psi	Yield strength, 1,000 psi	Elongation, % in 2 in.	BHN, 500 kg, 10 mm
13	DC	12.0	...	...	...	...	39	21	2.0	
43	SC	...	...	...	...	...	19	8	8.0	40
	PM	5.0	...	...	...	...	23	9	10.0	45
	DC	...	...	...	...	...	30	16	9.0	
85	DC	5.0	4.0	...	...	...	40	24	5.0	
108	SC	3.0	4.0	...	...	...	21	14	2.5	55
A108	PM	5.5	4.5	...	...	...	28	16	2.0	70
112	SC	...	7.0	...	1.7	...	24	15	1.5	70
113	SC	2.0	7.0	...	1.7	...	24	15	1.5	70
122-T61	SC	...	10.0	0.2	...	...	41	40	...	115
-T65	PM	...	...	...	...	...	48	36	...	140
A132-T65	PM	12.0	0.8	1.2	...	2.5	47	43	0.5	125
D132-T5	PM	9.0	3.5	0.8	...	0.8	36	28	1.0	105
195-T4	SC	0.8	4.5	...	...	...	32	16	8.5	60
-T6	SC	...	...	...	...	...	36	24	5.0	75
B195-T4	PM	2.5	4.5	...	...	...	37	19	9.0	75
B195-T6	PM	...	...	...	...	...	40	26	5.0	90
212	SC	1.2	8.0	...	...	...	23	14	2.0	65
214	SC	...	...	3.8	...	...	25	12	9.0	50
A214	PM	...	...	3.8	1.8	...	27	16	7.0	60
218	DC	...	...	8.0	...	...	45	27	8.0	
220-T4	SC	...	...	10.0	...	...	46	25	14.0	75
319-F	SC	...	...	...	...	...	27	18	2.0	70
-T6	SC	6.3	3.5	...	...	...	36	24	2.0	80
355-T6	SC	5.0	1.3	0.5	...	...	35	25	3.0	80
-T6	PM	...	...	...	...	...	43	27	4.0	90
356-T6	SC	7.0	...	0.3	...	...	33	24	3.5	70
-T6	PM	...	...	...	...	...	40	27	5.0	90
360	DC	9.5	...	...	...	...	44	27	3.0	
380	DC	9.0	3.5	...	...	...	45	26	2.0	

* Compiled from information in "Casting Alcoa Alloys," Aluminum Co. of America.
† Alcoa (Aluminum Co. of America) designation.
‡ SC = sand cast, PM = permanent-mold cast, DC = die cast.

deformation. Above 400°F, however, additional planes become active and the plasticity of magnesium and many of its alloys is improved.

Commercially pure magnesium or primary magnesium has a minimum purity of 99.8 per cent and usually contains small amounts of aluminum, iron, manganese, silicon, and copper.

Approximately half the magnesium produced is used in alloy form for structural purposes, primarily in the aircraft and missile industries. Magnesium is used as an alloying element in aluminum, zinc, lead, and other nonferrous alloys. It has found increasing use in photo-engraving because of its light weight and rapid but controlled etching characteristics.

Magnesium has a great affinity for oxygen and other chemical oxidizing agents. It is used as a deoxidizer and desulfurizer in the manufacture of nickel and copper alloys, also as a "getter" in the manufacture of vacuum tubes. Because of its high chemical activity, it finds use in the production of uranium and zirconium by thermal reduction with magnesium.

Magnesium anodes provide effective corrosion protection for water heaters, underground pipelines, ship hulls, and ballast tanks.

12·27   Alloy designation and temper. The American Society for Testing Materials (ASTM) has published a system of alloy nomenclature (Specification B275-61) and temper designation (Specification B296-61) for light metals and alloys. This system has been officially adopted by The Magnesium Association for all magnesium alloys. The temper designation is the same as that adopted by The Aluminum Association for aluminum alloys and is covered in Sec. 12·18. The designation for alloys and unalloyed metals is based on their chemical-composition limits as follows (from ASTM Designation B275-61 by permission of the American Society for Testing Materials):

Alloys

(a) Designations for alloys consist of not more than two letters representing the alloying elements (Note 1) specified in the greatest amount, arranged in order of decreasing percentages, or in alphabetical order if of equal percentages, followed by the respective percentages rounded off to whole numbers and a serial letter (Notes 2 and 3). The full name of the base metal precedes the designation, but it is omitted for brevity when the base metal being referred to is obvious.

(b) The letters used to represent alloying elements should be those listed in Table 12.8.

Table 12·8   Letters representing alloy elements

A	Aluminum	M	Manganese
B	Bismuth	N	Nickel
C	Copper	P	Lead
D	Cadmium	Q	Silver
E	Rare earths	R	Chromium
F	Iron	S	Silicon
G	Magnesium	T	Tin
H	Thorium	Y	Antimony
K	Zirconium	Z	Zinc
L	Beryllium		

(c) In rounding-off percentages, the nearest whole number shall be used. If the decimal is followed by a 5, the nearest even whole number shall be used.

(d) When a range is specified for the alloying element, the rounded-off mean should be used in the designation.

(e) When only a minimum percentage is specified for the alloying element, the rounded-off minimum percentage should be used in the designation.

NOTE 1.   For codification, an alloying element is defined as an element (other than the base metal) having a minimum content greater than zero either directly specified or computed in accordance with the percentages specified for other elements. The amount present is the mean of the range (or the minimum percentage if only that is specified) before rounding off.

NOTE 2. The serial letter is arbitrarily assigned in alphabetical sequence starting with A (omitting I and O) and serves to differentiate otherwise identical designations. A serial letter is necessary to complete each designation.

NOTE 3. The designation of a casting alloy in ingot form is derived from the composition specified for the corresponding alloy in the form of castings. Thus, a casting ingot designation may consist of an alloy designation having one or more serial letters, one for each product composition, or it may consist of one or more alloy designations.

Unalloyed Metals

Designations for unalloyed metals consist of the specified minimum purity, all digits retained but dropping the decimal point, followed by a serial number (Note 2). The full name of the base metal precedes the designation, but it is omitted for brevity when the base metal being referred to is obvious.

As an example, for magnesium alloy AZ92A, "A" represents aluminum, the alloying element specified in the greatest amount; "Z" represents zinc, the alloying element specified in the second greatest amount; "9" indicates that the rounded-off mean aluminum percentage lies between 8.6 and 9.4; "2" signifies that the rounded-off mean zinc percentage lies between 1.5 and 2.5; and "A" as the final letter indicates that this is the first alloy whose composition qualified assignment of the designation AZ92.

12·28 Magnesium alloys. Although most magnesium alloys are ternary alloys, they may be considered as based upon four binary-alloy systems. These are magnesium-aluminum, magnesium-zinc, magnesium–rare earths, and magnesium-thorium. In each case the solvus line on the magnesium-rich side shows a decrease in solubility of the alloying element in solid magnesium as the temperature decreases. This indicates that certain alloy compositions may be strengthened by age hardening.

For example, the maximum solubility of aluminum in magnesium is 12.7 per cent at 818°F, decreasing to 3.2 per cent at 400°F. Alloys containing over 6 per cent aluminum, which includes all the Mg-Al casting alloys, are therefore heat-treatable.

The solubility of zinc in solid magnesium varies from 8.4 per cent at 644°F to 1.7 per cent at 300°F. Alloys in the composition range of 4 to 8 per cent zinc show the most potent precipitation-hardening effects of any of the magnesium-based binary systems.

Magnesium-Aluminum–based Alloys. This group includes the magnesium-aluminum-manganese (AM) and the magnesium-aluminum-zinc (AZ) casting alloys.

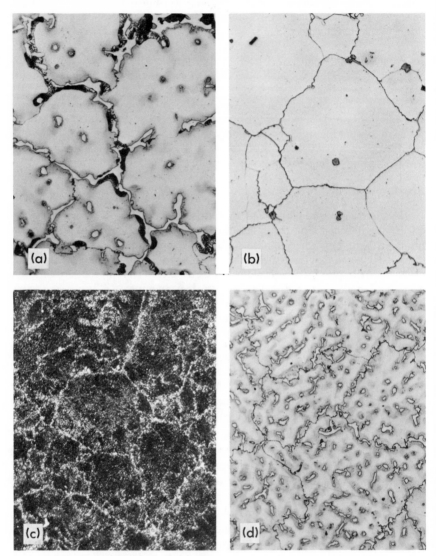

Fig. 12·22   The microstructures of magnesium alloy AZ92A, 250×.   (a) Sand-cast, etched in phosphopicral; (b) sand-cast, solution-treated, etched in glycol; (c) sand-cast, solution-treated and artificially aged, etched in acetic glycol; (d) permanent-mold cast, etched in phosphopicral.   (The Dow Metal Products Company)

The AM100A alloy is popular for pressuretight sand and permanent-mold castings with a good combination of tensile strength, yield strength, and elongation.

The sand-casting alloys AZ63A and AZ92A are used for normal-temperature applications. If the operating stresses are not too high, they may give satisfactory service at temperatures as high as 350°F. AZ63A is used where maximum toughness or ductility along with moderately high yield strength is required. AZ92A is used where maximum yield strength plus good pressuretightness is required. The microstructures of AZ92A alloy are shown in Fig. 12·22. The structure in the sand-cast condition (Fig. 12·22a) shows a network of massive $Mg_{17}Al_{12}$. The eutectic was originally composed of $Mg_{17}Al_{12}$ and α solid solution rich in magnesium. However, the eutectic has "separated"; the α phase has joined the primary α grains, leaving behind the compound as a white network. Subsequent slow cooling after solidification has allowed precipitation of the compound in fine lamellar form, primarily at the grain boundaries. The compound may be retained in solution by the relatively rapid cooling after solution treatment (Fig. 12·22b). Subsequent artificial aging causes precipitation of the compound as fine particles within the grains (Fig. 12·22c). Because of the more rapid cooling in permanent-mold casting as compared with sand casting, the structure (Fig. 12·22d) shows finer particles of the compound and no lamellar constituent. AZ91C and AZ81A are gradually replacing AZ63A for applications requiring good ductility and moderate yield strength.

AZ91A and AZ91B alloys are especially suited for die casting. The castings are pressuretight with good yield strength and ductility.

The wrought alloy M1A (containing 1.2 per cent manganese) is a low-cost, relatively low-strength magnesium alloy. It has excellent weldability, corrosion resistance, and hot formability.

The AZ31 alloys are widely used as general-purpose extrusion alloys having good strength and formability. Since they contain only 3 per cent aluminum, they are not heat-treatable and attain their properties by strain hardening. AZ31 with low calcium content, known as PE alloy, is widely used for magnesium photoengraving sheet in the printing industry.

AZ61A has excellent strength and ductility and is used mainly as an extrusion and forging alloy.

AZ80A alloy, containing 8.5 per cent aluminum, is a heat-treatable alloy used for extruded products and press forgings. It offers an excellent combination of high strength and moderate elongation.

Magnesium-Zinc–based Alloys. These are essentially magnesium-zinc-zirconium (ZK) and magnesium-zinc-thorium (ZH) casting alloys.

The effect of zirconium additions, up to about 0.7 per cent, to magnesium alloys is one of grain refinement. Zirconium completely eliminates the coarse-grained, columnar cast structure, thus increasing the mechanical properties.

The casting alloys ZK51A and ZK61A attain the highest combination of tensile yield strength and ductility of any magnesium casting alloys. This is due to the strong age-hardening effect of the magnesium-zinc binary system and the fine-grain effect of zirconium. Unfortunately, the high zinc content requires very careful foundry control to produce sound castings free of microporosity and hot cracks. The addition of thorium (ZH62A) helps to reduce these problems with little effect on mechanical properties, while the addition of a rare-earth metal (ZE41A) also reduces the above problems with some reduction in mechanical properties.

The wrought alloy ZK60A is the highest-strength extrusion alloy for solid and hollow shapes. It has good toughness and may be heat-treated to improve its properties further. The replacement of zirconium by a rare-earth metal (ZE10A) results in a cheaper and tougher alloy.

Magnesium–Rare Earth–based Alloys. This group includes the magnesium–rare earth–zirconium (EK) and magnesium–rare earth–zinc (EZ) casting alloys.

Improvement in elevated-temperature properties is obtained by a high recrystallization temperature and by precipitates at the grain boundaries that are stable at high temperature to minimize creep. The addition of rare-earth elements to magnesium satisfies both requirements, so that these alloys are suitable for use up to 500°F.

Casting alloys EK30A, EK41A, and EZ33A all have similar mechanical properties, but EZ33A shows poorer corrosion resistance because of the presence of zinc.

When the rare-earth addition contains 50 per cent cerium, it is known as *mischmetal* and is used as a low-cost commercial alloy.

The rare-earth elements are not used as the principal addition in any wrought-magnesium alloys.

Magnesium-Thorium–based Alloys. The group includes the magnesium-thorium-zirconium (HK) and magnesium-thorium-zinc (HZ) casting alloys. Thorium, like the rare-earth elements, greatly improves the elevated-temperature properties of magnesium.

Casting alloys HK31A and HZ32A are used for applications in the range of 350 to 700°F where properties better than those of the rare earth–containing alloys are needed. HK31A is particularly good for short-time elevated-temperature uses where high stresses are encountered, while HZ32A is preferred where long-time lower-stress properties are important.

HK31A is also used as a wrought sheet alloy for high-temperature applications. Other wrought alloys in this group are the extrusion alloy HM31XA and the sheet alloy HM21A, both of which are magnesium-thorium-manganese alloys. These have the best high-temperature properties of any wrought-magnesium alloy.

The nominal composition and typical mechanical properties of some cast- and wrought-magnesium alloys are given in Table 12·9.

12·29 Corrosion resistance of magnesium alloys. The resistance of magnesium alloys to atmospheric corrosion depends upon the alloying element, the amount present, indoor or outdoor exposure, and humidity. At low values of humidity (below 10 per cent), magnesium alloys show good corrosion resistance, but the resistance decreases with increasing humidity. During indoor exposure, the magnesium alloys show better corrosion resistance then those containing aluminum, but the reverse is true under outdoor exposure conditions. With aluminum content above 9 per cent and zinc content above 5 per cent, corrosion resistance is decreased. Experimental results indicate that the corrosion resistance of magnesium compares favorably with that of aluminum alloys and is superior to that of low-carbon steel in industrial atmospheres. Under marine exposure, the purity of the alloy seems to be a controlling factor in determining corrosion resistance. Controlled-purity cast alloys show a far superior corrosion resistance under marine conditions than uncontrolled-purity alloys.

The corrosion resistance of magnesium alloys in aqueous salt solutions is dependent upon the presence of impurities such as iron, copper, nickel, and cobalt.

The effect of heat treatment on the corrosion resistance of magnesium alloys in salt solutions varies with the heat-treating temperature, rate of cooling, alloying elements, and impurity content. In the magnesium-manganese alloy M1, heat treatment in the range of 500 to 900°F greatly increases the corrosion rate and the tendency to pit. However, heat treatment at about 1050°F, followed by rapid cooling, completely eliminates pitting and increases corrosion resistance.

12·30 Joining magnesium alloys. Magnesium and magnesium alloys may be joined by most of the common fusion and mechanical fastening methods. These include shielded-metal arc welding, gas welding, electric resistance seam and spot welding, riveting, bolting, self-fastening devices, and adhesive bonding. Arc welding, spot welding, and riveting are the most commonly used methods.

In all magnesium alloys, the solidification range increases and the melting point and shrinkage decrease with an increase in alloy content. Alloys containing up to 10 per cent aluminum aid weldability by refining the grain structure. Alloys containing more than 1 per cent

Table 12.9 Nominal composition and typical mechanical properties of magnesium alloys at room temperature*

Alloy and temper	Nominal composition, %						Tensile strength, 1,000 psi	Tensile yield strength, 1,000 psi	Elongation, %	BHN, 500 kg, 10 mm	Compressive yield strength, 1,000 psi
	Al	Mn	Zn	Th	Zr	Rare earths					
Sheet, annealed	99.8% Mg minimum						23–28	13–15	3–15	40–41	10–12
Sheet, hard temper							26–32	17–20	2–10	45–47	15–17
Sand and Permanent-mold Casting Alloys											
AM100-T6	10.0	0.1					40	22	1	69	19
AZ63A-T6	6.0	0.2	3.0				40	19	5	73	19
AZ81A-T4	7.5	0.15	0.7				40	12	15	55	12
AZ91C-T6	9.0	0.2	0.7				40	19	5	70	19
AZ92A-T6	9.0	0.1	2.0				40	22	3	81	22
ZK51A-T5			4.5		0.7		40	24	8	65	24
ZK61A-T5			6.0		0.7		…	27	…	68	27
ZK61A-T6			6.0		0.7		…	28	…	70	28
ZH62A-T5			5.7	1.8	0.7		39	26	4	70	
ZE41A-T5			4.25		0.5	1.25	30	20	3.5	62	20
EK30A-T6					0.6	4.0	23	16	3	45	16
EK41A-T6					0.2	3.0	25	18	3	50	18
EZ33A-T5			2.7		0.5	3.0	23	16	3	50	16
HK31A-T6				3.25	0.7		32	15	8	66	15
HZ32A-T5			2.0	3.25	0.75		27	13	4	55	16
Die-casting Alloys											
AZ91A and B-F	9.0	0.2	0.7				33	22	3	63	24
Extruded Bars and Shapes											
M1A-F		1.2					37	26	12	44	12
AZ31B-F	3.0	0.2	1.0				38	29	15	49	14
AZ61A-F	5.5	0.2	1.0				45	33	16	60	19
AZ80A-T5	8.5		0.5				55	40	7	80	35
ZK60A-T5			5.5		0.5		53	44	11	82	36
Sheet and Plate Alloys											
AZ31B-H24	3.0	0.2	1.0				42	32	15	73	26
HK31A-H24				3.25	0.7		37	29	8	…	23
HM21A-T8		0.5		2.0			34	25	10	…	15
ZE10A-H24			1.25			0.17	38	28	13	…	24

* Compiled from information in "Metals Handbook," 1961 edition, American Society for Metals, Metals Park, Ohio.

zinc have a tendency to crack when hot (*hot short*) and may result in weld cracking. Thorium alloys have no tendency toward hot shortness.

Failure of welded joints usually occurs in the heat-affected zone next to the weld rather than the weld itself. This is most likely due to some grain growth of the base metal.

Welds in some magnesium alloys, particularly the Mg-Al-Zn series, are susceptible to stress-corrosion cracking. This is due to the high residual stresses set up in the welding process. These residual stresses may be relieved by a suitable stress-relief treatment.

Adhesive bonding is a comparatively new method of joining. Since no drilling is required, there is less stress concentration and better fatigue strength in adhesive-bonded joints as compared with other types. The adhesive fills the spaces between contacting surfaces and acts as an insulator between any dissimilar metals in the joint. Adhesive bonding allows the use of thinner materials and takes better advantage of the weight saving possible with magnesium. This method of joining is particularly suited for joining stiffeners to sheet and is used in aircraft and radar applications.

Riveting is the most common method of joining magnesium, since it gives joints of good strength and efficiency, is a fairly simple method, and does not require highly skilled labor.

NICKEL AND NICKEL ALLOYS

12·31 Nickel. Nickel is characterized by good resistance to corrosion and oxidation. It is white in color and has good workability and good mechanical properties. It forms tough, ductile solid-solution alloys with many of the common metals. Approximately 60 per cent of the nickel produced is used in stainless and nickel alloy steels. Most of the remainder is used in high-nickel alloys and for electroplating. Because of its high corrosion resistance and hardness, nickel makes an ideal coating for parts subjected to corrosion and wear. Although nickel is often given a flash coating of chromium to increase wear resistance, most of the corrosion protection is due to the heavy nickel undercoat.

Cast nickel is sometimes used for corrosion-resistant castings, particularly where contamination with copper or iron must be avoided. Small amounts of silicon and manganese are added to facilitate the production of sound, ductile castings.

Wrought nickel is not adversely affected by cold working, welding, or heating. Its mechanical properties are similar to those of mild steel. It retains its strength at elevated temperatures and its ductility and toughness at low temperatures. The electrical conductivity of

Table 12·10   Nominal composition and typical mechanical properties of commercial nickels*

Material	Nominal composition (essential elements), %	Condition	Tensile strength, psi	Yield strength, 0.2% offset, 1,000 psi	Elongation, % in 2 in.	BHN
Nickel (pure)	Ni 99.99	Annealed	8.5	46	30	100
A nickel (wrought)	99.40 Ni(+Co), 0.06 C, 0.25 Mn, 0.15 Fe, 0.05 Si, 0.05 Cu, 0.005 S	Annealed	70	20	40	110
		Hot-rolled	75	25	40	170
		Cold-drawn	95	70	25	210
		Cold-rolled	105	95	5	
D nickel	95.00 Ni(+Co), 0.10 C, 4.75 Mn, 0.05 Fe, 0.05 Si, 0.02 Cu, 0.005 S	Annealed	75	35	40	140
		Hot-rolled	90	50	35	150
		Cold-drawn	100	80	25	190
Nickel (cast)	95.6 Ni, 0.5 Cu, 0.5 Fe, 0.8 Mn, 1.5 Si, 0.8 C	As cast	57	25	22	110
Duranickel	93.90 Ni(+Co), 0.15 C, 0.25 Mn, 0.15 Fe, 0.005 S, 0.55 Si, 0.05 Cu, 4.50 Al, 0.45 Ti	Annealed	100	45	40	160
		Annealed, age-hardened	170	125	25	330
		Spring temper	175	...	5	320
		Spring, age-hardened	205	...	10	370
Permanickel	98.65 Ni(+Co), 0.25 C, 0.10 Mn, 0.10 Fe, 0.005 S, 0.06 Si, 0.02 Cu, 0.45 Ti, 0.35 Mg	Annealed	105	45	45	160
		Annealed, age-hardened	175	125	25	325
		Spring temper	180	...	5	
		Spring, age-hardened	210	195	10	

* "Properties of Some Metals and Alloys," The International Nickel Co.

nickel, while not so high as that of copper or aluminum, is satisfactory for current-carrying leads and terminals in many electronic applications.

The most important commercial grades of nickel are A nickel, D nickel, E nickel, permanickel, and duranickel.

A nickel is the basic material, containing 99 per cent minimum nickel including cobalt. Cast commercial nickel contains approximately 2 per cent silicon to improve fluidity and castability. A nickel is used where strength combined with resistance to corrosion and oxidation is required. Rolled nickel is used by the chemical and soap industries for the construction of evaporators, jacketed kettles, heating coils, and other processing equipment.

D nickel and *E nickel* conform generally to the composition of A nickel, the important difference being the inclusion of about 4.5 and 2.0 per cent, respectively, of manganese replacing a like amount of nickel. The addition of manganese improves the resistance to atmospheric attack at elevated temperatures. The mechanical strength of D nickel, both at normal and at elevated temperatures, is somewhat greater than that of A nickel, and it has better resistance to attack by sulfur. D nickel is used extensively for spark-plug electrodes, ignition tubes, radio-tube grid wires, and marine-boiler refractory bolts. Since E nickel has a lower manganese content than D nickel, its mechanical properties are intermediate between A and D nickel. Typical uses are for spark-plug wires and as electrical lead-in wires for furnaces.

Duranickel is a wrought, age-hardenable, corrosion-resisting, nickel-aluminum alloy. It offers a combination of high strength (comparable to that of heat-treated steels) and the excellent corrosion resistance of nickel. Duranickel springs are used as laundry clips, jewelry parts, and optical frames. This alloy is also used for instrument parts such as diaphragms, bellows, snap-switch blades, and in the sports field for fish-hooks and parts of fishing tackle.

Permanickel is an age-hardenable, high-nickel alloy having mechanical properties and corrosion resistance similar to those of duranickel. In addition, good electrical and thermal conductivity is present. Its resistance to softening at elevated temperatures is somewhat inferior to that of duranickel, and it should be used in place of duranickel only in applications where higher electrical conductivity and better magnetic properties are essential.

The chemical composition and typical mechanical properties of the commercial grades of nickel are given in Table 12·10.

12·32 Nickel alloys. The most common alloying elements with nickel are copper, iron, chromium, silicon, molybdenum, manganese, and aluminum.

Nickel-Copper–base Alloys. Copper is completely soluble in nickel and is added to increase formability, decrease price, and still retain the corrosion resistance of nickel. *Monel* is the most important of the nickel-copper alloys, containing approximately two-thirds nickel and one-third copper. Monel has high corrosion resistance to acids, alkalies, brines, waters, food products, and the atmosphere. It has mechanical properties higher than those of the brasses and bronzes, but lower than those of alloy steels. It also has good toughness and fatigue strength and finds considerable use in elevated-temperature applications. It does not oxidize at a destructive rate below approximately 1000°F in sulfur-free atmospheres and for some applications may be used at temperatures up to 1500°F. Monel has widespread use in the chemical, pharmaceutical, marine, power, electrical, laundry, textile, and paper-equipment fields.

R Monel is a nickel-copper alloy which contains high sulfur to improve machinability. It is produced primarily for automatic screw-machine work.

K Monel contains approximately 3 per cent aluminum, which makes the alloy age-hardenable. Thus it is possible to obtain a nonmagnetic corrosion-resistant material with extra strength and hardness. Some typical applications of K Monel are marine pump shafts, springs, aircraft instruments, ball bearings, and safety tools.

H Monel and *S Monel*, containing 3 and 4 per cent silicon, respectively, are casting alloys that combine high strength, pressuretightness, nongalling, and antiseizing characteristics along with resistance to corrosive attack. Both alloys have similar mechanical properties, but H Monel, containing less silicon, has better machinability. Typical applications include valve seats, pump liners, and impellers.

Constantan (45 per cent nickel, 55 per cent copper) has the highest electrical resistivity, the lowest temperature coefficient of resistance, and the highest thermal emf against platinum of any of the copper-nickel alloys. The first two properties are important for electrical resistors while the last property is desirable for thermocouples. The copper-constantan and iron-constantan thermocouples were discussed in Chap. 1.

Nickel-Silicon-Copper–base Alloys. The best-known commercial alloy in this group is *Hastelloy D*. It contains 10 per cent silicon and 3 per cent copper. It is a casting alloy which is strong, tough, and extremely hard. It can be machined only with difficulty and is generally finished by grinding. Its most important characteristic is its excellent corrosion resistance to concentrated sulfuric acid at elevated temperatures. It is used for evaporators, reaction vessels, pipelines, and fittings in the chemical industry.

Nickel-Chromium-Iron–base Alloys. A variety of binary nickel-chromium and ternary nickel-chromium-iron alloys are used as electrical-resistance alloys. Some nominal compositions are 80Ni-20Cr (*Chromel A, Nichrome V*, and others) used as electric heating elements for household appliances and industrial furnaces; 60Ni-16Cr-24Fe (*Chromel C, Nichrome*, and others) used as electrical heating elements for toasters, percolators, waffle irons, heater pads, hair driers, and hot-water heaters, also in high-resistance rheostats for electronic equipment and as dipping baskets for acid pickling; 35Ni-20Cr-45Fe used for heavy-duty rheostats. Many of the above alloys show good resistance to oxidation, heat fatigue, and carburizing gases. They are widely used in cast and wrought form for heat-treating equipment, furnace parts, carburizing and nitriding containers, cyaniding pots, and other equipment that must withstand temperatures up to about 1800°F.

Inconel, with a nominal composition of 76Ni-16Cr-8Fe, combines the inherent corrosion resistance, strength, and toughness of nickel with the extra resistance to high-temperature oxidation of chromium. The first applications for Inconel were in food-processing equipment such as heaters, coolers, regenerators, pasteurizers, and holding tanks for pasteurizing milk. Inconel is outstanding in its ability to withstand repeated heating and cooling in the range of zero to 1600°F without becoming brittle and is used for exhaust manifolds and heaters of airplane engines. It is used extensively in the furnace and heat-treating field for nitriding containers, carburizing boxes, retorts, muffles, and thermocouple-protection tubes.

Inconel X is an age-hardenable Inconel. Hardening is secured by additions of titanium (2.25 to 2.75 per cent) and aluminum (0.4 to 1 per cent). A considerable portion of its high room-temperature strength is retained at temperatures up to 1500°F. Typical applications include parts that require high strength and low plastic-flow rate at temperatures up to 1500°F, such as gas turbine, supercharger, and jet-propulsion parts, and springs for temperatures up to 1000°F.

Nickel-Molybdenum-Iron–base Alloys. Hastelloy A (57Ni-20Mo-20Fe) and *Hastelloy B* (62Ni-28Mo-5Fe) are the two best-known alloys in this group. These alloys are austenitic and therefore do not respond to age hardening. By cold working, it is possible to obtain strength and ductility comparable to those of alloy steel. These alloys are noted for their high resistance to corrosion by hydrochloric, phosphoric, and other nonoxidizing acids. They are used in the chemical industry for equipment to handle, transport, and store acids and other corrosive materials.

Nickel-Chromium-Molybdenum-Iron–base Alloys. The remainder of the Hastelloy alloys fall into this group, the best-known one being *Hastelloy C* (54Ni-17Mo-15Cr-5Fe-4W). These alloys are characterized by their high corrosion resistance to oxidizing acids such as nitric, chromic, and sulfuric acids. They generally have good high-temperature properties and are resistant to oxidizing and reducing atmospheres up to 2000°F. They are used in the chemical industry, when dealing with strong oxidizing acids, for pump and valve parts, spray nozzles, and similar applications. *Hastelloy X* (47Ni-9Mo-22Cr-18Fe) has outstanding strength and oxidation resistance up to 2200°F. It is used for many industrial-furnace applications and for aircraft parts such as jet-engine tail pipes afterburners, turbine blades, and vanes.

Nickel-Chromium-Molybdenum-Copper–base Alloys. The alloys in this group were originally developed as materials resistant to both sulfuric and nitric acids over a wide range of concentration and exposure conditions. Two casting alloys are *Illium B* (50Ni-28Cr-8.5Mo-5.5Cu) and *Illium G* (56Ni-22.5Cr-6.5Mo-6.5Cu). They provide superior corrosion resistance in machinable high-strength casting alloys. Typical applications are thrust and rotary bearings and pump and valve parts where high hardness is required in corrosive environments. *Illium R* (68Ni-21Cr-5Mo-3Cu) is a machinable wrought alloy that provides heat and corrosion resistance. It is used for pump and valve shafting, hardware items, tubing, sheet, and wire.

The nominal chemical composition and typical mechanical properties of some nickel alloys are given in Table 12·11.

12·33   Nickel-iron alloys. The nickel-iron alloy system is shown in Fig. 12·23. Accurate phase boundaries below about 1100°F have not yet been established because of the sluggishness of structural changes at low temperatures. Nickel and iron are completely soluble in the liquid state and solidify as solid solutions. Nickel lowers progressively the γ to α transformation in iron. Alloys that contain up to 6 per cent nickel are ferritic. As the nickel content increases, the alloys have an increasing tendency to air-harden on slow cooling. Alloys with 6 to about 30 per cent nickel are martensitic after fast cooling. After slow cooling or reheating, they decompose into α plus γ phases. The amount of each phase present is dependent upon the nickel content, heat treatment, and amount of cold working. Alloys containing more than 30 per cent nickel are predominantly austenitic and nonmagnetic. Alloys of iron and nickel, containing 20 to 90 per cent nickel, have wide application because of their useful thermal expansion and magnetic and thermoelastic properties.

As the nickel content is increased above 25 per cent, thermal expansion falls off sharply, becoming almost invariable, for ordinary ranges in temperature, at 36 per cent nickel. Further additions of

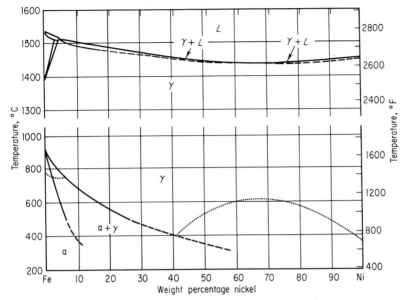

Fig. 12·23   The iron-nickel alloy system. (*From "Metals Handbook,"* **1948** *edition, p.* **1211,** *American Society for Metals, Metals Park, Ohio*)

nickel result in an increase in thermal expansion.   Figure 12·24 shows the effect of nickel on the coefficient of linear thermal expansion of iron-nickel alloys at room temperature.   The 35 per cent nickel alloy is known as *Invar*, meaning invariable, and is used where very little change in size with change in temperature is desirable.   Typical applications include length standards, measuring tapes, instrument parts, variable condensers, tuning forks, and special springs.

In the range of 30 to 60 per cent nickel, it is possible to select alloys of appropriate expansion characteristics to fit particular applications. Alloys containing 68 per cent iron, 27 per cent nickel, and 5 per cent molybdenum, or 53 per cent iron, 42 per cent nickel, and 5 per cent molybdenum have high coefficients of thermal expansion.   They are used in combination with a low-expansion alloy to produce movement. Applications include thermostatic bimetals, thermoswitches, and other temperature-regulating devices.

Fig. 12·24   Effect of nickel on the coefficient of linear thermal expansion of iron-nickel alloys at room temperature. (*After Guillaume from "Metals Handbook,"* **1961** *edition, American Society for Metals, Metals Park, Ohio*)

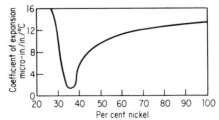

Table 12·11 Nominal composition and typical mechanical properties of some nickel alloys[a]

Material	Nominal composition (essential elements), %	Condition	Tensile strength, 1,000 psi	Yield strength, 0.2% offset, 1,000 psi	Elongation, % in 2 in.	BHN
Monel (wrought)	66.15 Ni(+Co), 31.30 Cu, 1.35 Fe, 0.90 Mn	Annealed	75	35	40	125
		Hot-rolled	90	50	35	150
		Cold-drawn	100	80	25	190
		Cold-rolled	110	100	5	240
Monel (cast)	64.0 Ni(+Co), 31.5 Cu, 1.5 Si	As cast	75	35	35	140
K Monel	65.25 Ni(+Co), 29.60 Cu, 2.75 Al, 0.45 Ti	Annealed	100	45	40	155
		Annealed[a]	155	100	25	270
		Spring temper	150	140	5	300
		Spring temper[a]	185	160	10	335
H Monel	63.0 Ni(+Co), 30.5 Cu, 3.2 Si	As cast	115	70[b]	10	265
Inconel (wrought)	77.0 Ni(+Co), 15.0 Cr, 7.0 Fe	Annealed	85	35	45	150
		Hot-rolled	100	60	35	180
		Cold-rolled[c]	135	110	5	260
Inconel X	72.85 Ni(+Co), 15.15 Cr, 6.80 Fe, 2.50 Ti, 0.75 Al	Annealed	115	50	50	150
		Annealed[a]	175	115	25	300

[a] "Properties of Some Metals and Alloys," The International Nickel Co.; "Metals Handbook," 1961 edition, American Society for Metals, Metals Park, Ohio.

[b] 0.5 per cent extension.

[c] Hard temper.

[d] Age-hardened.

Table 12·11 (Continued)

Material	Nominal composition (essential elements), %	Condition	Tensile strength, 1,000 psi	Yield strength, 0.2% offset, 1,000 psi	Elongation, % in 2 in.	BHN
Hastelloy alloy A	Bal. Ni, 22 Mo, 22 Fe, Mn, Si	As cast	73	44	10	180
		Rolled[e]	115	50	44	210
Hastelloy alloy B	Bal. Ni, 28 Mo, 5 Fe, Mn, Si	Sand-cast[e]	80	50	9	199
		Rolled[e]	120	56	50	215
Hastelloy alloy C	Bal. Ni, 16 Mo, 16 Cr, 5 Fe, 4 W, Mn, Si	Sand-cast[e]	78	50	5	199
		Rolled[e]	130	71	45	204
Hastelloy alloy D	Bal. Ni, 10 Si, 3 Cu, Mn	Sand-cast[e]	118	118	0–2[f]	321
Hastelloy alloy X	47 Ni, 9 Mo, 22 Cr, 8 Fe, C, W	Wrought sheet	114	52	43	90[f]
		Sand-cast	65	42	11[f]	89[g]
Illium B	50 Ni, 28 Cr, 8.5 Mo, 5.5 Cu	Grade B1 (2.5–4.5% Si)[h]	61–67	50–62[i]	1.0–4.5	200–240
		Grade B4 (6.1–6.3% Si)[h]	45–51	45–51[i]	0.5 max	325–360
Illium G	56 Ni, 22.5 Cr, 6.5 Mo, 6.5 Cu	Cast	68	50	32	200
Illium R	68 Ni, 21 Cr, 5 Mo, 3 Cu	Solution-treated	112.8	50.2	45.7	162
		20% cold-worked	142.3	128.1	11.5	238

e Annealed.
f In 1 in.
g Rockwell B.
h Grade defined by silicon content.
i Elastic limit.

Alloys containing approximately 28 per cent nickel, 18 per cent cobalt, and 54 per cent iron have coefficients of expansion closely matching those of standard types of glass. They are used for matched glass-to-metal seals under the trade names of *Kovar* and *Fernico*. A 46 per cent nickel alloy, called *Platinite*, has the same coefficient of expansion as platinum. A 42 per cent nickel alloy covered with an oxidized copper plating is known as *Dumet wire* and is used to replace platinum as the "seal-in" wire in vacuum tubes.

An alloy containing 36 per cent nickel and 12 per cent chromium known as *Elinvar* has a zero thermoelastic coefficient; that is, the modulus of elasticity is almost invariable over a considerable range in temperature. It is used for hair springs and balance wheels in watches and for similar parts in precision instruments.

Permalloys include several nickel-iron alloys in the range of 78 per cent nickel that have high magnetic permeability under the influence of very weak magnetizing forces. They also have low hysteresis losses and low electrical resistivity. Permalloy parts are used as loading coils in electrical communication circuits.

The aluminum-nickel-cobalt-iron alloys, commonly called *Alnico*, containing 8 to 12 per cent aluminum, 14 to 28 per cent nickel, 5 to 35 per cent cobalt, have outstanding magnetic properties. These are widely used as permanent magnets in motors, generators, radio speakers, telephone receivers, microphones, and galvanometers.

By variation in the percentage of nickel and proper additions of cobalt, chromium, copper, and molybdenum, different combinations of magnetic properties can be secured.

LEAD AND LEAD ALLOYS

12·34 Lead. The major properties of lead include heavy weight, high density, softness, malleability, low melting point, and low strength. It has lubricating properties, low electrical conductivity, high coefficient of expansion, and high corrosion resistance.

By far the largest tonnage of lead is used in the manufacture of storage batteries, followed by the use of tetraethyl lead as the anti-knock ingredient in high-test gasoline. Lead compounds are used in the manufacture of many high-grade paints.

The high weight of lead makes it suitable for use as weights and counterbalances, its high density for shielding against β rays and γ rays, its softness for gaskets and for calked joints in cast-iron pipe, and its flexibility for cable sheathing. As a coating on wire, lead acts as a drawing lubricant. Advantage is taken of the high corrosion resistance of lead by its use for equipment in the chemical industry, as a roofing material, and in the plumbing industry as pipe for transporting water and chemicals. Lead is used to improve the machinability of bronzes, brasses, and free-machining steels.

12·35 Lead alloys. Antimony and tin are the most common alloying elements of lead. The antimony-lead phase diagram is shown in Fig. 6·24. This is a simple eutectic system with the eutectic composition at 11.2 per cent antimony. Antimony is generally added to lead to raise the recrystallization temperature and to increase hardness and strength as shown by the values in Table 12·12. Lead-antimony

Table 12·12   Properties of cast lead-antimony alloys*

Antimony, %	Tensile strength, psi	BHN
0	2,500	4.0
1	3,400	7.0
2	4,200	8.0
3	4,700	9.1
4	5,660	10.0
5	6,360	11.0
6	6,840	11.8
7	7,180	12.5
8	7,420	13.3
9	7,580	14.0
10	7,670	14.6
11	7,620	14.8
12	7,480	15.0
13	7,380	15.2
14	7,000	15.3

* From "Lead in Modern Industry," Lead Industries Association, New York, 1952.

alloys contain from 1 to 12 per cent antimony and are used for storage-battery plates, cable sheathing, collapsible tubes, and for building construction.

The lead-tin alloy system is shown in Fig. 6·25. Like the lead-antimony diagram, it is also a simple eutectic system with the eutectic point located at 61.9 per cent tin and 361°F. Although lead-tin alloys are most commonly used for their melting characteristics, as in solder, tin also increases hardness and strength, as shown by the values in Table 12·13. The most widely used solders are those containing about 40 per cent tin and 60 per cent lead or 50 per cent each, with or without small percentages of antimony. *Terne metal*, a lead-tin alloy containing from 10 to 25 per cent tin, is used to coat steel sheets for roofing and automotive fuel-tank applications.

Lead alloys containing bismuth, tin, and cadmium form a low-melting-point eutectic. These alloys are useful in electric fuses, sprinkler systems, and boiler plugs.

Lead-tin-antimony alloys are widely used in the printing industry as type metals. The lead base provides low cost, low melting point, and ease in casting; additions of antimony provide hardness and wear resistance and also lower the casting temperature; additions of tin increase fluidity, reduce brittleness, and impart a finer structure.

Table 12·13   Properties of lead-tin alloys*

Tin, %	Tensile strength, psi	BHN
5	3,200	8.0
10	4,100	11.5
15	4,900	12.0
20	5,400	11.7
30	6,200	12.4
40	6,600	13.0
50	7,000	14.3
60	7,200	10.7

* From "Lead in Modern Industry," Lead Industries Association, New York, 1952.

Electrotype metal, being used only as a backing material for the electroformed copper shell and not required to resist wear, contains the lowest percentages of tin and antimony. Foundry type metal, on the other hand, is used exclusively to cast type for hand composition. Since the cast type is used over and over again, it requires the hardest, most wear-resistant alloy that is practical to use. Foundry type metal contains the largest amounts of tin and antimony, and generally includes up to 2 per cent copper as an additional hardener. Linotype and Intertype casting machines die-cast an entire line of type characters at each casting. It is important that the alloy used should have a low melting point and a short temperature range during solidification. Therefore, the ternary eutectic alloy or compositions near this are preferred. Figure 12·25 shows the microstructure of linotype metal containing 12 per cent antimony, 4 per cent tin, and 84 per cent lead. This alloy has a liquidus temperature of 463°F and a solidus temperature of 462°F, and the structure is almost entirely a ternary eutectic mixture.

Lead-base bearing alloys are known commercially as *babbitts* or *white metal* alloys. One group includes the alloys of lead-tin-antimony and usually arsenic while the other group includes alloys of lead and tin with small percentages of calcium, barium, magnesium, and sodium.

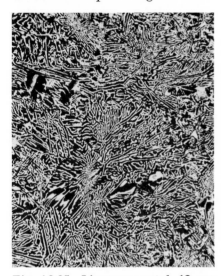
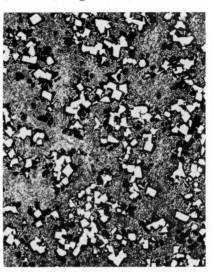

Fig. 12·25 Linotype metal, 12 per cent antimony, 4 per cent tin, 84 per cent lead. Almost entirely a ternary eutectic structure, 300×. (*American Smelting and Refining Company*)

Fig. 12·26 Lead-base bearing alloy, 15 per cent antimony, 5 per cent tin, 80 per cent lead. Cubes of primary antimony-tin compound (white) in a binary eutectic mixture of lead and tin solid solutions, 75×. (*American Smelting and Refining Company*)

Figure 12·26 shows the microstructure of a lead-base bearing alloy. It consists of cubes of primary antimony-tin compound in a binary eutectic mixture of lead and tin solid solutions. These alloys are used for automotive connecting rods, main and camshaft bearings, diesel-engine bearings, railroad-car journal bearings, and many electric-motor bearings.

The nominal composition and typical mechanical properties of some lead alloys are given in Table 12·14.

TIN AND TIN ALLOYS

12·36 Tin. Tin is a white, soft metal that has good corrosion resistance and good lubricating properties. It undergoes a polymorphic

Table 12·14   Nominal composition and typical

Alloys	Nominal composition, %				Condition
	Pb	Sb	Sn	Others	
Chemical lead	99.9+	...	...	...	Rolled sheet
Corroding lead	99.73+	...	...	...	Sand-cast Chill-cast
Arsenical lead	Bal.	...	0.10	0.15 As, 0.10 Bi	Extruded sheath
Calcium lead	Bal.	...	...	0.028 Ca	Extruded and aged
Soft solders	97.5	...	1	1.5 Ag	...
	95	...	5	...	...
	80	...	20	...	...
	50	...	50	...	...
Antimonial lead	99	1	...	...	Extruded and aged
	91	9	...	...	Chill-cast
Hard lead	96	4	...	...	Cold-rolled 95%
	94	6	...	...	Cold-rolled 95%
Type metal	95	2.5	2.5	...	...
	80	14	6	...	...
	86	11	3	...	Cast
	78	15	7	...	...
	61	25	12	2 Cu	...
Lead-base babbitt:					
SAE 13	85	10	5	...	...
SAE 14	75	15	10	...	Chill-cast
SAE 15	83	15	1	1 As	...
G	83.5	12.75	0.75	3 As	...

* "Metals Handbook," 1961 edition, American Society for Metals, Metals Park, Ohio.

transformation from the normal tetragonal structure (white tin) to a cubic form (gray tin) at a temperature of 55.8°F. This transformation is accompanied by a change in density from 7.30 to 5.75, and the resulting expansion causes disintegration of the metal to coarse powder known as *tin pest*. However, the transformation is very sluggish, and considerable undercooling is necessary to initiate it. Common impurities in tin tend to delay or inhibit the change so that, under ordinary conditions, the transformation is of no practical importance.

Over half the primary tin used in this country goes into the coating of other metals, primarily steel in the manufacture of tin cans. Tin-coated copper tubing is useful for handling fresh waters that contain large percentages of carbon dioxide and oxygen. The use of tin as an alloying element in copper, aluminum, and lead has been discussed in preceding sections.

12·37   Tin alloys. Lead is alloyed with tin to produce several soft solders that have higher strength than the lead-base solders. Tin solders containing 5 per cent antimony or 5 per cent silver are preferred

mechanical properties of some lead alloys*

Tensile strength, psi	Yield strength, psi	Elongation, %	BHN	Typical uses
2,385	1,180	29	. . .	Material of construction in the chemical industry
1,800	800	30	3.2–4.5	Storage batteries, cable sheathing,
2,000	. . .	47	4.2	paint, calking, antiknock fluid, liquid metal for heat treating
2,500	. . .	40	4.9	Cable sheathing
4,500	. . .	25	. . .	Cable sheath and creep-resistant pipe
. . .	. . .	. . .	13	
3,400	1,500	50	8	⎫
5,800	3,650	16	11.3	⎬ Coating and joining metals, body solder
6,100	4,800	60	14.5	⎭
3,000	. . .	50	7	Cable sheathing
7,500	. . .	17	15.4	Storage-battery grids
4,020	. . .	48.3	. . .	Rolled sheet and extruded pipe
4,100	. . .	47		
. . .	. . .	. . .	12.4	Electrotype
. . .	. . .	. . .	23	Stereotype
. . .	. . .	. . .	19	Linotype
. . .	. . .	. . .	24	Monotype
. . .	. . .	. . .	. . .	Foundry type
10,000	. . .	5	19	Light loads; car journal bearings
10,500	. . .	4	22	Moderate loads: blowers, pumps
10,350	. . .	2	20	High loads; diesel-engine bearings
9,800	. . .	1.5	22	Elevated-temperature bearing; trucks

for electrical equipment because these solders have higher electrical conductivity than the high-lead alloys.

The most common alloying elements for tin are antimony and copper to produce pewter and the tin-base babbitts that are used for high-grade bearing applications. Figure 12·27 shows a typical microstructure of tin-base babbitt. There are CuSn rods arranged in a

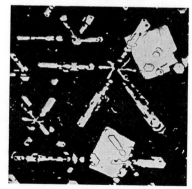

Fig. 12·27 Tin-base hard babbitt of 84 per cent tin, 7 per cent copper, and 9 per cent antimony, 50×. Star-shaped CuSn compound and rectangular crystals of SnSb compound in a ductile ternary eutectic matrix. (*By permission from R. M. Brick and A. Phillips, "Structure and Properties of Alloys," 2d ed., McGraw-Hill Book Company, Inc., New York, 1949*)

Table 12·15   Nominal composition and typical

Alloy	Nominal composition, %					Condition
	Sn	Sb	Cu	Pb	Ag	
Tin (pure)	99.8 min	...	...	...	...	Cast
Hard tin	99.6	...	0.4	...	...	80% reduction
Antimonial tin solder	95	5	...	...	...	Cast
Tin-silver solder	95	...	...	...	5	Sheet
Soft solder	70	...	...	30	...	Cast
	63	...	...	37	...	Cast
Tin babbitt	91	4.5	4.5	...	...	Chill-cast
	89	7.5	3.5	...	...	Chill-cast
	84	8	8	...	...	Die-cast
	65	15	2	18	...	Die-cast
White metal	92	8	...	...	...	Chill-cast
Pewter	91	7	2	...	...	Annealed sheet

* "Metals Handbook," 1961 edition, American Society for Metals, Metals Park, Ohio.
† In 4 in.
‡ Compressive yield (0.125 per cent offset).

star-shaped pattern and large cubes of SnSb compound, all in a ductile tin-rich ternary eutectic. The SnSb cubes are extremely hard and contribute to the excellent wear resistance of babbitt.

The nominal composition and typical mechanical properties of some tin alloys are given in Table 12·15.

ZINC AND ZINC ALLOYS

12·38   The principal use of zinc is as a coating for steel to prevent corrosion. It is more highly anodic than steel, and in a corrosive atmosphere, the zinc coating acts as the sacrificial anode. Thus the zinc is consumed while protecting the steel from any attack. Metallic zinc coatings may be applied by various methods such as hot-dip galvanizing, electrogalvanizing, painting, metallizing or spraying of molten metal, and by sherardizing or cementation. Steel products that are galvanized include bolts, chains, fencing, hardware, pipe and tubing, screws, sheets, tanks, wire, and wire cloth.

In *sherardizing*, parts to be coated are tightly packed with zinc dust in an airtight container, which is then revolved and heated to a temperature slightly below the melting point of zinc. In the presence of heat, the zinc impregnates the surface and diffuses into the steel, providing a thin uniform coating.

Zinc oxide is used in the manufacture of dental cement, enamels, floor tiling, glass, glazes, matches, paint, pottery, rubber goods, tires, and tubes.

mechanical properties of some tin alloys*

Tensile strength, psi	Yield strength, psi	Elongation, % in 2 in.	BHN	Typical uses
3,100	. . .	55†	5.3	Electrotinning, alloying
4,000	. . .	. . .	. . .	Collapsible tubes and foil
5,900	. . .	38†	. . .	Solder for electrical equipment
4,600	3,600	49	. . .	Solder for electrical equipment
6,800	. . .	. . .	12	For joining and coating of metals
7,500	. . .	32†	14	
9,300	4,400‡	2	17	Automotive applications, better
11,200	6,100‡	. . .	24	corrosion and wear resistance than
10,000	. . .	1	30	lead-base bearing alloys
7,800	. . .	1.5	23	
7,200	. . .	. . .	20	Castings for costume jewelry
8,600	. . .	40	9.5	Vases, candlesticks, book ends

Zinc can be easily worked into various shapes and forms by common fabricating methods. Pure zinc has a recrystallization temperature below room temperature, so that it "self-anneals" and cannot be work-hardened at room temperature. The presence of natural impurities or added elements raises the recrystallization temperature. Therefore, the less pure grades of wrought zinc will show an increase in hardness and strength with working.

For deep-drawing purposes a relatively pure zinc should be used. Typical applications include drawn and extruded battery cans, eyelets, grommets, laundry tags, and address plates. The addition of lead and cadmium results in higher hardness, stiffness, and uniform etching quality. It is used for weatherstrips, soldered battery cans, and photoengraver's plate. For added stiffness, good creep resistance, and easy work hardening, alloys containing from 0.85 to 1.25 per cent copper are recommended. A wrought-zinc alloy containing from 0.50 to 1.50 per cent copper and 0.12 to 1.50 per cent titanium has outstanding creep resistance and is used for corrugated roofing, leaders, and gutters.

The 4 per cent aluminum, 0.04 per cent magnesium, and up to 3.5 per cent copper alloy has been used in the form of heavy rolled plate in the aircraft industry and for dies in the blanking of aluminum-alloy sheet and thin steel.

The major use of zinc as a structural material is in the form of alloys for die castings. The zinc die-casting alloys are low in cost, easy to cast, and have greater strength than all die-casting metals except the copper alloys. They can be cast to close dimensional limits,

Table 12·16   Typical mechanical properties of some zinc alloys*

Material compositions, approx. %	Treatment	Tensile strength, psi	Elongation, % in 2 in.	BHN, 10-mm ball
Wrought Alloys				
Commercial rolled zinc	Hot-rolled†	19,500	65	38
(deep drawing),	Hot-rolled‡	23,000	50	38
0.08 max Pb,	Cold-rolled†	21,000	40	
bal. Zn	Cold-rolled‡	27,000	40	
Commercial rolled zinc,	Hot-rolled†	21,000	52	43
0.05–0.10 Pb,	Hot-rolled‡	25,000	30	43
0.05–0.08 Cd,	Cold-rolled†	22,000	40	
bal. Zn	Cold-rolled‡	29,000	30	
Commercial rolled zinc,	Hot-rolled†	23,000	50	47
0.25–0.50 Pb,	Hot-rolled‡	29,000	32	47
0.25–0.45 Cd,	Cold-rolled†	25,000	45	
bal. Zn	Cold-rolled‡	31,000	28	
Copper-hardened rolled	Hot-rolled†	24,000	20	52
zinc alloy,	Hot-rolled‡	32,000	15	60
0.85–1.25 Cu,	Cold-rolled†	32,000	5	
bal. Zn	Cold-rolled‡	40,000	3	
Rolled zinc alloy,	Hot-rolled†	28,000	20	61
0.85–1.25 Cu,	Hot-rolled‡	36,000	10	80
0.006–0.016 Mg,	Cold-rolled†	37,000	20	
bal. Zn	Cold-rolled‡	48,000	2	
Casting Alloys				
Zamak-3, SAE 903, ASTM AG40A (XX111), 3.5–4.3 Al, 0.03–0.08 Mg, 0–0.15 max Cu, bal. Zn (99.99%)	Die-cast	41,000	10	82
Zamak-5, SAE 925, ASTM AG41A (XXV), 3.5–4.3 Al, 0.03–0.08 Mg, 0.75–1.25 Cu, bal. Zn (99.99%)	Die-cast	47,600	7	91
Zamak-2, SAE 921, ASTM (XX1), 3.5–4.5 Al, 0.02–0.10 Mg, 2.5–3.5 Cu, bal. Zn (99.99%)	Sand-cast	20,000– 30,000	. . .	70–100
Zamak-5 (same as above)	Sand-cast	20,000– 30,000	. . .	70–100

* American Zinc Institute, New York.
† Longitudinal direction.
‡ Transverse direction.

are machined at minimum cost, and their resistance to surface corrosion is adequate for a wide range of applications. They are usually limited to service temperatures below 200°F since above this temperature their tensile strength is reduced 30 per cent and their hardness 40 per cent.

The two die-casting alloys in general use are known as *Zamak*-3 (ASTM AG40A, SAE 903) and *Zamak*-5 (ASTM AG41A, SAE 925). They both contain about 4 per cent aluminum and 0.04 per cent magnesium. Zamak-3 has slightly higher ductility and retains its impact strength better at slightly elevated temperature. Zamak-5, containing about 1 per cent copper, is somewhat harder and stronger and has slightly better castability. They are used for automotive parts, household utensils, building hardware, padlocks, toys, and novelties. The maximum composition limit of certain impurities such as lead (0.007 per cent), cadmium (0.005 per cent), and tin (0.005 per cent) must be strictly observed to minimize intergranular corrosion.

The composition and typical mechanical properties of some zinc alloys are given in Table 12·16.

PRECIOUS METALS

The precious-metals group includes silver, gold, and the six platinum metals platinum, palladium, iridium, rhodium, ruthenium, and osmium. This group is characterized by softness, good electrical conductivity, and very high corrosion resistance to common acids and chemicals.

12·39 Silver and silver alloys. The photosensitivity of silver and certain silver salts, coupled with their ease of reduction, forms the basis for photography. Silver-clad copper, brass, nickel, and iron are used for electrical conductors, contacts, and chemical equipment. A recent development is the use of silver coatings on glass, ceramics, and mica to provide a conducting base for subsequent electroplating of electronic devices. The high reflectivity and ease of electroplating make silver useful in reflectors, silverware, and jewelry.

Silver-Copper Alloys. The silver-copper alloy system is shown in Fig. 12·28. It is a simple eutectic-type system with the eutectic point located at 28.1 per cent copper and 1435°F. The maximum solubility of copper in silver is 8.8 per cent, and the slope of the solvus line indicates the possibility of age-hardening certain alloy compositions. *Sterling silver* (7.5 per cent copper) and *coin silver* (10 per cent copper) are age-hardenable alloys, but little commercial use is made of this heat treatment because of the close temperature control required. The 28 per cent copper eutectic alloy finds some use as a brazing solder. Coin silver is used for United States silver coins and for electrical contacts.

Silver-Copper-Zinc. Silver alloys in this group are known as *silver solders* or *silver brazing alloys.* In addition to silver, copper, and zinc, they often contain cadmium and tin. In brazing, the physical mechanism of bonding is similar to that of soft soldering, except that it takes place at a higher temperature. There is no melting of the material being joined, and the bond is achieved by interfacial penetration of

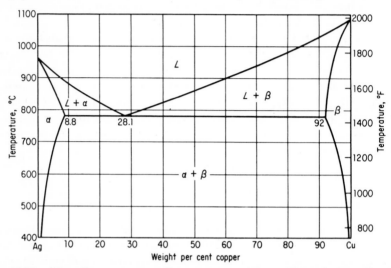

Fig. 12·28   The silver-copper alloy system. (*From "Metals Handbook,"* **1948** *edition, p.* **1148,** *American Society for Metals, Metals Park, Ohio*)

the brazing alloy. The important property of these alloys is the temperature at which they melt and flow freely into a joint. By suitable variation of composition, it is possible to obtain brazing alloys that melt anywhere from 1100 to 1550°F. Silver brazing alloys are used for many applications in the joining of ferrous and nonferrous materials.

12·40   Gold and gold alloys. Aside from the use of gold alloys for coinage, jewelry, and dental products, they have many industrial applications. The very high corrosion resistance, nontarnishing characteristics, good electrical conductivity, and ease of electroplating make gold coating suitable for electrical applications. Electroplated gold is used in wave guides, on grid wires, on contacts, on vibrating components, and as a thin film on glass for selective light filters. Other industrial applications of high-purity gold include thermal-limit fuses to protect electrical furnaces, as a target in X-ray apparatus, as a freezing-point standard, for the lining of chemical equipment, and as a high-melting solder for vacuumtight pressure welds.

A 70 per cent gold–30 per cent platinum alloy, with a solidus temperature of 2242°F, is used as a high-melting-point platinum solder.

Gold-palladium-iron alloys develop very high resistivity after proper heat treatment and are used primarily for potentiometer wire. The alloy having the highest resistivity contains 49.5 per cent gold, 40.5 per cent palladium, and 10 per cent iron.

12·41 Platinum and platinum alloys. Platinum is the most important and most abundant metal in the platinum group. The important properties of platinum are high corrosion resistance, high melting point, white color, and ductility. It forms extensive ductile solid solutions with other metals. In the unalloyed form, platinum is used for thermocouple and resistance-thermometer elements, electrical contacts, crucibles and laboratory ware, dental foil, electrodes, heat- and corrosion-resistant equipment, and for jewelry. It is also used as a catalyst in the production of sulfuric acid, vitamins, and high-octane gasolines.

Most of the important binary platinum alloy systems show complete solid solubility, so that the increase in hardness and strength obtained by alloying is due to solid-solution hardening. The hardening effect of alloying additions upon platinum is shown in Fig. 12·29. Of the metals shown, nickel produces the greatest hardening effect and palladium the least. In general, the effect of alloying additions on tensile strength parallels the effect on hardness.

Platinum-Rhodium Alloys. These contain between 3.5 and 40 per cent rhodium. Rhodium is the preferred alloying element to platinum for most applications at high temperatures under oxidizing conditions. The 10 per cent rhodium alloy is the most popular one in this group. It is the standard catalyst for the oxidation of ammonia in the manufacture of nitric acid. This alloy shows excellent resistance to molten glass and is used for nozzles in glassworking equipment. The 10 per cent rhodium–90 per cent platinum alloy, with its composition carefully controlled, serves as the positive side of the widely used rhodium-platinum vs. platinum thermocouple. The 3.5 per cent rhodium alloy is used for crucibles as an alternative to pure platinum. Platinum-rhodium alloys containing between 10 and 40 per cent are used as windings in furnaces operating between 2800 and 3275°F.

Platinum-Iridium Alloys. Platinum alloyed with 0.4 to 0.6 per cent iridium is employed for crucibles and other laboratory ware. The rich color, high mechanical properties, and excellent corrosion and tarnish resistance of the 5 to 15 per cent iridium alloys make them the preferred metal for jewelry. Electrical contacts for dependable service in magnetos, relays, and thermostats generally contain between

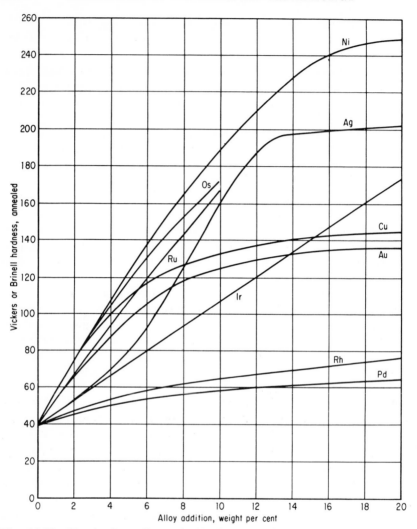

Fig. 12·29 Hardening effect of alloying additions on platinum. (*The International Nickel Co.*)

10 and 25 per cent iridium.   The 25 or 30 per cent iridium alloys are used for hypodermic needles and as electrodes for aircraft spark plugs.

Platinum-Ruthenium Alloys.   The alloys in this group have properties and applications similar to those of the platinum-iridium group. Ruthenium is harder to work than iridium, the practical limit of workability being about 15 per cent ruthenium.   The 5 per cent ruthenium alloy is used in jewelry and in medium-duty electrical contacts.   The 10 per cent alloy is used for contacts in aircraft magnetos and the 14 per cent alloy in heavy-duty contacts. Platinum-ruthenium alloys are also employed for aircraft spark-plug electrodes, hypodermic needles, and pen nibs.

Platinum-Nickel Alloys. This group of alloys, containing up to 20 per cent nickel, has good strength at elevated temperature. The 5 per cent nickel alloy is used for long-life oxide-coated cathode wires in electron tubes.

Platinum-Tungsten Alloys. The most popular alloys in this group contain 4 and 8 per cent tungsten. Typical applications include aircraft spark-plug electrodes, electrical contacts, for grids in power tubes for radar, potentiometer wire, strain gauges, and for hard corrosion-resisting instrument bearings.

A platinum 23 per cent cobalt alloy has unusual magnetic properties and is used as a permanent magnet in small instruments where a very short magnet is essential.

12·42 Palladium and palladium alloys. Palladium resembles platinum in many respects and is second to it in importance. The principal advantage of palladium as compared with platinum is its lower cost. The major application of palladium is in telephone relay contacts. It is also used as a catalyst to remove oxygen from heat-treating atmospheres and as a filter for purification of hydrogen gas. Palladium leaf is used for decorative effects in bookbinding, glass signs, and trim.

Like platinum, palladium forms complete solid solutions with almost all alloying elements. The hardening effect of alloying additions on palladium is shown in Fig. 12·30. Of the metals shown, ruthenium and nickel are very effective hardeners while platinum is least effective.

Palladium-Silver Alloys. Alloys containing 1, 3, 10, 40, 50, and 60 per cent palladium are widely used for electrical contacts. The 60 per cent palladium alloy is employed for electrical contacts operating at reasonably high currents and for precision resistance wires. The lower-palladium-content alloys are used for contacts in low-voltage relays and regulators. Palladium-silver alloys are used for brazing stainless steel and other heat-resistant alloys.

Palladium-silver alloys that have additions of copper, gold, zinc, and platinum are age-hardenable and yield high mechanical properties after heat treatment.

12·43 Iridium. Iridium is the most corrosion-resistant element known. Pure iridium has been used for crucibles in studying slag reactions at very high temperatures, and as extrusion dies for very high melting glasses.

The main use of iridium is as a hardening addition to platinum. Small amounts of iridium, up to about 0.1 per cent, are used for refining the grain size and improving the mechanical properties of gold- and silver-base casting alloys.

12·44 Osmium. Osmium has a high melting point and cannot be worked even at very high temperatures. Osmium and its alloys have high hardness, high wear resistance, and good corrosion resistance.

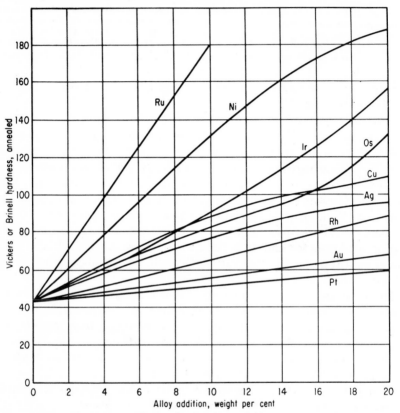

Fig. 12·30 Hardening effect of alloying additions on palladium. (*The International Nickel Co.*)

Typical applications include fountain-pen nibs, phonograph needles, electrical contacts, and instrument pivots.

12·45 Rhodium. Rhodium is similar to platinum in color and has considerably higher reflectivity. It has exceptionally high corrosion resistance, almost equal to that of iridium. Rhodium provides a nontarnishing electroplate with high reflectivity. It is used as a finishing plate in the jewelry field and for reflectors for motion-picture projectors and aircraft searchlights. A thin rhodium plate is sometimes used on the surfaces of sliding electrical contacts The main use of rhodium is as an alloying addition to platinum and palladium.

12·46   Ruthenium.   This element cannot be cold-worked but may be forged at temperatures above 2800°F.   The general corrosion resistance of ruthenium approaches that of iridium.   The metal is rarely used in the pure form except as a catalyst for the synthesis of certain hydrocarbons.   It is employed mainly as a hardener for platinum and palladium.

Typical mechanical properties of some metals and their alloys are given in Table 12·17.

12·47   Electrical contacts.   Since many of the precious metals and their alloys are widely used for electrical contacts, this particular application will be discussed in greater detail (The H. A. Wilson Company, Union, N.J.).

The properties of an ideal contact material are:

High electrical conductivity for maximum current-carrying capacity

Low temperature coefficient of resistance to keep contact resistance as nearly uniform as possible

High thermal conductivity to decrease temperature rise of contact and reduce tendency toward oxidation

Low surface contact resistance to utilize minimum contact pressure

High melting point to prevent the formation of molten bridges, loss of material, and surface roughening

High boiling point to prevent local vaporization and loss of material during arcing

High corrosion resistance to prevent an increase in contact resistance

High nonwelding and nonsticking characteristics

High hardness and toughness to prevent mechanical wear and failure, particularly in parts that operate at high frequencies or under high contact pressures

It is apparent, from the properties listed, that no one metal or alloy can be a universal contact material.   The practical selection of a contact material is based upon combining two or more desirable properties while minimizing the less advantageous properties for a particular application.

The contact materials may be classified according to contact properties in the following groups:

High conductivity: silver and silver alloys

Corrosion- and oxidation-resistant: platinum and related alloys

Refractory and arc-resistant: tungsten and molybdenum

High conductivity plus arc-resistant: powder-metallurgy compacts

Silver and Silver Alloys.   Silver has the highest electrical and thermal conductivity of all the contact materials.   The oxides of silver decompose at relatively low temperatures because of arcing, reverting to metallic silver, thus maintaining low contact resistance.   Silver is used

Table 12.17 Properties of some metals and alloys*

Metal or alloy and nominal composition	Condition	Tensile strength, 1,000 psi	Yield strength, 1,000 psi	Elongation, % in 2 in.	BHN	Modulus of elasticity, 10⁶ psi
Silver (99.9+)	Annealed	23	12	45	30	10.5
	Cold-rolled	43	48	6	90	
Sterling silver, 92.5 Ag, 7.5 Cu	Hard	64	50	4	125	10.5
Silver brazing alloy,	Annealed	41	20	26	65	
60 Ag, 25 Cu, 15 Zn	Annealed	58	45	38	110	13
	Cold-drawn	89	75	9	160	
Gold (pure)	Hard	30	...	2	49	
	Annealed	17.5	...	40	28	10.8
Platinum	Hard	65	...	2	101	
(commercial)	Annealed	27	...	28	65	22
Platinum-iridium,	Hard	80	...	2	169	
90 Pt, 10 Ir	Annealed	53	34	23	104	25
Platinum-rhodium,	Hard	93	...	3	169	
90 Pt, 10 Rh	Annealed	50	18.3	36	79	21.2
Platinum-ruthenium,	Hard	145	...	2	210	
90 Pt, 10 Ru	Annealed	91	...	28	156	31.5
Palladium	Hard	55	...	...	91	
(commercial)	Annealed	30	7.6	30	47	16.3
Palladium-silver,	Hard	100	94	...	176	
60 Pd, 40 Ag	Annealed	47	15	40	87	22.4
Iridium (pure)	Annealed	90	34	...	175	75
Rhodium (pure)	Annealed	80	...	...	119	50
Osmium (pure)	Arc-melted button	...	...	...	400†	81
Ruthenium (pure)	Forged	74	...	...	390†	60
Molybdenum	As-rolled	100	75	30	250	46
(99.9+)	Recrystallized	70	50	45	190	
Tantalum	Annealed sheet	60	45	37	55	27
(99.9+)	Unannealed sheet	110	100	3	123	
Tungsten (pure)	Hard wire	600	540	0.8	...	53
Titanium (99.8+)	Annealed	90	70	2.3	200	16.5
Zirconium (pure)	Annealed	36	16	31	77	11

* From "Properties of Some Metals and Alloys," The International Nickel Co.
† Vickers pyramid hardness

for sensitive contacts under light and intermediate pressure. They operate satisfactorily if current and voltage do not become excessive. The principal disadvantages of silver are its low hardness, low melting point, tendency to form sulfide films, and tendency to build up on one electrode under excessive current conditions. These disadvantages are minimized by the addition of alloying elements, principally copper, cadmium, zinc, nickel, manganese, platinum, palladium, and iron. The effect of alloying is to increase hardness, raise the melting point, reduce material loss or transfer, increase resistance to welding or sticking, increase resistance to erosion by arcing, and increase corrosion resistance.

Platinum, Palladium, and Gold. The outstanding property of the alloys in this group is their corrosion resistance to surrounding atmospheres and the sureness of making contact under light pressures. The metals are able to maintain low contact resistance over long periods because of their resistance to oxidation at the high local temperatures reached in arcing. Since these metals are soft, they are rarely used in the pure form. They are alloyed to obtain higher hardness without undue sacrifice of corrosion resistance or surface-contact resistance. The most common alloying elements are iridium, ruthenium, osmium, rhodium, and silver. Copper, nickel, and iron are also used as alloying elements.

Tungsten and Molybdenum. Tungsten and molybdenum have the unique property of high resistance to arc erosion along with very high melting points, high boiling points, and high resistance to welding and pitting. They are used in applications requiring high contact pressures and where the contacts have to operate frequently or continuously. The chief disadvantage of tungsten and molybdenum is their tendency to form oxides, particularly where severe arcing takes place. In some applications these disadvantages may be overcome by using very high contact pressures, by incorporating a wiping action in the contacts, or by use of protective circuits to suppress excessive arcing.

Powder-metallurgy Compacts. Silver and tungsten do not alloy with each other by the ordinary process of melting and casting. These metals, however, may be combined by using the techniques of powder metallurgy (discussed in Chap. 16) to produce alloys which are homogeneous and have high physical properties. It is thus possible to take advantage of the high electrical conductivity of silver or copper and the high arc resistance of tungsten or molybdenum. These materials are designed to operate under conditions of heavy current and voltage and are also often used in low-current high-frequency applications.

Typical combinations in this group are silver-tungsten, silver-molybdenum, silver–tungsten carbide, silver–molybdenum carbide, copper–tungsten carbide, and copper-tungsten. Other compositions are manufactured by powder metallurgy to take advantage of the high electrical conductivity of silver and copper and the semirefractory properties of cadmium oxide, iron, graphite, and nickel.

Many of these compositions can be produced in strip and wire form and may be drilled, rolled, swaged, drawn, formed, bent, and extruded without difficulty. They may be used as replacements for fine silver or silver alloys in some applications, since they give greater resistance to sticking and welding, have improved mechanical properties, and possess greater resistance to electrical erosion.

QUESTIONS

12·1   What is the most important property of copper?

12·2   Explain why copper is a suitable material for automobile radiators.

12·3   Explain the reasons for the difference in microstructure of Figs. 12·1 and 12·2.

12·4   What would be the temper of 0.25-in.-diameter copper wire cold-drawn from 0.50-in-diameter soft wire?

12·5   What is "season cracking"?   How may it be minimized?

12·6   What is dezincification?   How may it be minimized?

12·7   How does the addition of lead to brass improve its machinability?

12·8   Which copper alloy would be best for the tubes in a marine heat exchanger?   Why?

12·9   Why are most copper-zinc alloys not age-hardenable?

12·10   Discuss the effect on corrosion resistance of copper by increasing additions of (a) zinc, (b) tin, (c) nickel.

12·11   Why is muntz metal heat-treatable?   Describe a typical heat treatment and the resulting microstructure.

12·12   What properties would be important in the choice of a copper-alloy spring?

12·13   Why is "manganese bronze" a misnomer?

12·14   Differentiate between the terms *brass* and *bronze*.

12·15   Why are tin bronzes suitable for use as bearings?

12·16   Why is beryllium suitable for tools in the petroleum industry?

12·17   What are the outstanding properties of cupronickel alloys?

12·18   What are the outstanding properties of aluminum?

12·19   Why do long-range electrical transmission lines use a steel core and an aluminum shell?

12·20   Explain the meaning of the digits in the following aluminum specifications: 2107-T4, 5056-H16, 7075-T6, 6061-0.

12·21   Why do many aluminum alloys respond to age hardening?   Give some examples.

12·22   Why do aluminum alloy 2017 rivets have to be refrigerated until used?

12·23   What outstanding properties are generally given an alloy by the addition of nickel?

12·24   What outstanding properties do aluminum-silicon alloys have?   Give some typical applications.

12·25   Which aluminum casting alloy develops the highest mechanical properties? Why?

12·26   What is meant by "anodizing" aluminum?

12·27   What are the outstanding properties of magnesium?   Of nickel?

12·28   What is the effect of zirconium additions to magnesium alloys?

12·29   What is the effect of a rare earth metal addition to magnesium?   Of thorium addition?

12·30   Compare aluminum and magnesium with regard to corrosion resistance.

12·31   Discuss the methods used to join magnesium alloys.

12·32   Give one application and the reasons for selection of the following nickel alloys: duranickel, permanickel, Monel, K Monel, constantan, Inconel, Inconel X, Hastelloy C, and Illium G.

12·33   Give the composition, special properties, and one application of the following iron-nickel alloys: Invar, Kovar, Platinite, and Elinvar.

12·34   What are the outstanding properties of lead?   Give one application for each property.

12·35   What property is important for fusilbe plugs?   Give the composition of a suitable alloy for this application.

12·36   What properties are important in alloys for type metals?

12·37   Why is "white metal" suitable for bearing applications?

12·38   Which type of soft solder is preferred for electrical equipment and why?

12·39   Compare the lead-base and tin-base babbitts with regard to properties and applications.

12·40   Why is it difficult to work-harden lead, tin, or zinc at room temperature?

12·41   Why is tin-coated steel used for tin cans to hold food and not zinc-coated steel?

12·42   What are the outstanding properties of (a) silver, (b) gold, and (c) platinum?

12·43   Which of the platinum metals has the highest corrosion resistance? Which has the highest modulus of elasticity?

REFERENCES

Alice, J.: "Introduction to Magnesium and Its Alloys," Ziff-Davis Publishing, Chicago, 1945.

Aluminum Company of America: "Casting Alcoa Alloys," Pittsburgh, Pa., 1951.

American Society for Metals: "Magnesium," Metals Park, Ohio, 1946.

American Society for Metals: "Metals Handbook," Metals Park, Ohio, 1948, 1961.

American Society for Metals: "Physical Metallurgy of Aluminum Alloys," Metals Park, Ohio, 1949.

Bunn, E. S., and R. A. Wilkins: "Copper and Copper-base Alloys," McGraw-Hill Book Company, Inc., New York, 1943.

Dow Chemical Company: "Magnesium Alloys and Products," Midland, Mich., 1955.

Ellis, O. W.: "Copper and Copper Alloys," American Society for Metals, Metals Park, Ohio, 1948.

Gibbs, L. E.: "Cold Working of Brass," American Society for Metals, Metals Park, Ohio, 1946.

International Nickel Co.: "Nickel and Its Alloys," "Nickel and Nickel-base Alloys," "Age-hardening Inco Nickel Alloys," "Engineering Properties of

Duranickel," "Engineering Properties of Inconel," "Engineering Properties of Monel," "Engineering Properties of Nickel," New York.

Lead Industries Association: "Lead in Modern Industry," New York, 1952.

Liddell, D. M.: "Handbook of Nonferrous Metallurgy," McGraw-Hill Book Company, Inc., New York, 1945.

Mondolfo, L. F.: "Metallography of Aluminum Alloys," John Wiley & Sons, Inc., New York, 1943.

National Bureau of Standards (U.S.).: Zinc and Its Alloys, *Natl. Bur. Std. (U.S.) Circ.* 395, 1931.

Raudebaugh, R. J.: "Nonferrous Physical Metallurgy," Pitman Publishing Corporation, New York, 1952.

Reynolds Metals Company: "Heat Treating Aluminum Alloys," 1948; "Aluminum Forming," 1952; "Finishes for Aluminum," 1951, Louisville, Ky.

Roberts, C. S.: "Magnesium and Its Alloys," John Wiley & Sons, Inc., New York, 1960.

Vines, R. F.: "The Platinum Metals and Their Alloys," The International Nickel Co., New York, 1941.

Chapter 13

WEAR OF METALS

13·1 Introduction. Wear may be defined as unintentional deterioration resulting from use or environment. It may be considered essentially a surface phenomenon. Wear is one of the most destructive influences to which metals are exposed, and the importance of wear resistance needs no amplification.

The displacement and detachment of metallic particles from a metallic surface may be caused by contact with another metal (metallic wear), by contact with either a metallic or nonmetallic abrasive (abrasion), or by contact with moving liquids or gases (erosion). Erosion is usually accompanied by some form of corrosion. The above three types of wear may be subdivided into wear under rolling friction or under sliding friction and, further, according to whether lubrication can or cannot be used.

Wear involving a single type is rare and in most cases both abrasive and metallic wear occur. Since in most machinery applications wear can rarely be avoided completely even with the best lubrication, it is common practice to use a hard metal and a relatively soft one together. The softer material is used (as in a bearing) for the part which is most economical to replace.

13·2 Mechanism of wear. In metallic wear, tiny projections produce friction by mechanical interference, with the relative motion of contacting surfaces increasing resistance to further movement. If the driving force is sufficient to maintain movement, the interlocked particles are deformed. If they are of a brittle material, they may be torn off. This leads to the conclusion that wear resistance will be improved by increasing the hardness to resist initial indentation, the toughness to resist tearing out of metallic particles, and the surface smoothness to eliminate the projections.

In abrasive wear, the abrading particles penetrate the metal and cause the tearing off of metallic particles. The ease with which the deformed metal may be torn off depends upon the toughness.

Therefore, hardness and toughness, the same properties that influence metallic wear, also determine abrasive wear. Of these two factors, hardness is probably the more important one.

13·3   Factors influencing wear. Lubrication is an important contributing factor to wear resistance, particularly in metallic wear. In "thick-film" lubrication, a sufficiently thick lubricating film completely eliminates metallic contact, and metallic wear is reduced to a negligible amount. This is, however, the ideal condition, and more frequently "boundary lubrication" occurs. This is the condition of intermittent metallic contact that occurs when the oil film cannot be continuously maintained. Under boundary conditions, the amount of wear depends upon speed, pressure, nature of the mating surfaces, and efficiency of the residual oil film. In many cases, however, lubrication is impractical or is not wanted, as in braking.

Although actual melting of the metal occurs only in rare instances, the effect of heat produced by dry wear can reduce wear resistance in several ways. It may temper hardened structures, may cause phase changes that increase hardness and brittleness, may decrease mechanical properties, and it accelerates corrosion reactions.

The dominant frictional factor for metallic materials is believed to be welding. Atoms of the same or crystallographically similar metals have very strong forces of cohesion. When two clean surfaces of the same metal actually touch each other, they will weld together because of atomic attraction. If, by friction, sufficient pressure is applied to break through any residual separating material such as oil, dirt, or adsorbed moisture, and the surfaces are in sufficient contact to have elastic or plastic deformation occur, then seizing or welding takes place. The softening of metals by high temperatures increases the ease of plastic deformation and facilitates welding. Seizing may cause complete stoppage, or if relative motion is not prevented, pieces of the opposite face may be pulled out. The resultant projection then may cause scoring, galling, and excessive local wear.

Many methods may be used to minimize the danger of seizing. One is to use thin layers of hard surfacing material. The use of at least one metal that forms some sort of lubricating film or thin, tightly adherent oxide, sulfide, or phosphide coating is frequently helpful. Aluminum oxide is very effective in preventing welding. For parts that operate under such high pressures that elastic deformation permits intimate contact, the best preventive method is a lubricant that combines with the metal surface to form a "corrosion" product of sufficient strength to keep the surfaces separated. The use of materials of high elastic limit will minimize seizure due to intimate contact produced by plastic deformation.

Impact is a factor in wear, since the suddenly applied load may cause plastic flow and a change in shape. Proper design should provide a surface compressive yield strength above the compressive stress produced by impact and sufficient support so that subsurface flow does not occur.

Fatigue failure is included in a discussion of wear since it is a gradual deterioration due to use. Proper design to eliminate stress concentrations at notches and sharp angles will increase fatigue strength. Since fatigue failures are always due to tensile stress, residual compressive stress at the surface will provide additional protection. This may be accomplished by case hardening, such as carburizing, and by shot peening.

13·4 Methods of testing for wear resistance. Since wear is not a simple phenomenon, wear resistance is represented by fewer standardized tests than other engineering properties. It is generally accepted that a "universal" wear test is not feasible. Therefore, equipment for wear testing must be designed to simulate actual service conditions. These tests should have proved reproducibility, should be able to rank various materials under consideration, and most important, should be validated by correlation with actual service data.

13·5 Protection against wear. Many materials and methods are available for protection against wear. The selection of a particular material and process requires a thorough analysis of the actual service conditions, a knowledge of applicability and limitations of the particular material and process, and the cost involved. The lack of engineering data available for comparisons imposes a need for good judgment on the engineer or technician who selects materials to withstand wear.

Various techniques for providing surface protection to wear are as follows:

Electroplating
Anodizing
Diffusion
Metallizing
Hard facing
Selective heat treatment

13·6 Electroplating. The wear resistance of a metal part can be improved by electroplating a harder metal on its surface. The metals most often plated on base materials are chromium, nickel, and rhodium. Indium plating has been used to reduce the wear of lead bearings.

Two types of chromium plating used industrially are known as *hard chromium* and *porous chromium*. The hard-chromium plate is the same as that used for decorative purposes but much thicker, usually from 0.0001 to 0.010 in.   Porous chromium plate has on its surface carefully controlled pits or channels to hold lubricants.   The term is misleading, since below the specially prepared surface, it is no more porous than ordinary hard-chromium plate.   The hardness of chromium plate is equivalent to 950 to 1050 Vickers.   Another factor contributing to the reduction of wear is the low coefficient of friction of chromium plate.   Chromium plating is used in the cylinders and piston rings of internal-combustion engines.   Nongalling is another useful property of chromium plate.   Force-fitted chromium-plated steel parts may be assembled and disassembled many times without seizing or galling.   The high corrosion resistance of chromium is helpful in reducing wear under corrosive conditions.

The hardness of nickel plate is from 140 to 425 Vickers depending upon the nickel-plating solution used.   Nickel plate is a good deal softer than chromium plate, but in many cases it is hard enough for the purpose and more economical.   A nickel plate may be finished by machining while a chromium plate must be ground.   The better throwing power of nickel-plating solutions as compared with chromium-plating solutions is an advantage in plating parts that have recesses.

The hardness of rhodium plate is from 540 to 640 Vickers, and its wear resistance is between those of nickel plate and chromium plate. Rhodium plate has high reflectivity, high heat resistance, and nontarnishing properties along with good hardness and wear resistance. The use of rhodium plate for reflectors of high-intensity light sources, for electrical contacts, and for slip rings and commutators has been mentioned in Chap. 12.

13·7   Anodizing.   The formation of an oxide coating by anodizing may be used to improve the wear resistance of certain metals.   The anodizing process is usually applied to aluminum, magnesium, zinc, and their alloys.   In anodizing, the work is the anode, and oxide layers are built up on the base metal.   Since the newest oxide layer always forms next to the base metal, in order for the process to continue, the previously formed oxide layers must be porous enough to allow the oxygen ions to pass through them.

Anodizing aluminum is simply a method of building up a much thicker oxide coating than may be obtained by exposure to air.   The Alumilite process developed by the Aluminum Company of America uses sulfuric acid as an electrolyte for anodizing.   The films produced are transparent, thicker, and more porous than those produced by other electrolytes.   Continued development resulted in Alumilite hard coatings, which are thicker and harder than ordinary anodic coatings. Aircraft parts such as hydraulic pistons, guide tracks, gears, cams, screws, swivel joints, and friction locks are made of hard-coated aluminum alloys.

The production of a hard wear-resistant surface by anodizing has greatly extended the uses of magnesium and its alloys. Flash anodic coatings are often used as a base for paint adherence.

Anodizing zinc produces a coating which has greater resistance to wear than chromate films. Anodic zinc coatings are used for cartridge cases, airplane propeller blades, wire-screen cloth, and refrigerator shelves.

13·8 Diffusion. Several processes improve wear resistance by diffusion of some element into the surface layers. These are:

Carburizing
Cyaniding
Carbonitriding
Nitriding
Chromizing
Siliconizing

The first four of these processes were discussed in detail in Chap. 8, and only the last two will be discussed here.

Chromizing consists of the introduction of chromium into the surface layers of the base metal. The process is not restricted to ferrous materials and may be applied to nickel, cobalt, molybdenum, and tungsten to improve corrosion resistance and heat resistance.

When it is applied to iron or steel, it converts the surface layer into a stainless-steel case. If the steel contains appreciable amounts of carbon (above 0.60 per cent), chromium carbides will precipitate, increasing wear resistance. The chromizing process most widely used employs the principle of transfer of chromium through the gas phase at elevated temperatures. The temperatures used range from 1650 to 2000°F. These high temperatures may produce some distortion and grain growth during treatment. Chromized high-carbon steels have a hardness of 800 to 1000 Vickers and a low coefficient of friction. Chromizing is used on drop-forging dies, tools, hydraulic rams, pistons, and pump shafts.

Siliconizing, or Ihrigizing, consists of impregnation of an iron-base material with silicon. The process is carried out in the temperature range of 1700 to 1850°F. The work is heated in contact with a silicon-bearing material such as silicon carbide, and chlorine gas is used as a catalyst. The case depth ranges from 0.005 to 0.1 in., depending mainly on the carbon content of the base material. The case produced contains approximately 14 per cent silicon and is essentially an iron-silicon solid solution. Siliconized cases are difficult to machine, although the hardness is only Rockwell B 80 to 85. The increase in wear resistance by siliconizing is due to a low coefficient of friction and nongalling properties. Siliconized cases have been used on pump shafts, conveyor chain links, cylinder liners, valve guides, valves, and fittings for the chemical and oil industry.

13·9 Metallizing. Metal spraying, or metallizing, has been used for many years in production salvage to build up dimensions that are undersize and to repair worn surfaces. It has found increased use for wear-resistant applications.

Metallizing is usually done by automatically feeding a metal wire at a controlled rate of speed through the metallizing tool, or "gun." Air, oxygen, and a combustible gas are supplied to the gun by means of hoses and form a high-temperature high-velocity flame around the wire tip. The wire tip is continuously melted off, and the liquid-metal particles are directed at the work by the high-velocity flame. When they strike the surface, the liquid-metal particles flatten out to form irregularly shaped disks. At the same time they are forced into surface pores and irregularities to provide some mechanical interlock with previously deposited material. Cooling is very rapid, and a thin oxide film forms on the exposed surfaces of the deposited particles. The nature of the oxides formed under metallizing conditions determines to a large degree the physical properties of the deposit. Metals that form dense, tenacious oxides having good physical properties, such as chromium steel, aluminum bronze, or silicon-aluminum alloys, show relatively high strength in the sprayed form. Metals which form loose, friable oxides, such as the brasses and copper, produce coatings of low strength.

Various methods have been developed for bonding sprayed metals to the base material. One of the most widely used methods is to spray a bonding coat of molybdenum 0.001 to 0.003 in. thick which forms a thin alloy layer. Molybdenum adheres to nearly all steels and many other metals and alloys but will not bond to copper, brass, bronze, or nitrided steels. Other bonding methods prepare the surfaces by abrasive blasting or by rough threading. The Fusebond method deposits rough, porous nickel on the surface to provide a good strong anchorage for sprayed coatings, but it cannot be used on brass, bronze, or copper.

The most important alloys used for metal spraying to increase wear resistance are type 420 chromium stainless steel, type 304 nickel-chromium stainless steel, Monel, 0.1 to 0.80 per cent carbon steel, aluminum iron bronze, tobin bronze, and molybdenum. Sprayed molybdenum is used on aluminum pulleys, plug gauges, high-speed spindles running in bronze bearings, and crankshafts. Sprayed stainless steel or Monel is used on turbine shafts. Diesel-engine parts such as crankshafts, bores, blocks, camshafts, and valve stems are metallized with molybdenum, stainless steel, or aluminum for increased wear resistance.

The wear resistance of sprayed metals is generally very good, but metallizing is not suitable for service involving heavy impact, extreme abrasion, or where highly localized loads are applied. Metallizing is best suited for applications involving light abrasive wear, for conditions where boundary lubrication exists, and to provide a wear-resistant or corrosion-resistant surface to inexpensive base materials.

13·10 Hard facing. The production of a hard wear-resistant surface layer on metals by welding is known as *hard facing*. This method is relatively easy to apply, requiring only the hard-facing alloys in the form of welding rods and an oxyacetylene flame or electric arc. The advantages of hard facing are that it may be applied to localized areas subjected to wear, hard wear-resistant compounds are available, and it provides effective use of expensive alloys and protection in depth.

The hard-facing material is provided in the form of an electrode or welding rod. These rods are generally used bare for oxyacetylene-gas welding and are flux-coated for electric-arc welding. The flux coating contains materials for arc stability, oxidation protection of the molten weld, fluxing of impurities, thermal and electrical insulation, and control of metal transfer. Oxyacetylene-gas welding produces smoother deposits that can be positioned more precisely, while the heating and cooling rates are slower. Electric-arc welding is less expensive, may be faster, and lends itself better to automatic equipment. Arc deposits are generally rougher, more likely to be porous, and tend to develop cracks because of the sharp temperature gradients due to rapid heating and cooling.

A great number of alloys of widely varying service characteristics are available in forms convenient for application by the arc- and gas-welding processes. A simplified classification of wear-resistant hard-facing alloys is given in Table 13·1.

As a starting point in alloy selection, consider the chromium-molybdenum grade of martensitic iron. It has good resistance to abrasion, good hot hardness up to 1000°F, excellent resistance to light impact, and high compressive strength. It welds easily at relatively low temperature and is adapted to both arc and gas welding. If impact is in the medium range, a martensitic steel should be tried, while heavy impact may require an austenitic steel. Nickel-base alloys and stainless steels are best for corrosion resistance while high chromium content is favored for oxidation resistance and erosion resistance. The tungsten carbide composites provide the best abrasion resistance.

Cobalt-base alloys should be considered for high-temperature service. The martensitic steels offer a good combination of impact and abrasion resistance.

Since toughness is inversely proportional to carbon content, variation in the carbon content within each group makes available alloys of different toughness.

Table 13·1   A graded series of wear-resistant alloys*

↑ Increasing toughness / Increasing abrasion resistance	1. Tungsten carbide	Maximum abrasion resistance; worn surfaces become rough
	2. High-chromium irons	Excellent erosion resistance; oxidation resistance
	3. Martensitic irons	Excellent abrasion resistance; high compressive strength
	4. Cobalt-base alloys	Oxidation resistance, corrosion resistance, hot strength, and creep resistance
	5. Nickel-base alloys	Corrosion resistance; may have oxidation and creep resistance
	6. Martensitic steels	Good combinations of abrasion and impact resistance; good compressive strength
	7. Pearlitic steels	Inexpensive; fair abrasion and impact resistance
	8. Austenitic steels	Work hardening
	Stainless steels	Corrosion resistance
	Manganese steel	Maximum toughness with fair abrasion resistance; good metal-to-metal wear resistance under impact

* "Surface Protection against Wear," American Society for Metals, Metals Park, Ohio, 1954.

Pearlitic steels are used mainly as build-up metal for welding or as the base for hard surfacing. Austenitic manganese steels are very tough and work-harden rapidly under impact (see Sec. 9·10). This alloy is used as a base for hard facing because of its toughness, as well as for overlays.

13·11 Selective heat treatment. The methods used for selective heat treatment are induction hardening and flame hardening. These are essentially shallow-hardening methods to produce a hardened case and relatively tough core. These methods were discussed in Chap. 8.

QUESTIONS

13·1 Differentiate between metallic wear, abrasive wear, and erosion.

13·2 Differentiate between "thick-film" lubrication and boundary lubrication.

13·3 Explain methods that may be used to minimize seizing.

13·4 What factors should be considered to set up a good wear test?

13·5 What would be a good method of reducing wear in a drawing die?   Why?

13·6 Aside from lubrication, how may wear be reduced in an automotive cylinder?

13·7 What are the advantages and disadvantages of nickel plating vs. chromium plating for wear resistance?

13·8 List the various diffusion processes for increasing wear resistance, and give a practical application of each.

13·9 What is the principle of metallizing to increase wear resistance?   Give some applications.

13·10 Give some applications of hard facing to improve wear resistance.

REFERENCES

American Society for Metals: "Metals Handbook," 1948 and 1961 editions, Metals Park, Ohio.

————: "Surface Protection against Wear and Corrosion," Metals Park, Ohio, 1954.

————: "Surface Treatment of Metals," Metals Park, Ohio, 1941.

American Society for Testing Materials: "Symposium on Wear of Metals," Philadelphia, Pa., 1937.

Avery, H. S.: "Hard Surfacing by Fusion Welding," American Brake Shoe Co., New York, 1947.

————: Hard Facing for Impact, *Welding J. (N.Y.)*, vol. 31, no. 2, pp. 116–143, 1952.

Burwell, J. T. (ed.): "Mechanical Wear," American Society for Metals, Metals Park, Ohio, 1950.

Riddihough, M.: "Hard Facing by Welding," Iliffe & Sons, Ltd., London, 1948.

Chapter 14

METALS AT HIGH AND LOW TEMPERATURES

14·1 Introduction. The terms *high* and *low* temperatures are entirely relative to our own natural environment. What is considered a high temperature for low-melting metals such as tin and lead may be considered a low temperature for a high-melting metal such as tungsten. Therefore, lower-melting metals will exhibit characteristics at low temperatures that will require relatively higher temperatures for other metals. For example, a temperature of about 1000°F may be necessary to recrystallize iron after cold working, but tin and lead will recrystallize at or near room temperature. The properties of metals are usually determined at room temperature, and our thinking about metals is based on their behavior at normal temperatures. When the temperature is changed, either higher or lower, changes in the behavior of metals often occur which may seriously affect their usefulness in a particular application.

METALS AT HIGH TEMPERATURES

14·2 Elevated-temperature tests. The behavior of metals observed by stressing at elevated temperatures depends upon the length of the test period. Since life expectancy of machine parts is usually high, it is not possible to run a test for many years to determine what to use in current construction. It is necessary to extrapolate from shorter-time tests. This extrapolation, however, must be done with great care from tests that will provide useful data. This is especially difficult for high-temperature applications, since changes in behavior will occur with time at temperature.

In high-temperature tests it is necessary to determine the dependence of ultimate strength (rupture strength) and yield strength (creep strength) on the time application of the stress. In investigating the plastic behavior of metals at elevated temperatures, it is convenient to apply a tensile load on the test specimen.   While this procedure, in many cases, does not duplicate service conditions, it is possible, by careful interpretation, for the data to provide useful information which can be applied to combined stress conditions.

Many tests have been developed for high-temperature studies, but the three most widely used ones are:

1. Creep tests at small deformations: low stresses and low strain rates for long time periods

2. Stress-rupture (creep-rupture) tests at larger deformations: higher stresses and larger strain rates for shorter periods of time

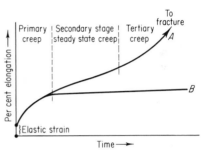

Fig. 14·1   Typical creep curves illustrating the stages of creep.

3. Short-time tensile tests at large deformations: high stresses and high strain rates available with the usual tension-testing equipment

14·3   Creep tests.   Creep is a property of great importance in materials used for high-temperature applications.   It may be defined as a continuing slow plastic flow under constant conditions of load or stress.   Creep is generally associated with a time rate of deformation continuing under stresses well below the yield strength for the particular temperature to which the metal is subjected.   It occurs at any temperature, though its importance depends upon the material and the degree to which freedom from continuing deformation is desired.

A creep test is simply a tension test run at constant load and constant temperature.   There is a means of measuring the elongation of the specimen very accurately and a means of heating the specimen under closely controlled conditions.   The total creep or per cent elongation is plotted against time for the entire duration of the test.   Two typical creep curves are shown in Fig. 14·1.

The various stages of creep are illustrated by curve *A*.   When the load is first applied, there is an instantaneous elastic elongation, then a primary stage of a transient nature during which slip and work hardening take place in the most favorably oriented grains.   The creep rate (tangent to the curve) is initially high and gradually slows to a minimum.   This is followed by a secondary stage of steady-state creep during which the deformation continues at an approximately constant rate.   During this stage a balance exists between the rate of work hardening and the rate of softening because of recovery or recrystallization.   In some cases, under moderate stresses, the creep rate may continue to decrease at a very slow rate and the secondary stage may continue for a very long time (curve *B*, Fig. 14·1).   However, if the stress is sufficiently high, there is a tertiary stage in which the creep rate accelerates until fracture occurs.

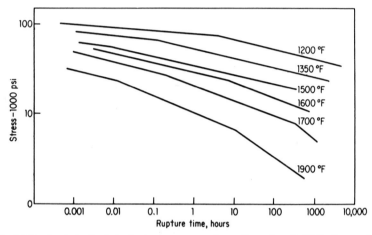

Fig. 14·2   Log-log plot of stress vs. rupture time for S-590 alloy.   (*From "High Temperature Properties of Metals," American Society for Metals, Metals Park, Ohio,* 1951)

There is little or no correlation between the room-temperature mechanical properties of a material and its creep properties.   Creep seems to be greatly affected by small variations in microstructure and prior history.   The grain size of the metal is an important factor in determining its creep characteristics.   Whereas at room temperature fine-grained materials show higher yield and ultimate strengths than coarse-grained materials, the reverse is true at elevated temperatures. It is believed that at high temperatures the grain boundaries may act as centers for the generation of dislocations which cause creep.

The presence of solute atoms, even in minor amounts, tends to retard creep by interfering with the motion of dislocations through the crystal.   A more potent factor in retarding creep is the presence of a strong, stable, finely dispersed second phase.

14·4   Stress-rupture tests.   These tests are conducted to determine the ability of a material to resist fracture at elevated temperatures. In stress-rupture tests the loads are high enough to cause comparatively rapid rupture. The time involved is usually between 10 and 400 hr, although some tests may run as long as 1,000 hr.

A series of specimens are broken at each temperature of interest, under constant load, the stresses being selected so fractures will occur from a few minutes to several hundred hours. The results are usually plotted in log-log coordinates, and if no structural changes occur during the test period, the relationship of rupture stress and time to rupture is linear. Typical stress-rupture data for S-590 (cobalt-chromium-nickel–base) alloy are shown in Fig. 14·2. Discontinuities in the straight lines are associated with changes in the

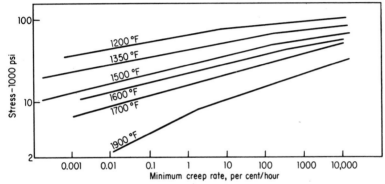

Fig. 14·3   Log-log plot of stress vs. minimum creep rate for S-590 alloy. *(From "High Temperature Properties of Metals," American Society for Metals, Metals Park, Ohio, 1951)*

alloy and indicate a change in the method of failure from transcrystalline low-temperature type to intercrystalline high-temperature type.

The principal differences between the stress-rupture and creep test are the testing time, the stress or strain rate level, and the sensitivity of control and measurement of temperature, load, and strain. It is possible before fracture to determine the elongation as a function of the time, as in an ordinary creep test. From these data, the steady-state or minimum creep rate at very high stresses may also be determined. The log-log plot of stress vs. minimum creep rate for S-590 alloy is shown in Fig. 14·3.

For some applications, such as superheater tubes, still tubes, piping, pipe fittings, sheet-metal parts, nozzle guide vanes, and boilers, only rupture data are important. For other applications, such as bolts, steam valves, steam-turbine blading, turbine rotors, turbine casings, and valve stems, creep data are considered most important.

Considering the fact that the load in the stress-rupture test is much higher than design values and that the test continues to fracture, there is some doubt as to the usefulness of the data obtained. Metal behavior at high loads, high rates of deformation, and short life may not be indicative of that at lower loads. As a method of rating different alloys or in comparison of two different lots of the same alloy, the stress-rupture test seems to show a correlation with creep tests at usable loads.

In some applications the design life is short. Guided missiles are designed for a life of 1 hr, and turbojet engines are frequently designed for 1,000-hr life. In these cases the test period can be as long as the design life, and stress-rupture data can sometimes be used directly in such designs. For applications of longer design life, for example, steam or gas turbines with a design life of 100,000 hr (13 years), it is necessary to extrapolate data obtained during shorter time periods.

Materials for high-temperature use are usually designed for a certain minimum creep after a stated period. The creep strength, which is the quantity used in design, is the stress required to produce a definite per cent deformation in a stated time. Some gas-turbine designers have set a standard of 0.1 per cent creep in 10,000 hr. This is equivalent to 0.01 per cent in 1,000 hr.

14.5 Short-time tension tests. These tests are used to study the effect of heating a sample and testing under strain rates that are available in the ordinary tensile-testing machine. Elastic properties at elevated temperatures are not real since their values depend upon the time between load applications, and their accuracy on the sensitivity of the extensometer. The duration of testing is usually only a few minutes, and the important effects of time at temperature are not measured. The short-time tension test fails to predict what will happen in a shorter or longer period of time and therefore has very little application. The test is sometimes used for rapid estimation of materials which may warrant further study, and the short-time tensile strength is frequently used as the 0.1-hr point on a rupture curve. The variation of the short-time yield and tensile strength of Inconel X with temperature is shown in Fig. 14·4.

14.6 Creep properties of various alloys. Plain-carbon and low-alloy steels are widely used for moderate-temperature applications, particularly below 900°F. An increase in carbon content improves the creep strength at lower temperatures where the carbides are present in lamellar form. The reverse may be true at higher temperatures where the carbides are spheroidized. The recommended structure of plain-carbon steels for high-temperature service is the normalized one. The annealed structure appears to be less stable and tends to spheroidize more rapidly, reducing creep strength. The use of aluminum as a deoxidizer in the manufacture of steel tends to produce fine grain, which lowers creep strength. Aluminum additions should be kept low, and their effect is considerably reduced by the presence of manganese and molybdenum.

In low-alloy steels, containing less than 10 per cent alloy, molybdenum and vanadium are most effective in raising the creep resistance. The carbon content is usually kept below 0.15 per cent. The 0.5 per

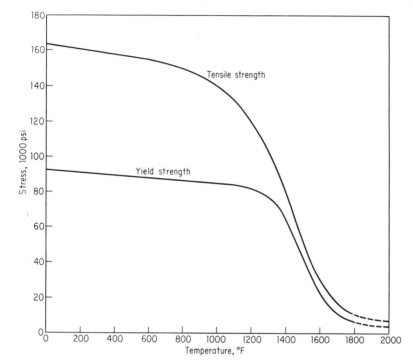

Fig. 14·4   Short-time yield strength and tensile strength of Inconel X at elevated temperatures. (*From "Metals Handbook," 1954 supplement, p. 42, American Society for Metals, Metals Park, Ohio*)

cent molybdenum steel is used for piping and superheater tubes up to 850°F. Above this temperature, spheroidization and graphitization tend to take place, with a reduction in creep strength. The addition of 1 per cent chromium to this steel increases the resistance to graphitization, and the steel is now used for piping and boiler tubes at temperatures to 1000°F.

The chromium-molybdenum-vanadium steels containing up to 0.50 per cent carbon are used in the normalized and tempered, or quenched and tempered condition. They have relatively high yield and creep strengths and are suitable for bolts, steam-turbine rotors, and other parts operating at temperatures up to 1000°F.

The straight-chromium (4xx series) stainless steels are used for elevated-temperature applications that require increased corrosion and oxidation resistance. Type 410 is used for bolts, steam valves, pump shafts, and other parts up to 1000°F. Type 422 is used for similar applications up to 1200°F. Both the above types are hardenable to a martensitic structure and are tempered about 100° above the operating temperature to promote stability of structure.

Type 430 (16 per cent Cr) and 446 (25 per cent Cr) are nonhardenable and ferritic. These grades, generally used in the annealed condition, have lower creep strength than the hardenable types but show greater oxidation resistance. Type 430 is used for heat-exchange equipment, condensers, piping, and furnace parts operating at temperatures to 1550°F. Type 446 is used for similar applications up to 2000°F.

The austenitic stainless steels (3xx series) show better creep properties than the 4xx series and better corrosion and oxidation resistance. Type 310 (25 per cent Cr, 20 per cent Ni) is used for furnace linings, boiler baffles, thermocouple wells, aircraft-cabin heaters, and jet-engine burner liners. Type 347 (18 per cent Cr, 11 per cent Ni, + Cb and Ta) is used for steam lines, superheater tubes, and exhaust systems in reciprocating engines and gas turbines operating up to 1600°F.

Another group of alloys that have good creep properties in the temperature range of 1200 to 1400°F are essentially chromium-nickel-molybdenum-iron alloys. Many contain small amounts of titanium and aluminum. Some trade names for alloys in this group are A-286, Discaloy, Incoloy 901, 16-25-6, and D-979. These alloys are used as forgings for turbine wheels, various other components of gas turbines, sheet-metal casings, housings, and exhaust equipment.

The nickel-base alloys such as M-252, Waspaloy, Rene 41, Hastelloy R-235, Inconel 700, Udimet 500, and Unitemp 1753 are widely used for aircraft applications. They are intended for use in the temperature range of 1400 to 1800°F. These alloys contain 50 to 70 per cent nickel, about 20 per cent chromium, up to 10 per cent molybdenum or tungsten, up to 20 per cent cobalt, and titanium and aluminum. They are used for manifolds, collector rings, and exhaust valves of reciprocating engines, and in sheet form for combustion liners, tail pipes, and casings of gas turbines and jet engines.

The cobalt-chromium-nickel–base alloys such as S-816, S-590, L-605, and N-155 are suitable for applications in the same range as the nickel-base alloys but have lower rupture strength. They are used for wheels and buckets of gas turbines.

All the commercial alloys mentioned above tend to lose their strength rapidly when heated above about 1700°F. It seems unlikely that alloys using these metals will raise the allowable operating temperature much above the present limit.   This limit is related to a great extent by the melting points of the base metals.   Most promising base metals for future high-temperature alloys are molybdenum (melting point

Table 14·1   High-temperature strength values for several alloys

Alloy	Temp, °F	Short-time tensile strength, psi	Stress-rupture strength, psi, 1,000 hr	Creep strength, psi	
				0.1% per 1,000 hr	0.01% per 1,000 hr
Carbon steel, 0.15 C,	800	55,000	. . .	26,800	18,500
annealed	1000	36,500	12,000	5,750	2,700
	1200	20,000	2,200	620	290
Carbon-molybdenum	800	60,000	. . .	30,000	21,000
steel, 0.15 C, 0.55 Mo	1000	45,000	25,000	10,800	6,700
	1200	27,000	4,400	2,000	700
Type 410 stainless	1000	48,000	19,000	12,000	
steel, 13 Cr	1200	25,000	7,000	2,200	
	1300	17,000			
Type 304 stainless	1000	60,000	35,000	17,000	12,000
steel, 19 Cr, 9 Ni	1200	46,000	14,000	7,000	4,000
	1300	37,000	9,000	3,900	
N-155 (low C),	1200	83,000	37,000	19,000	16,000
0.15 C, 21 Cr,	1350	60,000	22,000	14,500	10,500
20 Ni, 20 Co,	1500	40,000	13,000	8,000	5,000
3 Mo, 3 W, 1 Cb,					
bal. Fe					
S-816, 0.4 C, 20 Cr,	1350	99,000	30,000	18,000	12,000
20 Ni, 45 Co, 3 Mo,	1500	78,000	17,000	11,500	8,100
4 W, 4 Cb	1600	60,000	9,500	6,500	5,000
Inconel X, 0.04 C,	1200	120,000	69,000	60,000	48,000
15 Cr, 73 Ni, 1 Cb,	1350	93,000	42,000	37,500	30,000
2.5 Ti, 0.7 Al, 7 Fe	1500	60,000	18,000	18,000	15,000

4730°F) and tungsten (melting point 6170°F).   These metals are relatively abundant and are available in high-purity form.   A recently developed molybdenum alloy containing 0.5 per cent titanium has higher rupture strength in the range of 1600 to 2000°F than any other commercial alloy.   Two disadvantages of these metals are their high density and their great susceptibility to oxidation.   This latter disadvantage may be overcome by the development of a suitable oxidation-resistant coating.

Some typical high-temperature strength valves for several alloys are given in Table 14·1.

METALS AT LOW TEMPERATURES

14·7 Effect of low temperature on properties. As the temperature is decreased below normal room temperature, the hardness, yield strength, and, with few exceptions, the ultimate strength and modulus of elasticity of all metals and alloys increase. The variation of yield and tensile strengths of iron, nickel, and copper with temperature is shown in Fig. 14·5.

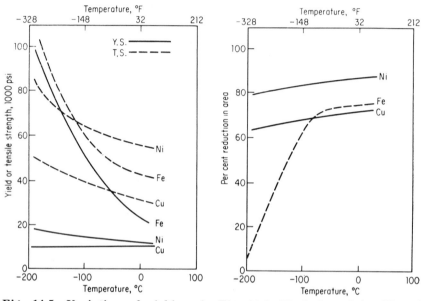

Fig. 14·5 Variation of yield and tensile strengths of iron, copper, and nickel with temperature. (*From "Behavior of Metals at Low Temperatures," American Society for Metals, Metals Park, Ohio,* 1953)

Fig. 14·6 Variation of ductility of iron, copper, and nickel with temperature. (*From "Behavior of Metals at Low Temperatures," American Society for Metals, Metals Park, Ohio,* 1953)

In regard to the effect of temperature on ductility, metals fall into two distinct groups, those which remain ductile at low temperatures and those which become brittle. An indication of the amount of ductility, or plastic deformation, before fracture may be obtained from a study of the fracture surface. A cup-cone type of fracture is typical of a ductile material which has failed in shear after plastic deformation when tested in tension. A brittle material fails by cleavage with no evidence of plastic deformation. As the temperature is decreased, face-centered-cubic metals fracture only by shear and show a gradual and continuous decrease in ductility. Metals with other crystal structures may fail by shear at room temperature, but with decreasing temperature the mode of fracture changes from shear (ductile) to cleavage (brittle).   The change in fracture often appears as a sharp drop in ductility.   The effect of temperature on the ductility of iron, copper, and nickel is shown in Fig. 14·6.   The tensile properties of some steels and nonferrous materials at low temperatures are given in Table 14·2.   Cleavage fractures of structural members are often sudden and unexpected and usually result in catastrophic brittle failure of the part.   Great interest in this problem developed during World War II when a number of welded ships failed in a brittle manner with almost explosive rapidity.   In some cases, the ship was split in two.

Fig. 14·7 Typical curve of impact value vs. testing temperature for a ferritic steel, showing transition temperature zone in which erratic values may be expected.   (*The International Nickel Company*)

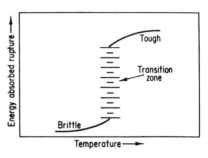

The steel used for ship plate was ductile at normal temperatures, yet the failure was of a brittle nature with little plastic deformation.

The tendency of steel to fail in a brittle manner is increased by stress concentration, increased speed of load application, and decrease of temperature.   These three factors are interrelated, and the effect of lowering the temperature is the easiest one to measure quantitatively. It is often possible to study the change from ductile to brittle fracture with decreasing temperature, provided that stress concentration and speed of load application are held constant.   These conditions are satisfied in the ordinary Charpy or Izod notched-bar impact test (see Sec. 1·31).   A rough approach to some degree of correlation with room-temperature and low-temperature toughness behavior is shown by the notched-bar impact test.   This test has become so common that most of the information on toughness has been obtained by it.

14·8   Effect of temperature on notched-bar test.   If tests on steel are made at many temperatures, a plot of energy absorbed vs. temperature will usually show a temperature range in which the impact values drop sharply as the temperature is lowered.   At the same time, the mode of fracture changes from a predominantly fibrous-shear type to a crystalline-cleavage type.   This is shown graphically in Fig. 14·7. Values in the transition range are often erratic since slight changes in conditions will affect the values.

Table 14.2   Tensile properties of some steels and nonferrous materials at low temperature*

Material and composition	Condition	Temp, °F	Yield strength, psi	Tensile strength, psi	Elongation, % in 2 in.	Reduction in area, %
Low-carbon steel, 0.13–0.14 C	As-rolled	70	54,700	66,300	29.7	71.8
	As-rolled	−85	67,700	80,700	33.6	70.3
	As-rolled	−292	...	121,300	26.5	55
	Annealed	70	42,700	45,700	27.5	77.5
	Annealed	−296		137,000	7.5	
	Annealed	−423	155,000	155,000	0.3	2.5
Ni steel, 0.13 C, 5.13 Ni, 0.41 Mn, 0.19 Cr, 0.15 Si	Oil-quenched and tempered 1200°F	68	...	103,000	25	74
		−242	...	153,000	25	57
		−319	...	175,000	21	50
Ni-Cr-Mo steel, 0.33 C, 0.67 Cr, 2.45 Ni, 0.64 Mo	Oil-quenched and tempered 1185°F	70	137,700	152,000	14	65
		6	141,000	154,500	15.6	64
		−90	145,000	163,000	15.6	62
		−292	183,500	201,500	17	63
Fe-Ni alloy, 0.16 C, 35.8 Ni, 0.86 Mn	Water-quenched	70	52,400	81,100	32	58
		−423	127,000	144,000	20	60
Commercially pure Ni	Annealed	70	24,600	65,500	42	78
		−112	27,600	76,400	43	73
		−292	27,600	97,000	53	74
Commercially pure Al	Hard-rolled	75	19,700	23,500	16	
		−112	21,350	24,700	18	
Al alloy 2017, 4 Cu, 0.5 Mn, 0.5 Mg	Solution-treated	75	45,500	68,000	15	
		−112	46,500	70,000	16	
Al alloy 2052, 2.5 Mg, 0.25 Cr	Hard-rolled	75	38,600	43,500	14	
		−112	39,200	45,600	18.5	
Pure copper	Annealed	75	8,600	31,400	48	76
		−112	10,100	38,500	47	74
		−292	15,000	50,800	58	77
Cu-Be, 2.56 Be	Water-quenched and aged	75	125,000	187,000	2.6	5
		−112	147,000	202,000	4	5
		−292	155,000	214,000	3	6
Cu-Zn, 30.5 Zn, 0.10 Fe	Annealed	75	28,200	51,100	49	77
		−112	27,300	57,100	60	79
		−292	29,600	73,500	75	73
Magnesium alloy M1, 1 Mn	Extruded	77	28,000	39,000	3.5	
		−110	30,900	52,000	3	
Magnesium alloy AZ63, 6 Al, 3 Zn	Cast, heat-treated, and aged	77	21,500	38,900	4.5	5.8
		−110	24,400	35,400	2.5	3.4
Ni alloy Monel, 28.86 Cu, 0.28 Mn	Annealed	75	20,900	70,800	41	75
		−112	27,100	85,300	40	74
		−292	29,600	113,000	51	72

* Compiled from data in "Metals Handbook," 1948 edition, American Society for Metals, Metals Park, Ohio.

The temperature at which some specified level of energy absorption or fracture appears is defined as the *transition temperature*. In ASTM specifications it is defined as the temperature at which specimens show a fracture of 50 per cent shear and 50 per cent cleavage. The lower the transition temperature the better is the steel able to resist the embrittling effect of stress concentration, high loading rate, or low temperature.   A study of available data for iron and steel indicates that their low-temperature behavior is affected by two classes of variables, namely, metallurgical factors and mechanical factors.

14·9   Metallurgical factors.   The important interrelated metallurgical factors affecting the low-temperature behavior of iron and steel are composition, deoxidation, heat treatment and microstructure, surface condition, and grain size.

Increasing carbon content decreases the notched impact strength at room temperature and raises the transition temperature (Fig. 14·8).

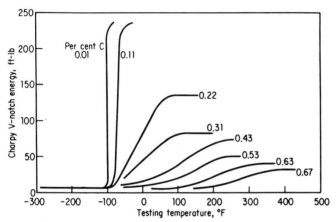

Fig. 14·8   Effect of carbon on the shape of the transition curve.   (*From "Metals Handbook," 1961 edition, p. 227, American Society for Metals, Metals Park, Ohio*)

The physical form of the carbon is also important.   When the cementite is spheroidized, it seems to be less harmful to low-temperature properties.

A manganese content of up to 1.5 per cent lowers the transition temperature as shown in Fig. 14·9 but does not change the shape of the transition curve.

Silicon, in amounts up to 0.30 per cent used to deoxidize steels, lowers transition temperature and improves notch toughness because a cleaner steel and a more uniform ferritic grain are produced.   Larger amounts have the reverse effect, and the presence of 4 per cent silicon results in a brittle structure even at room temperature.

The use of aluminum in addition to silicon for the deoxidation of steel seems to have a beneficial effect on the notch toughness of medium-carbon steels.   The room-temperature impact resistance is improved and the transition temperature is lowered as the amount of aluminum is increased up to about 0.10 per cent.   The relatively fine

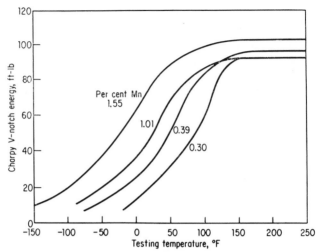

Fig. 14·9   Effect of manganese on Charpy V-notch values of a 0.30 per cent carbon steel.   (*From "Metals Handbook," 1961 edition, p.* 227, *American Society for Metals, Metals Park, Ohio*)

ferritic grain size usually found in aluminum-treated cast and wrought steels contributes largely to the improved toughness.

For a particular type of steel and strength level, fine-grained steels have higher notch toughness than coarse-grained steels.   The transition temperature is lowered as the grain size decreases.   This is illustrated by Fig. 14.10.   The fine-grained condition is usually due to a deoxidation practice that uses silicon, aluminum, or vanadium.

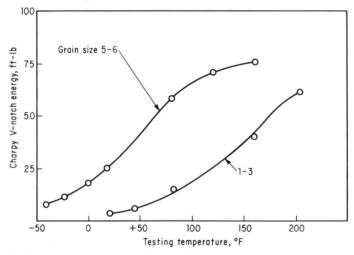

Fig. 14·10   Effect of grain size on notch toughness of 1030 steel.   (*From· "Metals Handbook," 1961 edition, p.* 227, *American Society for Metals, Metals Park, Ohio*)

Nickel is the most effective alloying element for increasing resistance to low-temperature embrittlement in steel and is one of the few alloying elements which improve the low-temperature ductility of iron. Nickel additions to steel increase room-temperature toughness, lower the transition temperature, and widen the transition-temperature range. The effects of variation in nickel content and temperature on the

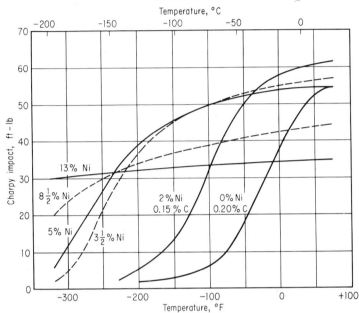

Fig. 14·11   Effect of nickel content on the resistance to low-temperature embrittlement of normalized low-carbon steels (keyhole notch). (*The International Nickel Company*)

Charpy keyhole impact values of low-carbon steels are shown in Fig. 14·11. The curves indicate that the transition temperature for 1020 killed steel is slightly below 0°F. The 2 per cent nickel steel retains considerable toughness down to −100°F. The 3½ and 5 per cent nickel steels seem to be best between −100 and −200°F. The 8½ per cent nickel steel shows only a gradual decrease in toughness with decrease in temperature. The 13 per cent nickel steel shows no transition temperature, and its room-temperature toughness remains at almost the same value over the entire test range.

Molybdenum, vanadium, and titanium have a similar effect on notch toughness. Small amounts tend to raise the transition temperature, but as the amount is increased, transition temperature is lowered.

The best microstructure for low-temperature toughness is that of tempered martensite. This structure gives the highest toughness and

Table 14.3 Toughness of some steels and nonferrous materials at low temperatures*

Material and composition	Condition	Room-temp tensile strength, psi or BHN	Notched-bar impact values							
			ft-lb	Temp, °F	ft-lb	Temp, °F	ft-lb	Temp, °F	ft-lb	Temp, °F
Bessemer structural steel, 0.10 C	As-rolled	55,000	37	148	26	68	4	32	3	0
Ni steel, 0.31 C, 3.47 Ni	Normalized 1675°F	192	49	75	32	0	17	-40	9	-100
	Oil-quenched, tempered 1050°F	217	106	75	106	0	105	-40	100	-100
Ni-Cr-Mo steel, 0.39 C, 0.71 Mn, 1.71 Ni, 0.75 Cr, 0.30 Mo	Normalized 1630°F	440	13	75	7	0	6	-40	5	-100
	Oil-quenched, tempered 1100°F	302	82	75	82	0	82	-40	77	-100
Fe-Ni alloy, 35.3 Ni	Annealed	…	28	75	19	-112	11.3	-310		
Ni-Fe alloy, 1.3 Fe	Annealed	…	27.6	75	27	-112	29.3	-310		
Commercially pure Al	Annealed	13,200	19	75	20	-112	21	-184	27	-292
Al alloy 17S, 3.72 Cu, 0.6 Mn, 0.6 Mg	Solution-treated	59,500	15	75	18	-105				
Al alloy 52S, 2.35 Mg, 0.12 Si, 0.14 Fe	As-rolled	31,500	58	75	58	-105				
Pure Cu, 99.98 Cu	Annealed	31,400	43	75	44	-112	44	-184	50	-290
Cu-Be, 2.56 Be	Water-quenched and aged	187,000	2	75	3	-112	3	-292		
Cu-Zn, 30.5 Zn, 0.10 Fe	Annealed	51,100	66	75	69	-112	78	-290		
Mg alloy M1, 1 Mn	Extruded	39,000	3.9	77	2.6	-110				
Mg alloy AZ63, 6 Al, 3 Zn	Cast, heat-treated, and aged	38,900	1.6	77	1.5	-110				
Ni alloy Monel, 28.86 Cu, 0.28 Mn	Annealed	70,800	90	75	90	-112	97	-292		

* Compiled from data in "Metals Handbook," 1948 edition, American Society for Metals, Metals Park, Ohio.

436

the lowest transition temperature compared with other microstructures of a specific steel (Fig. 14·12). The notch toughness of martensite decreases with increasing amounts of bainite. Retained austenite has only a slight effect on transition temperature.

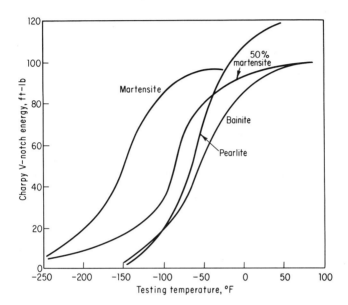

Fig. 14·12 Effect of microstructure on notch toughness of Cr-Mo low-carbon steel. (*From "Metals Handbook," 1961 edition, p. 235, American Society for Metals, Metals Park, Ohio*)

Carburized or nitrided surfaces tend to lower the notch toughness of carbon and alloy steels. This is due to the hard, less ductile surface layers that resist plastic bending under shock loads. Decarburization favors plastic bending and may slightly increase notch toughness; however, it will reduce fatigue strength.

Notched-bar impact values of some steels and nonferrous materials at low temperatures are given in Table 14·3.

14·10   Mechanical factors. The mechanical factors that affect notched-bar impact results are the stress concentration and the strain rate. The stress concentration is determined by the sharpness of the notch. Decreasing the radius of the notch increases the stress concentration, which tends to produce brittle behavior at higher temperatures. The strain rate is determined by the striking velocity of the pendulum, and the energy absorbed is very sensitive to the striking velocity when the steel is near the transition temperature. High striking velocity has the same effect as lowering the test temperature and tends to exaggerate brittle behavior.

To summarize, the best notch-toughness properties are obtained by selecting a fine-grained, low-carbon, fully killed, nickel-alloy steel which has been quenched to a fully martensitic structure and tempered to the desired hardness level.

It must be emphasized that notched-bar impact values apply only to the conditions under which the test was run. The results cannot be used in design and serve only to compare different factors under those conditions. Any attempt to use these values for structures of different size or different strain rates must be done with extreme care. The values become significant for design only when correlated with a particular structure in a particular kind of service.

QUESTIONS

14·1   What factors should be considered when testing at elevated temperatures as compared with testing at room temperature?

14·2   Define *creep*. Why is this property important for high-temperature application?

14·3   Give a specific application where creep properties would be important in design?

14·4   Draw a typical creep curve and explain the stages of creep.

14·5   What metallurgical factors affect the creep characteristics of metals?

14·6   What are the limitations on the use of stress-rupture data?

14·7   Which alloying elements are most effective in raising the creep strength of steels?

14·8   What is the effect of low temperatures on the mechanical properties of metals?

14·9   What is meant by *transition temperature?* How is it measured?

14·10   What factors influence brittle failure?

14·11   What are the limitations on the use of notched-bar data for the performance of actual parts?

14·12   Differentiate between a shear fracture and a cleavage fracture.

14·13   What alloying element is most effective in improving the low-temperature toughness of steel?

REFERENCES

American Society for Metals: "Behavior of Metals at Low Temperatures," Metals Park, Ohio, 1953.

————: "Creep and Recovery," Metals Park, Ohio, 1957.

————: "High Temperature Properties of Metals," Metals Park, Ohio, 1961.

————: "Metals Handbook," 1948 and 1961 editions, Metals Park, Ohio.

Clark, F. H.: "Metals at High Temperatures," Reinhold Publishing Corporation, New York, 1950.

International Nickel Company: "Nickel Alloy Steels," 2d ed., 1949.

Parker, E. R.: "Brittle Behavior of Engineering Structures," John Wiley & Sons, Inc., New York, 1957.

Savitsky, E. M.: "The Influence of Temperature on the Mechanical Properties of Metals and Alloys," Stanford University Press, Stanford, Calif., 1961.

Seigle, L., and R. M. Brick, Mechanical Properties of Metals at Low Temperatures; A Survey, *Trans. ASM*, vol. 40, p. 813, 1948.

Sully, A. H.: "Metallic Creep," Interscience Publishers, Inc., New York, 1949.

Chapter 15

CORROSION OF METALS

15·1 Introduction. Corrosion is a deterioration of metals by chemical action. Generally it is slow, but persistent in character. In some instances the corrosion products exist as a thin adherent film which merely stains or tarnishes the metal and may act as a retardant to further corrosive action. In other cases, the products of corrosion are bulky and porous in character, offering no protection.

The basic cause of corrosion is the instability of metals in their refined forms. The metals tend to revert to their natural states through the processes of corrosion.

15·2 Electrochemical principles. Corrosion is essentially an electrochemical process resulting in part or all of the metal being transformed from the metallic to the ionic state. Corrosion requires a flow of electricity between certain areas of a metal surface through an electrolyte. An electrolyte is any solution that contains ions. Ions are electrically charged atoms or groups of atoms. Pure water, for example, contains positively charged hydrogen ions (H^+) and negatively charged hydroxyl ions (OH^-) in equal amounts. The electrolyte, therefore, may be plain water, salt water, or acid or alkaline solutions of any concentration. To complete the electric circuit, there must be two electrodes, an anode and a cathode, and they must be connected. The electrodes may be two different kinds of metals or they may be different areas on the same piece of metal. The connection between the anode and the cathode may be by a metallic bridge, but in corrosion it is usually achieved simply by contact. In order for electricity to flow there must be a potential difference between the electrodes.

At the anode, atoms of the metal enter the solution as positive ions. The corresponding negative electrons travel through the metal to the cathode area. At the cathode, the electrons will neutralize positively charged ions that reach the cathode from the solution. These positive ions are usually hydrogen ions which become neutral atoms and may combine to form hydrogen gas. The basic electrochemical reaction may be written as

$$A + B^+ \rightarrow A^+ + B$$

Corrosion, the disintegration or eating away of a metal, almost always occurs at areas that act as anodes. The amount of metal A which dissolves is proportional to the number of electrons flowing, which in turn is dependent upon the potential and the resistance of the metal.

In order for corrosion to continue it is necessary to remove the corrosion products from the anode and the cathode. In some cases, the evolution of hydrogen gas at the cathode is very slow and the accumulation of a layer of hydrogen on the metal slows down the reaction. This is known as *cathodic polarization*. However, oxygen dissolved in the electrolyte can react with accumulated hydrogen to form water, thus allowing corrosion to proceed. Metallic ions may be removed as insoluble oxides or hydroxides.

15·3 Factors influencing corrosion. One of the most important factors in influencing corrosion is the difference in electrical potential of dissimilar metals when coupled together and immersed in an electrolyte. This potential is due to the chemical natures of the anodic and cathodic regions. Some indication of which metals may be anodic as compared with hydrogen is given by the standard electromotive-force series (Table 15·1). The standard hydrogen cell is assigned a value of zero, and the potential developed by a half cell of the metal in question coupled to a standard half cell is compared with that of the hydrogen cell. The listing in Table 15·1 is in decreasing order of activity. The more active metals at the top of the list exhibit a stronger tendency to dissolve than those at the bottom. A metal higher in the series will displace a metal lower in the series from solution.

The electromotive series holds only for metals under conditions for which the series was determined. The electrolytes contained particular concentrations of salts of the same metal that was being studied. Under actual conditions, in other electrolytes, their behavior may be different. Instead of the electromotive series, a somewhat similar galvanic series is used which is based on experience with combinations of metals in a great variety of environments. Table 15·2 gives such a series for a number of metals and alloys in sea water moving at high velocity. In any couple, the metal near the top of this series will be anodic and suffer corrosion, while the one nearer the bottom will be cathodic and receive some galvanic protection. The difference in electrical potential between two metals is related to distance between them in the galvanic series. A metal coupled with another close to it

Table 15·1   Electromotive-force series*

Electrode reaction	Standard electrode potential $E°$, volts, 25°C	Electrode reaction	Standard electrode potential $E°$, volts, 25°C
$K = K^+ + e^-$	-2.922	$Co = Co^{++} + 2e^-$	-0.277
$Ca = Ca^{++} + 2e^-$	-2.87	$Ni = Ni^{++} + 2e^-$	-0.250
$Na = Na^+ + e^-$	-2.712	$Sn = Sn^{++} + 2e^-$	-0.136
$Mg = Mg^{++} + 2e^-$	-2.34	$Pb = Pb^{++} + 2e^-$	-0.126
$Be = Be^{++} + 2e^-$	-1.70	$\frac{1}{2}H_2 = H^+ + e^-$	0.000
$Al = Al^{3+} + 3e^-$	-1.67	$Cu = Cu^{++} + 2e^-$	0.345
$Mn = Mn^{++} + 2e^-$	-1.05	$Cu = Cu^+ + e^-$	0.522
$Zn = Zn^{++} + 2e^-$	-0.762	$Ag = Ag^+ + e^-$	0.800
$Cr = Cr^{3+} + 3e^-$	-0.71	$Pd = Pd^{++} + 2e^-$	0.83
$Ga = Ga^{3+} + 3e^-$	-0.52	$Hg = Hg^{++} + 2e^-$	0.854
$Fe = Fe^{++} + 2e^-$	-0.440	$Pt = Pt^{++} + 2e^-$	~1.2
$Cd = Cd^{++} + 2e^-$	-0.402	$Au = Au^{3+} + 3e^-$	1.42
$In = In^{3+} + 3e^-$	-0.340	$Au = Au^+ + e^-$	1.68
$Tl = Tl^+ + e^-$	-0.336		

* Courtesy of the International Nickel Company.

on this list will usually corrode more slowly than when coupled with one further below it.

The relative concentration of both ions involved in the reaction has a definite influence on the electrical potential. If the metallic-ion concentration is increased relative to the reducible ion concentration, there will be a reduction in potential.

If the metallic ion is removed by the formation of an insoluble

Table 15·2   Galvanic series of metals and alloys in sea water*

Anodic (Corroded) End

Magnesium	Aluminum brass
Zinc	Red brass
Aluminum	Copper
Cadmium	Aluminum bronze
Aluminum alloys	Copper-nickel alloys
Low steel	Nickel
Alloy steel	Inconel
Cast iron	Silver
Stainless steel	Stainless steel (passive)
Muntz metal	Monel
Yellow brass	Titanium

Cathodic (Protected) End

* Courtesy of The International Nickel Company.

compound which is precipitated on the anode, and this film is adherent and impervious to the corroding solution, complete insulation results and corrosion stops. Oxide films of this type are formed on aluminum and chromium, which accounts for their superior corrosion resistance. A porous oxide or metallic coating tends to increase corrosion, especially when the part is exposed to alternating periods of immersion and drying.

The effect of dissolved oxygen on the corrosion rate is twofold: the formation of oxides and as a cathodic depolarizer. If the oxide formation removes metallic ions from the metal, corrosion will be increased. The effect of oxide film on the metal was mentioned previously. If the oxygen acts to remove hydrogen from around the cathode, corrosion will be increased. The effectiveness of oxygen in removing hydrogen is influenced by the amount of cathode area. With a large cathode the hydrogen that reaches it will spread out and will be more accessible for removal by reaction with oxygen. This is why it is poor practice to couple a large cathode with a small anode. This may be illustrated by the following example. If steel plates are joined by copper rivets and immersed in sea water for several months, the copper rivets will remain in good condition and there will be no significant acceleration of the corrosion of the steel near the rivets. If, however, copper plates are joined by steel rivets and immersed under the same conditions, the steel rivets will be attacked very severely (Fig. 15·1).

Agitation acts to increase the corrosion rate by bringing fresh corroding solution into contact with the metal.

Differences in potential from point to point on a single metal surface cause corrosion known as *local action* and may be due to impurities on the surface or differences in surface structure or environment. A difference in environment, such as the difference in concentration of metal ions in the corroding solution at one point on the metal surface as compared with another point on the metal surface, will cause corrosion by local action. This difference in metal-ion concentration can be set up when a metal is in contact with a solution where the velocity is greater at one point than at another. This situation can be created by spinning a metal disk through salt water. Since the metal nearer the center of the disk moves more slowly than at the edge, this allows metal ions to accumulate near the center and be swept away near the edge. At the edge, the region of highest velocity, metal-ion concentration will be the least, and severe corrosion will take place in this region (Fig. 15·2). For this application, a metal must be chosen that will be able to hold its protective film right up to the outer edge under these conditions.

Other factors such as the presence of other ions in solution, the temperature of the solution, and the existence of stray electric currents may materially affect the corrosion rate.

(a)

Fig. 15·1 Influence of area relationship between cathode and anode illustrated by copper-steel couples after immersion in sea water. (a) Copper rivets with small area in steel plates of large area have caused only slight increase in corrosion of steel. (b) Steel rivets with small area in copper plates of large area have caused severe corrosion of steel rivets. (*The International Nickel Company*)

15·4 Specific corrosion types. Specific descriptions are generally used for certain types of industrially important corrosion. When the entire surface of the metal is attacked to the same degree, it is known as *uniform corrosion*. This type is unusual in metals, since they are rarely so homogeneous that the surface will be evenly corroded.

Pitting corrosion is an example of nonuniform corrosion resulting from inhomogeneities in metal due to inclusions, coring, and distorted zones. These inhomogeneities set up differences of potential at

(b)

localized spots to cause deep isolated holes. Figure 15·3 shows an electrolytically formed pit. The large pit formed when the surface was penetrated in a small area, then grew rapidly into a large cavity under the surface. Progressive growth of the cavity caused further penetration of the surface from below. Part of the roof of the cavity then collapsed. Figure 15·4 shows pitting on a metal surface resulting from localized corrosion under marine organisms that became attached to the surface while immersed in sea water. Pitting of the base metal occurs when there is a break in the protecting layer or film. For example, when the chromium plate in a steel auto bumper is broken, pitting of the exposed steel takes place.

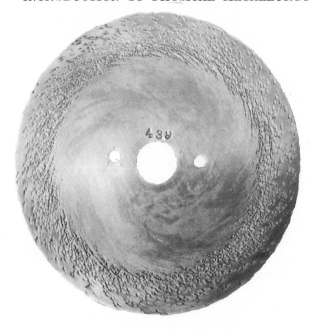

Fig. 15·2   Severe corrosion in region of high velocity on an admiralty-brass disk after rotation in sea water.   (*The International Nickel Company*)

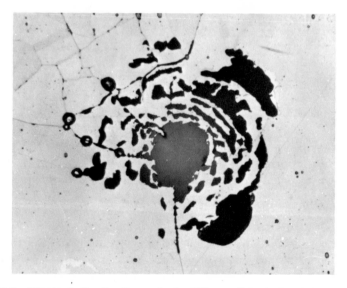

Fig. 15·3   Electrolytically formed pit, 350×.   (*M. A. Streicher, Du Pont Research Laboratory*)

Intergranular corrosion is another example of nonuniform corrosion when a potential difference exists between the grain boundaries and the rest of the alloy. This type of corrosion usually takes place when precipitation of a phase from a solid solution occurs. Since precipitation usually takes place faster at the grain boundaries, the material in the vicinity of the grain boundary becomes depleted of the dissolved element, creating a difference of potential, and the grain boundary

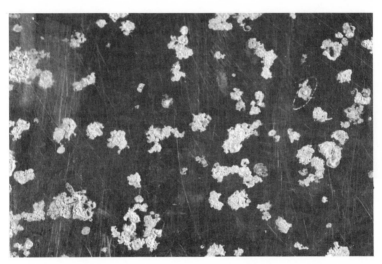

Fig. 15·4 Pitting corrosion due to marine organisms while metal was immersed in sea water. (*The International Nickel Company*)

will dissolve preferentially (Fig. 15·5). Often a visual examination of the part will not reveal the extent of the damage, and in most cases there is an appreciable loss in mechanical properties.

Preferential corrosion of one of the components may even occur in single-phase solid-solution alloys. Dezincification in brass (see Sec. 12·6) is an example of this kind of corrosion (Fig. 12·5).

Stress corrosion is acceleration of corrosion in certain environments when metals contain internal tensile stresses due to cold working (see Sec. 12·6). Figure 15·6 shows a stress-corrosion crack in stainless steel.

Galvanic corrosion occurs at the interface where two metals are in contact in a corroding medium. This type of corrosion, illustrated in Fig. 15·7, was discussed in Sec. 15·2.

Intergranular corrosion and stress corrosion have a very serious effect on the mechanical properties of the metal. The reduction in strength is not due to the amount of metal removed but rather to the stress concentration produced by the fine cracks. Table 15·3 (page 450) gives an idea of the effect of the type of corrosion on properties.

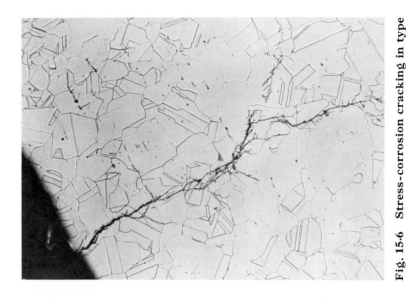

Fig. 15.6 Stress-corrosion cracking in type 304 stainless steel. A bend was exposed to chloride-containing water, 250×. (M. A. Streicher, Du Pont Research Laboratory)

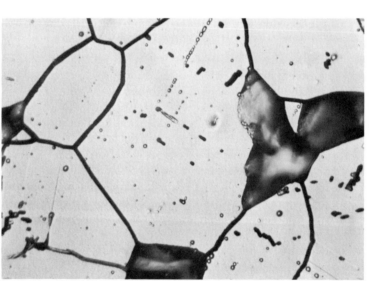

Fig. 15.5 Intergranular corrosion in type 316 stainless steel after 27-hr exposure in boiling ferric sulfate–sulfuric acid solution, 500×. (M. A. Streicher, Du Pont Research Laboratory)

A type of corrosion that has become increasingly important is liquid-metal corrosion. In certain types of nuclear reactors for the production of atomic power, liquid metals such as bismuth and sodium are used as the heat-transfer medium. The path of the liquid metal is a closed loop with one leg at high temperature in the reactor core and the other

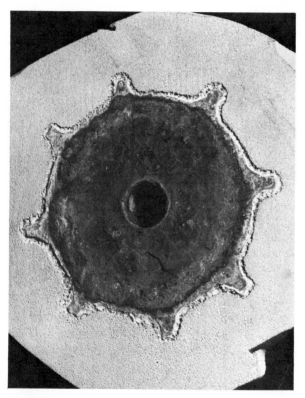

Fig. 15·7 Galvanic corrosion of magnesium where it is in close contact with a steel core around which the magnesium was cast. (*The International Nickel Company*)

leg at lower temperature in a heat exchanger. The solubility of a solid in the liquid usually increases with temperature. Therefore, there is a tendency for the solid to dissolve up to its solubility limit in the high-temperature leg and be deposited, because of the lower solubility limit, in the cooler leg. The hot leg is continually corroded and the cold leg becomes plugged with the deposited corrosion products. This phenomenon is essentially one of mass transfer which leads to gradual deterioration of the metal in the hot zone. The most effective method of controlling this type of corrosion is by use of inhibitors in

Table 15·3   Effect of corrosion type on properties*

Type	Weight loss, %	Depth of penetration, %	Loss of properties, %		
			Tensile strength	Yield strength	Elongation
Uniform	1	1	1	1	1
Pitting	0.7	5	7	5	15
Intergranular	0.2	15	25	20	80
Stress	0.1	100	100	100	100

* By permission from L. F. Mondolfo and O. Zmeskal, "Engineering Metallurgy," McGraw-Hill Book Company, Inc., New York, 1955.

the liquid metal.   Zirconium has been used as an effective inhibitor in liquid bismuth to decrease the liquid-metal corrosion of iron by mass transfer.

15·5 Methods for combating corrosion. Many methods are used industrially to prevent corrosion by selection of the proper alloy and structure, or by surface protection of a given material.   The most important are:

1. Use of high-purity metals
2. Use of alloy additions
3. Use of special heat treatments
4. Proper design
5. Cathodic protection
6. Use of inhibitors
7. Surface coatings

In most cases, the use of high-purity metals tends to reduce pitting corrosion by minimizing inhomogeneities, thereby improving corrosion resistance.

Alloy additions may reduce corrosion by several methods.   For example, austenitic stainless steels, when cooled through a temperature range of about 900 to 1400°F, precipitate chromium carbides at the grain boundaries.   This precipitation depletes the boundaries of chromium and makes them more susceptible to intergranular corrosion. This type of corrosion may be avoided either by reducing the carbon to a low value (below 0.03 per cent) or by converting the carbide to a more stable form.   The latter method is more widely used and involves the addition of titanium or columbium.   These elements have a great affinity for carbon, producing very stable carbides that are not soluble in austenite at elevated temperature.   This leaves very little carbon available for combination with chromium and results in what is known as a *stabilized* stainless steel.   Some alloy additions improve corrosion resistance by forming, or helping the formation of, adherent, nonporous surface oxide films. This is particularly true of manganese and aluminum additions to copper alloys, molybdenum additions to stainless steels, and magnesium additions to aluminum.

Heat treatment which leads to homogenization of solid solutions, especially in cast alloys that are subject to coring, tends to improve corrosion resistance. Stress-relief treatments following cold working are widely used to improve the resistance of alloys susceptible to stress corrosion.

Proper design should keep contact with the corroding agent to a minimum. Joints should be properly designed to reduce the tendency for liquids to enter and be retained. Contact between materials far apart in the electromotive series should be avoided. If this cannot be done, they should be separated by rubber or plastic to reduce the possibility of galvanic corrosion.

Cathodic protection is obtained by placing the metal that would normally corrode in electrical contact with one that is above it in the galvanic series. The more active metal thus becomes the anode. This is essentially a galvanic battery in which the corroding metal is made to function as the cathode. The metals generally used to provide this type of protection are zinc and magnesium. In some cases, the protective direct current is obtained by an external voltage source. The anode in this case usually consists of a relatively inert material such as carbon, graphite, or platinum. The structures most frequently protected by this method are underground pipelines, hulls of ships, and boilers. For the protection of underground pipe, anodes are buried some 8 to 10 ft from the pipe. The depth of the hole should be sufficient to locate the anode in permanently moist soil. Individual anodes are connected to a *collector* wire which in turn is brazed to the pipeline. The current discharges from the anode to the soil, collects on the pipeline, and returns to the anode through the connecting wire. For the cathodic protection of ship hulls, zinc or magnesium anodes are fastened to the rudder and to the hull itself in the region around the propeller. Magnesium anodes have become widely used to provide cathodic protection in domestic and industrial water heaters and elevated water-storage tanks.

Inhibitors are chemicals which, when added to the corrosive solution, reduce or eliminate its corrosive effect. In most cases, the inhibitor will form a protective layer on the metal surface. Inhibitors are added to the antifreeze mixtures used in automobile radiators. Oxidizing agents when added to the corrosive solution will produce oxide films on aluminum, chromium, and manganese.

Surface coatings include paints, salt and oxide films, and metallic coatings.

Paints and other organic coatings are primarily used to improve the appearance of the surfaces and structures. The use of paint for corrosion protection only is secondary and of little economic importance to the paint industry. Paint provides a protective film to the metal and is effective only as long as the film is unbroken.

Salt and oxide films are obtained by reacting the metal with a solution which produces the desired film. Some examples are: A chromate pickle protects magnesium by forming a film of magnesium chromate, *Parkerizing* or *Bonderizing* for ferrous alloys protects by forming a phosphate film, anodizing for aluminum and magnesium forms a thick oxide film, and passivating for stainless steels also forms an oxide film.

Metallic coatings may be obtained by a variety of methods such as metallizing, hot dipping, electroplating, diffusion, and cladding.

Metallizing was discussed in Chap. 13 in regard to surface coating for wear resistance. Practically all metallized coatings for corrosion use are either zinc or aluminum. These metals are used primarily for corrosion work on iron and steel because steel is cathodic to them and hence is protected electrochemically in spite of any porosity or minor voids in the coating. Grit or sand blasting is almost universally used for cleaning and preparing the surface prior to spraying. Most coating systems employ supplementary organic sealers or top coats. The sealers are usually vinyl and chlorinated rubber applied over inhibiting primers.

Hot dipping is used mainly to apply a coating of zinc, tin, cadmium, aluminum, or lead to steel. The hot-dip process has a wide range of applicability, but the coating applied must contend with a brittle diffusion layer of intermetallic compounds at the interface. This may result in poor adhesion and a tendency to flake on bending unless the thickness of the diffusion layer is properly controlled. The hot-dip process usually includes the operations of pickling with inhibited acid to produce a clean surface; fluxing to facilitate wetting; dipping the article in a molten bath of controlled composition; and wiping, shaking, or centrifuging the dipped piece to regulate the thickness and uniformity of the coating.

Zinc coating, or *galvanizing*, is applied to a greater tonnage of steel products than any other method of metallic coating. The major applications of zinc coating on steel products include roofing and siding sheets; wire and wire products for all outdoor exposure; articles fabricated from sheet steel such as boilers, pails, cans, and tanks; hardware for outdoor use; pipe and conduit; and exposed structural steel. Tin plate is widely used in the familiar tin can. Terne metal is sheet steel plated in a lead bath to which tin has been added to ensure bonding.

It is more expensive than zinc, but much cheaper than tin. It is used for gasoline tanks and as a roofing material. Aluminizing, hot-dipped aluminum coating on steel, is used for applications that require a combination of resistance to corrosion and heat, such as mufflers and tail pipes of automotive engines.

Electroplated coatings are used extensively for decorative purposes, but for industrial applications the most important single function is for corrosion protection. In addition to corrosion protection and appearance, electroplated coatings are applied to obtain other surface properties such as wear resistance, high electrical conductivity, good solderability, and high or low light-reflecting ability. Nickel and chromium plates provide wear resistance (see Chap. 13); silver and copper are best for electrical conductivity; silver, copper, tin, and cadmium improve solderability; chromium and rhodium have high resistance to tarnish.

Zinc coatings are used on iron and steel products which require primarily corrosion protection. These include nuts, bolts, screws, nails, hardware, and electrical conduit. Cadmium coatings are used as substitutes for zinc coatings but are not quite so good for outdoor exposure. Cadmium plating is also used for radio chassis and electronic equipment since it is readily solderable. Chromium coatings are used on automobile trim, plumbing fixtures, hardware, and appliances. These coatings are very thin and rather porous and normally offer little protection against corrosion. Therefore, they are usually applied over thicker coatings of nickel or copper. Nickel coatings are used principally as an underplate for chromium, silver, gold, and rhodium plating. Nickel has good corrosion resistance but is tarnished by the atmosphere. Copper coatings are used as an undercoat for nickel and chromium coatings, particularly on zinc-base die castings. The greatest use of electroplated tin coatings is for food containers. These coatings may be made thinner than those made by the conventional hot-dipping method.

The use of chromium and silicon as diffusion coatings for wear resistance has been discussed in Chap. 13. In addition to the above two metals, aluminum and zinc diffusion coatings are also used to provide corrosion protection. All diffusion-coating processes follow essentially the same procedure and are based on the same principles. The part to be coated is placed in contact with a powder containing the metal to provide the coating. At elevated temperature there is a transfer of the metal to the base material, through the vapor phase, usually by means of a suitable catalyst. Holding at temperature or reheating without the powder after the initial penetration will allow further diffusion to the desired depth. The process of alloying steel with aluminum by diffusion is called *calorizing*. Calorized steel is highly resistant to oxidation and corrosion by hot gases, particularly sulfurous gases. Calorized parts are used in furnaces that employ fuels high in sulfur; bolts for use up to 1400°F; salt, cyanide, and lead pots; and oil refineries. Zinc impregnation is obtained by a process known as *sherardizing*. The principal application of sherardizing is for small steel parts, such as bolts, nuts, and washers, or for castings exposed to the atmosphere.

Cladding is a method by which the coating becomes an integral part of the material. This may be accomplished by casting or hot working. Casting is best suited when there is a considerable difference in the melting points of the cladding material and the base material. Hot rolling is the more widely used method for cladding. Slabs or sheets of the cladding material are strapped to an ingot of the base material. After heating to the rolling temperature, the straps are removed and the entire assembly is rolled. The heat and pressure during rolling weld the two materials together. The cladding may be of the same base material as the core. Alclad is the name applied to aluminum alloys which are clad with pure aluminum to improve corrosion resistance (see Fig. 12·21). Steel may be clad with nickel, nickel-chromium, or nickel-copper alloys. Aside from corrosion resistance, cladding is sometimes done to obtain a combination of properties that are not available by any other method. Copper-clad steel wire is a good example. The copper exterior provides high electrical conductivity and good corrosion resistance, while the steel core provides high tensile strength. This wire is produced by pouring molten copper into a mold containing a round, heated steel billet. A weld that is able to withstand cold working is produced between the two metals. After solidification, the composite billet is hot-rolled to a rod and then drawn to the desired size.

QUESTIONS

15·1   Explain the mechanism of electrochemical corrosion.

15·2   Why does corrosion generally occur at the anode?

15·3   What is the limitation on the use of the electromotive series (Table 15·1) in the corrosion of metals?

15·4   How does the distance between metals in the galvanic series (Table 15·2) affect corrosion rate?

15·5   Why do aluminum and chromium show superior corrosion resistance?

15·6   List and explain four types of corrosion.

15·7   Explain *cathodic protection*.

15·8   List seven methods of corrosion protection and explain why each method is effective.

REFERENCES

American Society for Metals: "Corrosion of Metals," Metals Park, Ohio, 1946.
————: "Metals Handbook," 1948 and 1961 editions, Metals Park, Ohio.
————: "Surface Protection against Wear and Corrosion," Metals Park, Ohio, 1954.
Burns, R. M., and W. W. Bradley: "Protective Coatings for Metals," American Chemical Society Monograph 129, Reinhold Publishing Corporation, New York, 1955.
Evans, U. R.: "Metallic Corrosion Passivity and Protection," Edward Arnold (Publishers) Ltd., London, 1946.
Hedges, E. S.: "Protective Films on Metals," Chapman & Hall, Ltd., London, 1937.
Hudson, J. C.: "The Corrosion of Iron and Steel," Chapman & Hall, Ltd., London, 1940.
International Nickel Co.: "Corrosion in Action," New York, 1955.
McKay, R. T., and R. Worthington: "Corrosion Resistance of Metals and Alloys," American Chemical Society Monograph 71, Reinhold Publishing Corporation, New York, 1936.
Speller, F. N.: "Corrosion," 3d ed., McGraw-Hill Book Company, Inc., New York, 1951.
Uhlig, H. H.: "The Corrosion Handbook," John Wiley & Sons, Inc., New York, 1948.

Chapter 16

POWDER METALLURGY

16·1   Introduction.   Powder metallurgy may be defined as the art of producing metal powders and using them to make serviceable objects.   Powder-metallurgy principles were used as far back as 3000 B.C. by the Egyptians to make iron implements.   The use of gold, silver, copper, brass, and tin powders for ornamental purposes was commonplace during the middle ages.

In 1829, Woolaston published a paper which described a process for producing compact platinum from platinum sponge powder.   Considered the first scientific work in the field of powder metallurgy, this laid the foundations for modern techniques.

It is interesting to note that in the nineteenth century more metallic elements were produced in powder form than in any other form.

The invention of the incandescent electric light by Edison required the development of a suitable filament material.   Powders of osmium, tantalum, and tungsten were used but the filaments were very brittle. It had long been evident that tungsten would make an ideal filament for the electric lamp, but to work tungsten into the necessary fine wire was beyond conventional metallurgy at the beginning of the twentieth century.   It remained for Coolidge, in 1909, to make the important discovery that tungsten can be worked in a certain temperature range and will retain its ductility at room temperature. Finely divided tungsten powder was compressed into small ingots which were sintered at temperatures below the melting point of tungsten.   These sintered ingots were brittle at room temperature but could be worked at elevated temperatures near the sintering temperature.   Subsequent working at the elevated temperature improved its ductility until a stage was reached where the metal was ductile at room temperature and could be drawn into wire with tensile strength approaching 600,000 psi.

The Coolidge method led to a new method of fabrication for refractory metals such as molybdenum, tantalum, and columbium. It also led to the development of cemented carbides and composite metals. At about the same time porous-metal bearings were manufactured using the technique of powder metallurgy. These and other applications will be discussed later in this chapter.

16·2 Powder-metallurgy processes. The two main operations of the powder-metal process are compacting and sintering.

Compacting, or pressing, consists in subjecting the suitably prepared powder mixtures, at normal or elevated temperature, to considerable pressure. The resulting powder compact is known as a *briquette* and is said, in this form, to be "green." It can be handled but it is relatively brittle.

Sintering is an operation in which the green briquettes are subjected to heat, usually in an inert atmosphere, at a temperature below the melting point of the solid metal. Sintering will give the required mechanical strength as well as other desired properties.

In addition to compacting and sintering, and depending upon application, other accessory operations may be added to the process. These include presintering, sizing, machining, and impregnation. Typical flow sheets showing steps in the manufacture of powder-metal parts are shown in Fig. 16·1.

16·3 Characteristics of metal powders. In all cases, the performance of the material during processing as well as the properties of the finished product depends to a large extent upon the basic characteristics of the powder material. Aside from the chemical composition and purity, the basic characteristics of a metal powder are particle size and size distribution, particle shape, apparent density, and particle microstructure.

Metal powders may be divided into sieve and subsieve size ranges. Those in the sieve-size class are usually designated according to the finest mesh through which all the powder will pass. If all the powder passes through a 200-mesh screen, it is designated as a minus 200-mesh powder, etc. The subsieve-size powders all pass through a 325-mesh sieve used in practice. The size of these powders may be specified by averaging the actual dimensions as determined by microscopic examination.

Particle-size distribution is important in the packing of the powder and will influence its behavior during molding and sintering. For practical purposes, the selection of a desirable size distribution for a specific application is usually based upon experience. In general, a finer powder is preferred over a coarser powder since finer powders have smaller pore size and larger contact areas, which usually result in better physical properties after sintering. Particle-size distribution

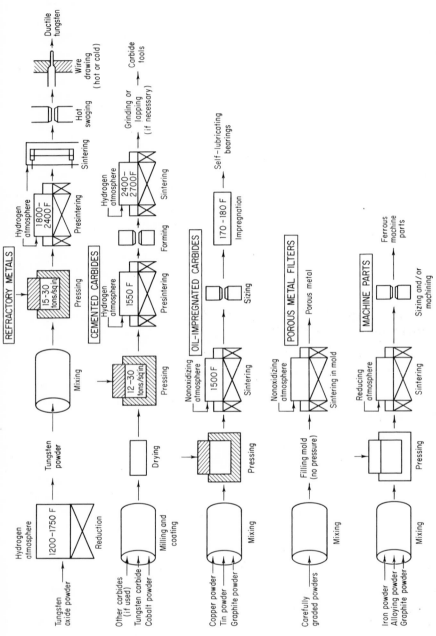

Fig. 16·1 Typical flow sheets showing steps in the manufacture of articles from metal powders. *(From "Metals Handbook," 1948 edition, p. 48, American Society for Metals, Metals Park, Ohio)*

is specified in terms of a sieve analysis, that is, the amount of powder passing through 100-, 200-, etc., mesh sieves.

Particle shape is important in influencing the packing and flow characteristics of powders. Spherical-shaped particles have excellent sintering qualities and result in uniform physical characteristics of the end product; however, irregular-shaped particles have been found superior for practical molding. The mechanism of packing involves three processes: the filling of gaps between larger particles by smaller ones, breakdown of bridges or arches, and mutual sliding and rotation

Table 16·1 Apparent densities of commercial metal powders*

Material	Specific gravity	Apparent density	Material	Specific gravity	Apparent density
Aluminum	2.70	0.7–1	Molybdenum	10.2	3–6.5
Antimony	6.68	2–2.5	Nickel	8.9	2.5–3.5
Cadmium	8.65	3	Silicon	2.42	0.5–0.8
Chromium	7.1	2.5–3.5	Silver	10.50	1.2–1.7
Cobalt	8.9	1.5–3	Tin	5.75	1–3
Copper	8.93	0.7–4	Tungsten	19.3	5–10
Lead	11.3	4–6	Zinc	7.14	2.5–3
Magnesium	1.74	0.3–0.7	Iron and steel	7.85	1–4

* By permission from C. G. Goetzel, "Treatise on Powder Metallurgy," vol. 1, Interscience Publishers, Inc., New York, 1949.

of particles. These processes are important in loading die cavities with metal powders.

Apparent density may be defined as the weight of a loosely heaped quantity of powder necessary to fill a given die cavity completely. A list of apparent-density ranges of a number of metal powders is given in Table 16·1. This property is of great importance for both molding and sintering operations. Powders with low apparent density require a longer compression stroke and deeper cavities to produce a briquette of given size and density. The tendency of the compact to shrink during sintering seems to decrease with increasing apparent density.

16·4 Preparation of metal powders. There is a definite relation between a particular method of powder production and desired properties of powder-metallurgy products. Many mechanical and chemical methods are used to produce powders for specific applications, but the three most important methods are atomization, reduction of oxides, and electrolytic deposition.

Atomization is the method most frequently used for metals having low melting points such as tin, lead, zinc, cadmium, and aluminum.

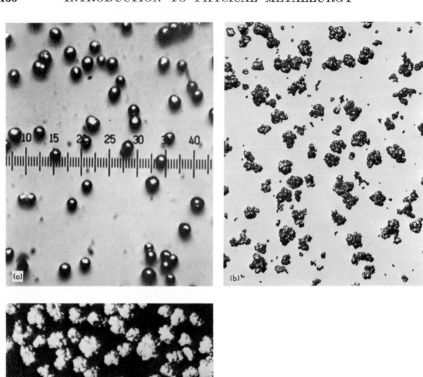

Fig. 16·2 Shape of powders produced by different methods. (*a*) Atomizing; (*b*) oxide reduction; (*c*) electrodeposition. (*Metal Powder Industries Federation*)

As the liquid metal is forced through a small orifice, a stream of compressed air causes the metal to disintegrate and solidify into finely divided particles. Atomized products are generally in the form of sphere-shaped particles (Fig. 16·2*a*). A wide range of particle-size distributions may be obtained by varying the temperature of the metal, pressure and temperature of the atomizing gas, rate of flow of metal through the orifice, and the design of the orifice and nozzle.

The principal advantage of the atomization process is its flexibility. It will produce powders of different degrees of fineness, and in the production of a given fineness, uniformity of particle-size distribution can be closely maintained.

The reduction of compounds of the metals (usually an oxide) provides a convenient, economical, and flexible method of producing powders. The largest volume of metallurgical powder is made by the process of oxide reduction. Mill scale or chemically produced oxides are reduced with carbon monoxide or hydrogen, and the reduced powder is subsequently ground. The nature, particle size, and distribution of the raw material and the conditions of reduction greatly influence the form of the deposited particles. If the oxide powder is graded before reduction, a high degree of size uniformity can be obtained in the reduced powder. The particles produced by oxide reduction are sponge-like in structure and are ideal for molding. The shape is generally jagged and irregular (Fig. 16·2b), and the particles are porous. This is the only practical method available for producing powders of the refractory metals such as tungsten and molybdenum. Oxide reduction is also an economical method of producing powders of iron, nickel, cobalt, and copper.

The method of electrolytic deposition is most suitable for the production of extremely pure powders of principally copper and iron. This process is essentially an adaptation of electroplating. By regulation of current density, temperature, circulation of the electrolyte, and proper choice of electrolyte, the powder may be directly deposited from the electrolyte. The deposit may be a soft spongy substance which is subsequently ground to powder, or the deposit may be a hard, brittle metal. Powders obtained from hard, brittle electrodeposits are generally not suitable for molding purposes. Most of the powder produced by electrolytic deposition for commercial applications is of the spongy type. The shape of electrolytic powder is generally dendritic (Fig. 16·2c). Although the resulting powder has low apparent density, the dendritic structure tends to give good molding properties because of interlocking of the particles during compacting.

16·5 Mixing. Proper blending and mixing of the powders is essential for uniformity of the finished product. Desired particle-size distribution is obtained by blending in advance the different types of powders used. Alloying powders, lubricants, and volatilizing agents to give a desired amount of porosity are added to the blended powders during mixing. The time for mixing may vary from a few minutes to several days, depending upon experience and the results desired. Overmixing should be avoided in many cases since it may decrease particle size and work-harden the particles.

16·6   Compacting.   The most important operation in powder metallurgy is compacting or pressing.   The ability to obtain a satisfactory pressed density often determines the feasibility of manufacture by powder metallurgy.   Most compacting is done cold, although there are some applications for which compacts are *hot-pressed*.

The usual sequence of operations in compacting consists in filling the die cavity with a definite volume of powder; application of the required pressure by movement of the upper and lower punches toward each

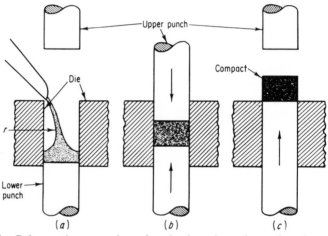

Fig. 16·3   Schematic operations for the forming of powdered parts.   (By permission from L. F. Mondolfo and O. Zmeskal, "Engineering Metallurgy," McGraw-Hill Book Company, Inc., New York, 1955)

other; and finally, ejection of the green compact by the lower punch. These operations are shown schematically in Fig. 16·3.

The pressures commonly employed range from 19 to 50 tons per sq in.   The pressure may be obtained by either mechanical or hydraulic presses.   Mechanical presses are available with pressure ratings of 10 to 150 tons and speeds of 6 to 150 strokes per minute.   The important features of mechanical presses are high-speed production rates, flexibility in design, simplicity and economy in operation, and relatively low investment and maintenance costs.   A mechanical press is shown in Fig. 16·4.   This is a 20-ton multiple-motion press combining one motion from above with two independent mechanically linked motions from below (Fig. 16·5).   The secondary lower motion allows the production of multilevel compacts with simplified tooling and can also be used as a movable core rod to assist in the production of thin-walled pieces.

Hydraulic presses have higher pressure ratings, up to 5,000 tons, but slower stroke speeds, generally less than 20 per minute.   These presses are used for higher-pressure, more complicated powder-metal parts.

Dies are usually made of hardened, ground, and lapped tool steels. When the powder to be compacted consists of hard abrasive particles, the die is generally constructed of two parts. The tough outer section supports the hardened polished wear-resistant insert which is the

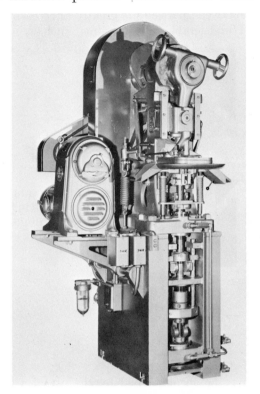

Fig. 16·4   Multiple-action 20-ton powder-metal mechanical press.   (*F. J. Stokes Corporation*)

working surface of the die. These replaceable liners are discarded when worn, and reduce the cost of die upkeep.

The punches are made of die steel heat-treated to be slightly softer than the die since they are usually easier to replace than the die. They must be perfectly aligned and very closely fitted.

16·7   Sintering.   The sintering process is usually carried out at a temperature below the highest melting constituent. In some cases the temperature is high enough to form a liquid constituent such as in the manufacture of cemented carbides where sintering is done above the melting point of the binder metal. In other cases, no melting of any constituent takes place.

Sintering furnaces may be either the electric-resistance type or gas- or oil-fired type. Close control of temperature is necessary to minimize variations in final dimensions. The very uniform and accurate temperature of the electric furnace makes it most suitable for this type of work.

Since bonding between particles is greatly affected by surface films, the formation of undesirable surface films, such as oxides, must be

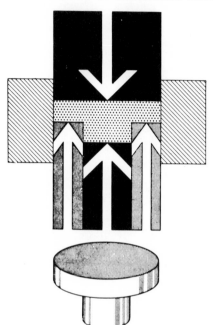

Fig. 16·5 The multiple actions of the press shown in Fig. 16·4. (*F. J. Stokes Corporation*)

avoided. This may be accomplished by the use of a controlled protective atmosphere. Another function of the atmosphere is to reduce such films if they are present on the powders before mixing and briquetting. The protective atmosphere should not contain any free oxygen and should be neutral or reducing to the metal being sintered. A dry hydrogen atmosphere is used in the sintering of refractory carbides and electrical contacts, but most commercial sintering atmospheres are produced by the partial combustion of various hydrocarbons. Natural gas or propane is often used for this purpose.

Sintering is essentially a process of bonding solid bodies by atomic forces. Sintering forces tend to decrease with increasing temperature, but obstructions to sintering such as incomplete surface contact, presence of surface films, and lack of plasticity all decrease more rapidly with increasing temperature. Thus elevated temperatures tend to favor the sintering process. The longer the time of heating or the higher the temperature, the greater will be the bonding between particles and the resulting tensile strength.

16·8 Hot pressing. This method consists in applying pressure and temperature simultaneously. Molding and sintering take place at the same time, which results in higher densities and greater productions. The advantages of hot pressing as compared with cold compacting and sintering are a reduction in gas content and shrinkage effects, and higher strength, hardness, elongation, and density. Hot pressing is used only to a limited extent primarily for the production of very hard cemented-carbide parts. The principal disadvantage of this method is the high cost of dies to stand up under pressure at elevated temperature.

16·9 Supplemental operations. For applications that require higher density or close dimensional tolerances, sintering is followed by a cold-working operation known as *coining* or *repressing*. Coining serves the purpose of condensing the sintered compact. It is possible to obtain considerable plastic deformation within the die, resulting in more complex shapes than may be made directly from powder. The restricted plastic deformation within the die also allows, in many cases, close dimensional tolerances to be held without the necessity of costly machining.

Heating for sintering may be interrupted at some intermediate temperature. This is known as *presintering*. At this point, the compact may have good machinability or be sufficiently soft to allow the use of operations that are not feasible after sintering.

In some cases, resintering after repressing will increase the mechanical properties considerably. As compared with straight sintered metal, resintering may increase the tensile strength of copper by about 60 per cent and of iron by about 30 per cent. Despite the increase in strength, resintering may result in large grain size and loss of dimensions due to shrinkage. This may require another sizing operation, which will increase the cost of the part.

Depending upon the particular application, the sintered compact may be heat-treated to obtain certain desirable properties. The heat treatment may be a stress-relief or annealing treatment. Suitable nonferrous alloy compositions may be age-hardened. Steels may be quench-hardened or case-hardened by carburizing, cyaniding, or nitriding.

Various finishing operations may be carried out to complete the manufacture of powder-metal parts. These include machining, shearing, broaching, burnishing, straightening, deburring, grinding, and sandblasting.

Protective surface coatings may be applied by electroplating, metal spraying, and many of the other methods described in Chap. 15.

Of the various joining methods, only brazing has been used extensively for powder-metallurgy products.

Impregnation is the means used to fill the internal pores in the sintered compact. This is carried out primarily to improve antifriction properties as in the self-lubricating bearings. Oil impregnation may be accomplished by dipping the parts in a container of hot oil, or by first drawing the air out of the pores by vacuum and then forcing the oil into the pores under pressure. Waxes and greases may also be used as impregnants. The use of a low-melting metal impregnant such as tin and lead babbitt alloys in a spongy matrix of nonferrous alloys tends to improve the bearing properties of the metal. Impregnation with liquid lead has been used to increase the specific gravity of iron-base parts.

16·10 Applications of powder metallurgy. Powder-metallurgy techniques are used for the production of refractory metals, composite metals, porous metals, and metal-nonmetal combinations, and as a more efficient production method for certain parts.

The high melting points of the refractory metals make it impossible to use the conventional melting and casting techniques. The use of the powder method for the manufacture of tungsten filaments was described at the beginning of this chapter. This technique offers the only practical method of producing molybdenum, tantalum, and other metals of the same group.

One of the outstanding uses of powder metallurgy is the combination of hard materials in a metallic matrix, which serves as the basis for cemented-carbide products. In the production of cemented-carbide cutting tools, a suitable mixture of the carbides of tungsten, tantalum, and titanium with cobalt as a binder is compacted and presintered. In this condition, the materials can be cut, machined, and ground to the final shape. The compact is then subjected to a high-temperature (about 2750°F) sintering operation during which the liquid cobalt binds the hard carbide particles into a solid piece. Cemented-carbide tools are noted for high compressive strength, red hardness, and wear resistance. Since they are relatively brittle, they are usually employed as brazed-on tips to a steel tool. They are also used as liners for wear-resistant applications.

Other examples in this classification are diamond-impregnated grinding wheels, drill-core bits, and dressing tools. These consist of diamonds embedded in cemented carbides or more plastic metals and alloys.

Metal-nonmetal combinations have found wide use in the manufacture of friction materials such as clutch facings and brake linings. These materials contain a metallic matrix of copper or bronze for heat conductivity, lead or graphite to form a smoothly engaging lining during operation, and silica or emery for frictional purposes. Iron is sometimes added to increase friction and prevent seizing. Copper-graphite combinations are used as current-collector brushes and in porous bronze and iron bearings.

Composite metals are metal combinations that retain the characteristics of each metal for particular applications. Powder metallurgy is particularly useful for alloys of metals that are not soluble in the liquid state or form monotectics. Casting tends to produce a two-layer alloy unless special techniques are used, whereas homogeneous mixtures are easily produced from powders. The electrical industry makes use of composite metals in the production of heavy-duty contacts which combine the high resistance to abrasion and arcing of a refractory metal such as tungsten with the high conductivity of silver or copper. Similarly, the lubricating qualities of lead are combined with the load-carrying ability of copper in the copper-lead bearings.

Controlled porosity of powder-metal parts has led to the production of porous bearings, gears, and filters. Self-lubricating bearings are made of bronze powder with controlled porosity after sintering. The pores are subsequently filled with oil. In operation, the load on the bearing and the increased heat set up by the moving part within the bearing force the oil out of the pores to provide automatic and uniform lubrication. Self-lubricating bearings are used extensively in the automotive industry and in washing machines, refrigerators, electric clocks, and many other types of equipment. Porous-metal gears are used in oil pumps for their lubricating properties. Metal filters, used in the chemical industry, are similar to the ceramic type but have higher mechanical strength and resistance to both mechanical and thermal shock.

Finally, in many applications the use of powder-metallurgy techniques results in more economical manufacture of the part. Where load conditions are not severe, small gears, cams, levers, sprockets, and other parts of iron, steel, brass, or bronze may be molded from powders to reduce greatly or completely eliminate expensive and time-consuming machining and other forming operations. For example, the gears of a gear-type oil pump must have accurately formed involute teeth or the pump will be inefficient. The machined gear is cut from a cast blank by a skilled machinist with about 64 per cent of the metal lost in chips. On the other hand, any semiskilled man can fill a hopper and operate a press which can turn out hundreds of these gears with dimensional accuracy and with less than 1 per cent of the metal as waste.

Small alnico permanent magnets containing aluminum, nickel, cobalt, and iron may be made from powders or by casting.   The cast alloy is difficult to machine, and finishing to dimensions must be done by tedious grinding.   These magnets may be molded of powders directly to size and shape and their dimensions held to acceptable tolerances during sintering.   In addition, a finer grain size and greater mechanical strength are obtained in the sintered magnets.

Fig. 16·6   Typical parts produced from powder metals.   (*F. J. Stokes Corporation*)

Some typical parts produced by powder-metallurgy techniques are shown in Fig. 16·6.

QUESTIONS

16·1   Why is particle-size distribution important in the packing of powders?

16·2   Discuss the importance of particle shape on the properties of sintered compacts.

16·3   List the three common methods of powder production and discuss their influence on the properties of the final product.

16·4   Contrast mechanical and hydraulic compacting presses with regard to advantages, disadvantages, and applications.

16·5   Why is sintering carried out in a controlled-atmosphere furnace?

16·6   Why do elevated temperatures tend to favor the sintering process although sintering forces tend to decrease with increasing temperature?

16·7   What are the advantages and disadvantages of hot pressing as compared with cold compacting and sintering?

16·8   Give three specific applications of powder-metallurgy parts.   Describe how these parts may be manufactured by other methods and give the advantages of the powder-metallurgy method.

16·9   Why is pore size important in the manufacture of self-lubricating bearings?   How may pore size be controlled?

REFERENCES

American Society for Metals: "Metals Handbook," 1948 edition, Metals Park, Ohio.

————: "Powder Metallurgy in Nuclear Engineering," Metals Park, Ohio, 1958.

American Society for Testing Materials: "Testing Metal Powders and Metal Powder Products," Philadelphia, 1953.

Baeza, W. J.: "A Course in Powder Metallurgy," Reinhold Publishing Corporation, New York, 1943.

Goetzel, C. G.: "Treatise on Powder Metallurgy," vols. 1, 2, and 3, Interscience Publishers, Inc., New York, 1949–1952.

Hausner, H. H.: "Powder Metallurgy," Chemical Publishing Company, Inc., New York, 1947.

The Iron and Steel Institute: "Symposium on Powder Metallurgy," Special Report 38, London, 1947.

Jones, W. D.: "Fundamental Principles of Powder Metallurgy," Edward Arnold (Publishers) Ltd., London, 1960.

Leszynski, W. J. (ed.): "Powder Metallurgy," Interscience Publishers, Inc., New York, 1961.

Schwartzkopf, P.: "Powder Metallurgy," The Macmillan Company, New York, 1947.

Wulff, J. (ed.): "Powder Metallurgy," American Society for Metals, Metals Park, Ohio, 1942.

Chapter 17

EXTRACTIVE METALLURGY

17·1 Introduction. Although this book is concerned primarily with the effect of chemical composition, mechanical treatment, and thermal treatment on the properties of metals and alloys, it is desirable to have some knowledge of how metals are obtained. This branch of metallurgy is known as *extractive metallurgy*. The fundamental processes in winning the metal from the ore will be covered in this chapter, and greater detail may be obtained from the appended references.

The outer 10 miles of the earth is known as the *earth's crust* and consists primarily of silica and alumina. The average composition of the crust is given in Table 17·1. It is surprising to realize that the

Table 17·1 Average composition of the earth's crust*

Element	% by weight	Element	% by weight
Oxygen	46.59	Chromium	0.037
Silicon	27.72	Carbon	0.032
Aluminum	8.13	Zirconium	0.026
Iron	5.01	Nickel	0.020
Calcium	3.63	Vanadium	0.017
Sodium	2.85	Copper	0.010
Potassium	2.60	Uranium	0.008
Magnesium	2.09	Tungsten	0.005
Titanium	0.63	Zinc	0.004
Phosphorus	0.13	Lead	0.002
Hydrogen	0.13	Cobalt	0.001
Manganese	0.10	Beryllium	0.001
Sulfur	0.052	Molybdenum	0.0006
Barium	0.050	Tin	0.0005

* Data from Clarke and Washington, "Composition of the Earth's Crust," Paper 127, U.S. Department of the Interior, 1924.

470

first eight elements in the table account for over 96.5 per cent of the earth's crust and that only three industrially important metals (aluminum, iron, and magnesium) are in this group.   Because many of the useful nonferrous metals occur in extremely small percentages, one may wonder how it is economically possible to obtain the pure metal.

Most metals are found in the combined state in the form of compounds called *minerals* while a few, notably gold, may be found in the free state.   Although Table 17·1 gives the average composition of the earth's crust, fortunately this crust is far from uniform.   Because of the action of several natural phenomena such as precipitation, crystallization, weathering, erosion, sedimentation, and consolidation, mineral deposits are often found in sufficient concentration so that the metals may be economically extracted.   Such a deposit is called an *ore* and consists of valuable minerals (values), elements chemically combined with the values (impurities), and extraneous mineral matter (gangue). The gangue is mechanically mixed with the values and is usually worthless.

Whether a metal may be economically extracted from an ore depends to a large extent upon the market price of the metal, and this varies with supply and demand.   The introduction of new extraction methods and improvements in existing methods may allow the use of ores that were formerly considered uneconomic.

The majority of minerals contain the metal combined with oxygen (oxide) or sulfur (sulfide).   The following metals are obtained mainly from oxide minerals: iron, tin, aluminum, chromium, tungsten, manganese, beryllium, and titanium.   Copper, lead, zinc, nickel, antimony, bismuth, cadmium, and molybdenum are obtained mainly from sulfide minerals.

Since no two ores are exactly alike, extraction methods vary considerably even for the same metal; however, there is a similarity in sequence of operations, as follows: ore → mining → concentration → metal extraction → refining → commercially pure metal or alloy.

A schematic diagram showing the actual sequence of operations in the extraction of a metal from an ore is known as a *flow chart*.   A typical flow chart is shown in Fig. 17·1 for nickel and in Fig. 17·2 for copper.

17·2   Mining.   There are two main methods of obtaining the ore: open-pit mining or underground mining.   As the name implies, open-pit mining is used when the deposit is at or close to the surface (Fig. 17·3).   Underground mining must be used when the deposit is in the form of veins or pockets deep underground.   A vertical shaft is usually drilled adjacent to the vein, and horizontal crosscuts or tunnels are

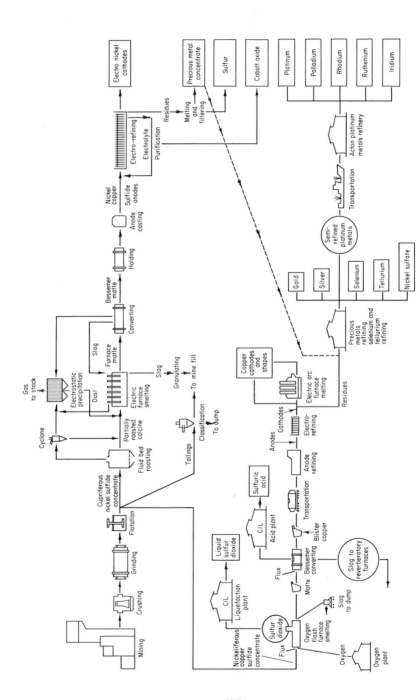

Fig. 17.1 Flow sheet for nickel. (*The International Nickel Company*)

dug to the vein. The operating and maintenance cost of hoisting, draining, and ventilation increase with the depth of the mine, and very rarely is it economically justifiable to extend a mine more than 1 mile in depth. As compared with underground mining, open-pit mining has the advantage of lower mining cost, use of larger mechanical

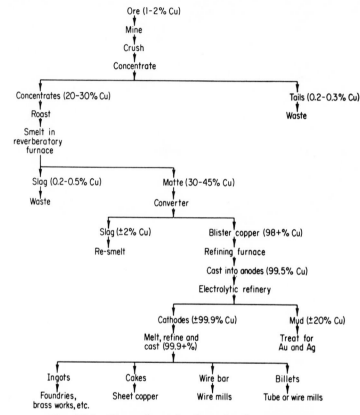

Fig. 17·2   Flow sheet for low-grade copper ore.

equipment, greater production, greater safety, and better working conditions. Some disadvantages of open-pit mining are: Overburden (rock and soil which covers the ore) must be removed, working time is subject to weather conditions, and operations are limited to moderate depth.

ORE DRESSING

17·3   Crushing.   In almost all cases, it is necessary to perform a series of mechanical operations to produce an enriched portion (concentrate) and to remove the waste material (tailings). This process is known as *ore dressing*.

Fig. 17·3   Open-pit mining of copper ore.   (*Phelps Dodge Corporation*)

The first steps in concentration are to reduce the size of mineral particles by feeding the ore through a series of crushers and grinders. *Primary crushing* is usually carried out by a jaw crusher, or a gyratory crusher.   A jaw crusher (Fig. 17·4) usually consists of two rectangular manganese-iron plates or jaws facing each other.   One plate is stationary and the other is movable, pivoted at either top or bottom.   The movable plate is caused to oscillate to and fro through a relatively short distance.   The ore is fed in between the two jaws, and the movable jaw on its forward swing crushes the lumps against the

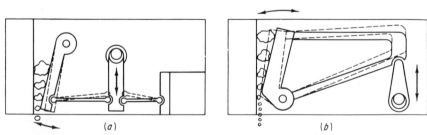

Fig. 17·4   Two types of jaw crushers.   (*a*) Double-toggle Blake crusher; (*b*) Dodge crusher.   (*By permission from D. M. Liddell, "Handbook of Nonferrous Metallurgy," McGraw-Hill Book Company, Inc., New York, 1945*)

stationary jaw. As it swings back, the broken ore falls downward through the opening at the end of the jaws. A gyratory crusher (Fig. 17·5) consists of a cone-shaped crushing head gyrating inside a stationary cone-shaped outer section which is open at top and bottom. The ore to be crushed is dumped on top of the crusher and is crushed by the same pinching action as described for the jaw crusher. Primary crushing usually reduces the mineral size to 2 to 3 in. The product of primary crushing is generally fed over a vibratory screen to remove all ore which is already crushed fine enough, thereby increasing the capacity of the secondary crusher.

Secondary crushers reduce the mineral size to ¼ to ⅜ in., ready for grinding or preliminary concentration operations. Secondary crushers

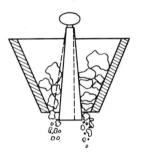

Fig. 17·5 Gyratory crusher. (*By permission from D. M. Liddell, "Handbook of Nonferrous Metallurgy," McGraw-Hill Book Company, Inc., New York*, 1945)

are usually of the gyratory or cone type (Fig. 17·6). These crushers are similar to those described under primary crushers except that they operate at relatively high speed (approximately 500 rpm) and are set to a much smaller discharge opening. When the ore is relatively soft and nonabrasive, a hammer mill (Fig. 17·7) may be used for crushing. The speed at which the hammers rotate is much greater than for any other type of crusher, thus increasing the wear on moving and wearing parts. For hard, abrasive ores, the wear on hammers and casing is excessive, and it is not economical to use this type of crusher.

17·4 Grinding. Grinding takes the product from the secondary crushers and reduces it to approximately 100-mesh (0.0058-in.) size. Grinding is usually done in a series of steps with intermediate screening and sizing devices. Grinding may be done either wet or dry, with the former more common.

There are many types of grinding machines or mills, but the most widely used is the rotating-drum mill. The mill consists of a horizontal, slowly rotating drum which is partially filled with freely moving grinding bodies. The grinding bodies may be metal balls, flint pebbles, or metal rods. Figure 17·8 shows the standard center-discharge cylindrical ball mill. The mill consists essentially of a drum rotating about its horizontal axis on hollow trunnions. Feed is introduced at the left trunnion by a scoop attached to, and rotating with, the drum. The mill is approximately half full of metal balls which grind the material by impact and attrition as they tumble down when the drum is rotated. The material being ground moves toward the discharge

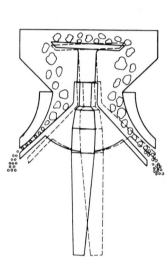

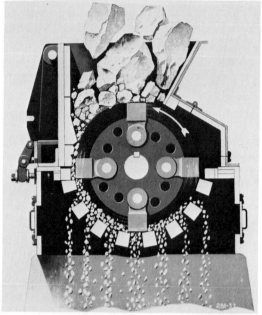

Fig. 17·6   Symons cone crusher. (*By permission from D. M. Liddell, "Handbook of Nonferrous Metallurgy," McGraw-Hill Book Company, Inc., New York, 1945*)

Fig. 17·7   Hammer mill. (*The Jeffrey Manufacturing Company*)

end, where it flows out of the hollow discharge trunnion in a ground state. Fineness of product and capacity depend upon speed, ball size, loading, size of feed, and hardness of material being ground.

The product from a ball mill is not uniform in size since grinding action will continue as long as a particle remains in the mill. This has led to the development of closed-circuit grinding (Fig. 17·9). The discharge from the mill is passed through a classifier where the oversize particles are separated from the fines and either sent back to the mill for regrinding or passed on to a second mill.

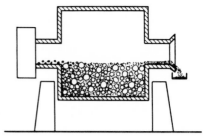

Fig. 17·8 Center-discharge cylindrical ball mill. (*By permission from D. M. Liddell, "Handbook of Nonferrous Metallurgy," McGraw-Hill Book Company, Inc., New York, 1945*)

17·5 Concentration. The purpose of classification and concentration is to effect a separation of the values from the gangue. This separation is generally not complete, but there should be only a very small amount of values to be discarded with the tailings.

Concentration methods are based on a difference in properties between values and gangue such as specific gravity, magnetic properties, and chemical properties.

There are a variety of gravity concentration methods that utilize the difference in specific gravity between the mineral and gangue. If

Fig. 17·9 Concentrator ball mill and classifier. (*American Smelting & Refining Company*)

two pieces of different materials having the same size and shape are dropped into still water, the one with the higher specific gravity will sink more rapidly than the other.

Separation may be carried out by placing the particles in a horizontal stream of water. The values, usually of greater specific gravity than the gangue, will settle out first. Separation may also be accomplished by placing the material in a vertical tank and adjusting the flow of a rising current of water so that the lighter gangue will rise while the

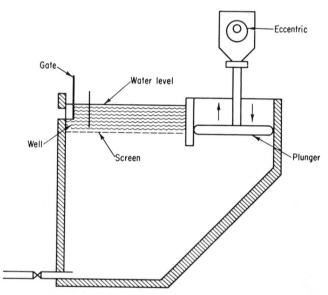

Fig. 17·10 Fixed-sieve plunger jig. (*By permission from M. Nord, "Textbook of Engineering Materials," John Wiley & Sons, Inc., New York, 1952*)

heavier values will sink. It is apparent that the degree of separation obtained by the above methods depends upon close control of size of the particles. Variation in the shapes of different particles and the difficulty in obtaining close sizing may be overcome by continuous classifiers. At any rate, it is rarely possible to obtain complete separation by these methods.

Jigging is a gravity concentration method utilizing short vertical impulses applied to a bed of loosely packed solids in water (Fig. 17·10). The jig consists of a hopper-shaped box divided into two compartments one of which contains a screen and the other a plunger actuated through an eccentric. Sized ore and water are continuously fed onto the screen. Action of the plunger forces water up through the screen and brings the ore into suspension. The lighter gangue is brought to the top where it is swept away by the flow of feedwater across the compartment while the heavier mineral particles sink onto the screen.

Roughly classified ore may be further concentrated by use of a *bumping table*. The water-suspended ore is fed onto a shallow table which is inclined toward the discharge end. The table is oscillated back and forth by a bumping mechanism. The heavier mineral particles settle in the depression formed by parallel strips of wood (riffles) and are moved by the bumping action to the opposite end of the table. The water washes the lighter gangue off the lower side.

The *sink-float* method depends on the use of a liquid medium whose specific gravity is between that of the gangue and that of the mineral to be separated. The heavy mineral sinks while the gangue floats. The limitation of this method is the difficulty of obtaining commercially available liquids of the desired density. This difficulty has been partially overcome by the use of a finely divided suspension of ferrosilicon or galena as the medium.

The most widely used concentration method is *flotation*. This method involves a combination of chemical and physical processes for the wet concentration of minerals (chiefly sulfides). Mineral particles whose surfaces have been made nonwettable adhere to oil-coated air bubbles and rise to the surface of the water where they remain suspended in a froth (Fig. 17·11). Gangue particles are wet by water and therefore sink. The mineral-rich froth is removed by paddles over the lip of the machine and proceeds to dewatering. It should be noted that this method operates in contradiction to the other gravity methods described. Successful operation of flotation requires that the ore be finely ground, that the mineral particles be conditioned with the proper chemicals to be made nonwettable, and that means be provided for the adherence of the minerals to the air bubbles. Accurate control of bubble size is also important for efficient flotation. The amount of mineral carried to the surface is determined by the surface area and not the size of the bubbles. Small bubbles present a greater total surface area and therefore provide a greater lifting force than large bubbles. This is illustrated in Fig. 17·12, which shows the greater amount of lead ore being floated by the small bubbles as compared with the large bubble.

Certain organic chemicals, known as *collectors*, link the collector molecule up to the mineral and then provide a water-repellent envelope around the mineral, thus allowing for their attachment to the air bubbles. Other organic chemicals, known as *frothers*, allow the air bubbles to emerge intact to the surface.

At first, flotation recovered nearly all the metal sulfides in one

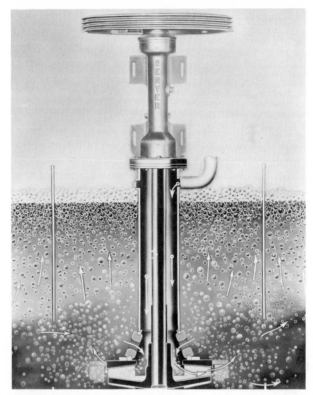

Fig. 17·11   Cross section of a flotation cell.   (*Denver Equipment Company*)

Fig. 17·12   Magnified photographs to show greater amount of lead ore being floated by small bubbles on left as compared with large bubble on right.   (*Denver Equipment Company*)

product. It is now possible to separate various sulfides from each other by differential flotation. By the use of reagents, known as *depressants*, the flotation of a particular mineral or minerals may be prevented temporarily or permanently. They inhibit the effect of the collector on a particular mineral. The depressed minerals may pass out with the tailings and be recovered in another flotation cell; or by the use of *activators*, minerals temporarily depressed may be caused to rise and be recovered in the same cell.

Fig. 17·13   Flotation machines. (*Anaconda Copper Mining Company*)

The flotation unit usually consists of several individual cells for roughing, scavenging, and cleaning (Fig. 17·13), thus producing a high-grade concentrate. For example, an ore containing 4 per cent lead or 6 per cent zinc yields a lead concentrate of 70 to 75 per cent lead and a zinc concentrate of 50 to 55 per cent zinc after flotation.

Magnetic separation may be used to separate magnetic minerals from nonmagnetic material. Figure 17·14 shows the cross section of a single-drum countercurrent type of magnetic separator.

Electrostatic separation is based on the principle that every mineral will take an electric charge on its surface if brought into contact with a high-potential source. The minerals are fed onto an electrically grounded rotor and are given a charge from a high-potential electrode mounted just above the rotor. The mineral particles of poor conductivity assume a surface charge and are attracted to and temporarily pinned to the rotor. Those particles of high conductivity do not assume a charge and fall away from the rotor.

In many cases, drying may be applied to the concentrate or crushed ore to remove absorbed water. This is usually done when the subsequent processes involve the use of heat. Figure 17·15 shows the flow sheet for mining and concentration of bauxite, the principal aluminum ore.

17·6   Metal extraction. The concentrate obtained from ore dressing must now be given further treatment to eliminate the remainder of the gangue and decompose the mineral in order to free the

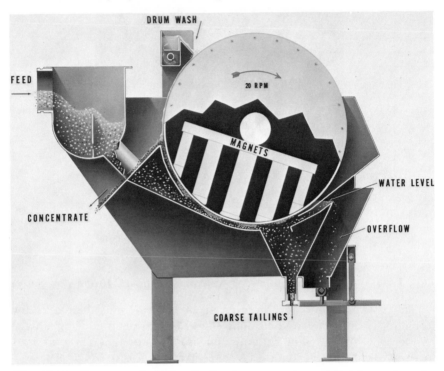

Fig. 17·14   Cross section of a single-drum countercurrent type of magnetic separator. (*The Jeffrey Manufacturing Company*)

metal. Metal-extraction and refining processes way be broadly classified under three types:

Pyrometallurgical, in which the burning of fuel supplies the heat for the reaction

Hydrometallurgical, in which the metal is obtained from the ore by use of some liquid solution

Electrometallurgical, in which electrical energy is used either to provide heat for decomposition or for electrolytic deposition of the metal from a solution

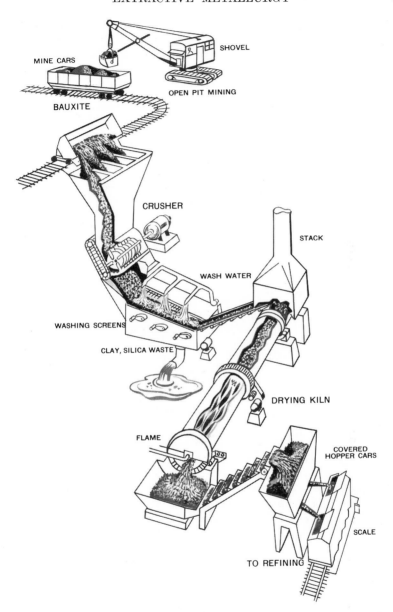

SHOVEL

MINE CARS

OPEN PIT MINING

BAUXITE

CRUSHER

STACK

WASH WATER

WASHING SCREENS

CLAY, SILICA WASTE

DRYING KILN

FLAME

COVERED
HOPPER CARS

SCALE

TO REFINING

Fig. 17·15 Flow sheet for mining and concentration of aluminum ore.
(*Aluminum Company of America*)

Many factors must be considered in the selection of a particular extraction process. Some factors are the kind of metal compounds in the concentrate (oxide, sulfide), the degree of concentration obtained, the particular properties of the metal to be extracted, required purity of the metal, tonnage to be treated, etc. Very often a combination of extraction processes may be employed. Table 17·2 gives the extraction processes used for recovery of the common nonferrous metals. Two different processes are indicated for the same type of zinc ore.

Table 17·2 Extraction processes for the recovery of the common nonferrous metals*

Metal	Raw material	Extraction and refining process		
		Pyro-metallurgy	Hydro-metallurgy	Electro-metallurgy
Aluminum	Bauxite	−	+	+
Copper	(a) Sulfide concentrate	+	−	+
	(b) Oxidized ore	−	+	+
Gold	Quartz ore	−	+	−
Lead	Sulfide concentrate	+	−	+
Magnesium	(a) Dolomite and magnesite	+	−	+
	(b) Sea water	−	+	+
Nickel	Sulfide concentrate	+	−	+
Silver	(a) Ore	−	+	+
	(b) Electrolytic slimes	+	−	+
Tin	Oxide concentrate	+	−	−
Zinc	Sulfide concentrate	+	−	−
		−	+	+

* By permission from W. H. Dennis, "Metallurgy of the Non-ferrous Metals," Pitman Publishing Corporation, New York, 1961.

If the plant is near a source of cheap fuel, the pyrometallurgical process is used, whereas if the plant is near a source of cheap electricity, the electrometallurgical process is used.

PYROMETALLURGICAL PROCESSES

These processes are sintering, calcining, roasting, smelting, distillation, and fire refining.

17·7 Sintering. Sintering consists in heating the particles to a temperature near their melting point. This high temperature causes the particles to stick together, forming a clinker and thereby increasing the particle size before smelting. Sintering is particularly useful following a concentration method which required small particles, such as flotation. If fine particles are charged into a blast furnace, some of the charge will be blown out with the flue gases.

The machine most widely used for sintering is the Dwight-Lloyd sintering machine shown in Fig. 17·16. The charge is automatically dropped from a feed hopper onto one end of an endless grate. The charge then passes under an *igniter* which sets fire to the surface of the charge as it enters the suction zone. The igniter is essentially a burner or firebox of suitable construction so that the hot products of combustion are deflected uniformly across the surface of the charge. The charge then enters the suction zone, which has a wind box or suction box under the traveling grate. The wind box is connected to a high-vacuum centrifugal fan which draws air through the charge while it is passing over the wind box. This causes the heat to travel down through the bed of material to be sintered. The most common depth of bed is 4 to 5 in. with lead and copper ores, and 8 to 10 in. with iron ores. The rate of travel of the grates is so adjusted that sintering is complete through the entire bed when the material reaches the end of the wind box. The sintered material drops off the end of the grates into a waiting car. The advantage of the Dwight-Lloyd sintering machine is that each step in the process is accomplished mechanically and automatically. All the factors that influence successful sintering, such as uniformity of mixture, thickness of layer, porosity, intensity of ignition, air supply, and time of sintering, have been converted into a series of mechanical controls that may be varied by a single operator.

17·8   Calcination.   Calcination is the decomposition of a compound to produce a solid and a gas, the gas being part of the original compound. The solid is usually an oxide. Typical calcining reactions are

$$FeCO_3 \rightarrow FeO + CO_2(g) \tag{17·1}$$

$$CuSO_4 \rightarrow CuO + SO_3(g) \tag{17·2}$$

$$2Al(OH)_3 \rightarrow Al_2O_3 + 3H_2O(g) \tag{17·3}$$

Figure 17·17 shows the sequence in operations to produce aluminum oxide from bauxite. The crushed bauxite is first mixed with a solution of lime and soda ash. When the mixture is heated under pressure, only the hydrated alumina (aluminum hydroxide) contained in the bauxite dissolves, while the solids and other impurities which remain are filtered out. The filtered solution is then cooled to precipitate the hydrated alumina. This aluminum hydroxide precipitate is filtered, washed, and then calcined in rotary kilns at 1800°F to produce pure alumina [reaction (17·3)]. The rotary kiln is a long cylindrical shell lined with refractory brick and inclined slightly downward. The slow rotation of the kiln causes the solids to roll along the bottom to the discharge where they are removed.

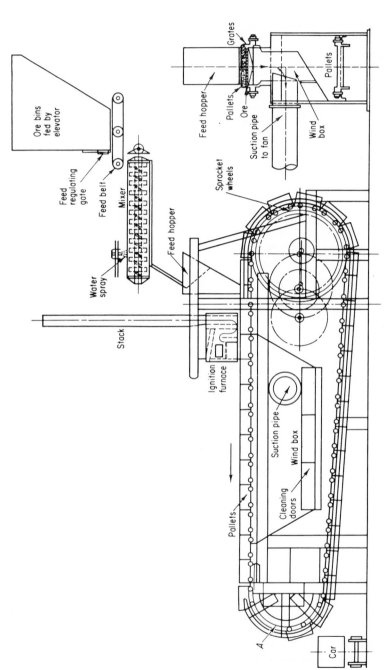

Fig. 17·16 Dwight-Lloyd sintering machine. (*By permission from D. M. Liddell, "Handbook of Nonferrous Metallurgy," McGraw-Hill Book Company, Inc., New York, 1945*)

486

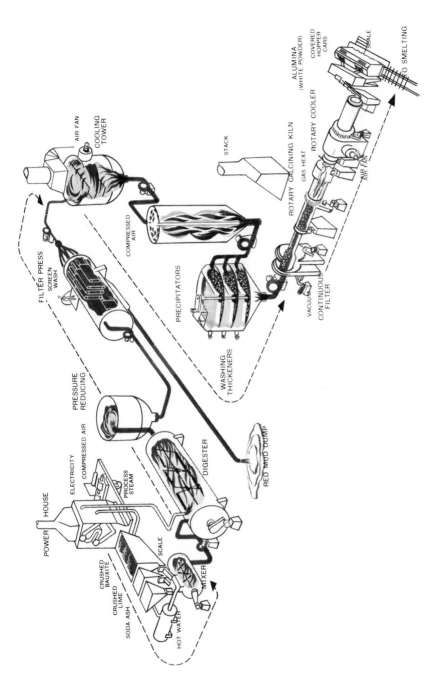

POWER HOUSE

ELECTRICITY
COMPRESSED AIR
PROCESS STEAM

CRUSHED BAUXITE
CRUSHED LIME
SODA ASH
HOT WATER

SCALE

MIXER

DIGESTER

RED MUD DUMP

PRESSURE REDUCING

AIR FAN
COOLING TOWER

FILTER PRESS
SCREEN WASH

COMPRESSED AIR

PRECIPITATORS

WASHING THICKENERS

STACK

ROTARY CALCINING KILN
GAS HEAT

VACUUM
CONTINUOUS FILTER

ROTARY COOLER
AIR FAN

ALUMINA (WHITE POWDER)
COVERED HOPPER CARS

SCALE

TO SMELTING

Fig. 17·17 Flow sheet for the production of alumina from bauxite. (*Aluminum Company of America*)

487

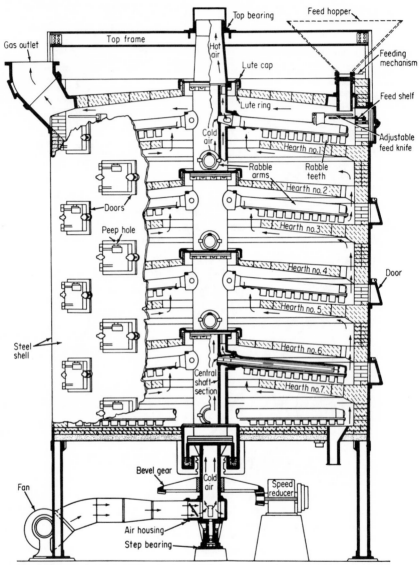

Fig. 17·18 Cross section of a multiple-hearth roaster. (*Nichols Engineering & Research Corporation*)

17·9   Roasting.   Roasting is a process in which heat and air are applied to an ore or concentrate, converting it to an oxide or sulfate. Roasting is usually preliminary to smelting.   In the case of lead and zinc concentrates, removal of the sulfur is essential before smelting. The presence of large amounts of sulfur during smelting leads to the formation of a matte or molten-sulfide layer.   A portion of the metal will be trapped in the matte and not extracted.   Typical reactions that form an oxide during roasting are

$$2PbS + 3O_2 \rightarrow 2PbO + 2SO_2 \qquad (17\cdot4)$$

$$2ZnS + 3O_2 \rightarrow 2ZnO + 2SO_2 \qquad (17\cdot5)$$

$$4FeS_2 + 11O_2 \rightarrow 2Fe_2O_3 + 8SO_2 \qquad (17\cdot6)$$

These reactions take place at relatively high temperatures and liberate heat (exothermic), so that the fuel required for roasting is small.

If the metal extraction is to be done by a hydrometallurgical process (leaching), it is necessary to produce a sulfate by roasting.   This may be done by lowering the furnace temperature to the range of 800 to 1000°F.   Typical reactions are

$$2PbO + 2SO_2 + O_2 \rightarrow 2PbSO_4 \qquad (17\cdot7)$$

$$2ZnO + 2SO_2 + O_2 \rightarrow 2ZnSO_4 \qquad (17\cdot8)$$

In the case of copper concentrates, a partial roasting is used to burn off part of the sulfur by oxidizing iron sulfides in preference to copper sulfides and leaving most of the copper as sulfides and sulfates.

The most widely used mechanical roaster is of the multiple-hearth type shown in Fig. 17·18.   The furnace usually consists of six to nine hearths and a central rotating shaft supporting two rotating *rabble arms* over each hearth.   Material to be roasted is dropped onto the top hearth.   The rabble teeth are placed at the proper angle to move the material from the center to the outside on one hearth, where it drops to the next one and is moved from the outside to the center, drops to the next hearth, and so on.   Heat is supplied from oil or gas burners at the bottom of the furnace.   Air required for roasting may be admitted wherever desired either from the outside or after use in cooling the rabble arms.

The Dwight-Lloyd sintering furnace, previously described, is extensively used for the roasting of lead and zinc concentrates.

In flash roasting, finely divided sulfide concentrates are injected by air into a combustion chamber, and ignition takes place while the

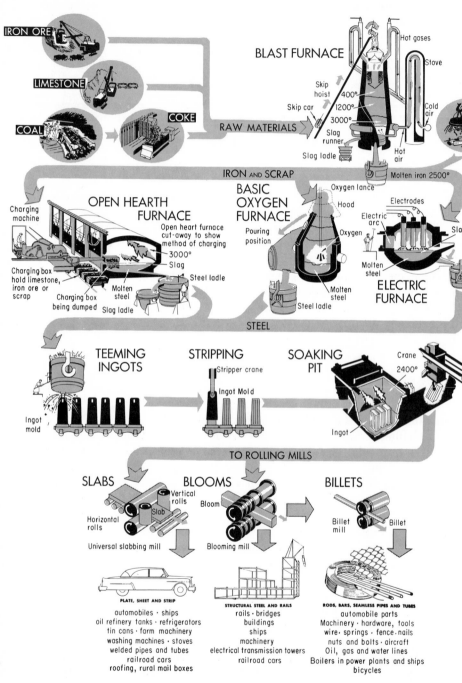

Fig. 17·19 Flow sheet for the production of steel. (*U.S. Steel Corporation*)

particles float down.   Oxygen is sometimes added to the combustion
air to increase the intensity of the reaction.   The heat liberated by
the burning of concentrates is usually sufficient to maintain the
required temperature.   Flash roasting is used on zinc sulfides and
iron sulfides (pyrites), the sulfur dioxide gas being recovered and used
for sulfuric acid manufacture.

17·10   Smelting.   Smelting consists of a high-temperature operation to produce either molten metal (reduction smelting) or molten
metallic sulfides (matte smelting).   Fluxes are usually added to combine with the gangue and form a slag that is removed periodically.
The two main types of furnaces used for smelting are the blast furnace
and reverberatory furnace.

The smelting of iron ore by reduction in a blast furnace is the
starting point in the manufacture of cast iron and steel and will be
discussed in greater detail.   A flow sheet for the production of steel is
shown in Fig. 17·19.

The raw materials used are iron ore, coke (reducing agent), and
limestone as a flux to combine with impurities and cause physical
separation.   The iron ores are primarily oxides: hematite (Fe_2O_3),
magnetite (Fe_3O_4), limonite ($Fe_2O_3 \cdot H_2O$), and siderite ($FeO \cdot CO_2$), while
the gangue consists largely of silica (SiO_2) along with manganese and
phosphorus.   Depending upon the type of ore, some preliminary ore-
dressing operations such as calcination, roasting, and concentration
may be applied.   Sintering of fine iron ore or blast-furnace dust with
coke and limestone has become common practice in most blast-furnace
plants.   The function of the flux is to combine with the gangue to
provide a fusible slag.   Since most gangues are acid in character
(silica), a basic flux such as limestone or magnesia is used.   The flux
also combines with sulfur, which may be present in the ore or fuel,
forming a sulfide which is removed in the slag.   The coke not only
serves as a reducing agent and a source of heat but also supplies
carbon and impurities which enter the pig iron.   The coke should be
low in sulfur and phosphorus, be porous to offer little resistance to
the upward flow of gases, and yet be strong enough to support the
weight of solids above it.   Coke is produced in coke ovens by heating
bituminous coal to approximately 2000°F.   At that temperature, the
moisture and *volatile matter* are driven off, leaving the ash and fixed
carbon in the form of coke.   The gases are collected and valuable
chemicals are extracted from them.   *Coal chemicals*, as they are called,
are used in the manufacture of nylon, plastics, synthetic rubber, dyes,
fertilizers, perfumes, and aspirin and other medicines.

The cross section of a blast furnace and heating stove is shown in
Fig. 17·20.   The blast furnace consists of a vertical steel shaft about

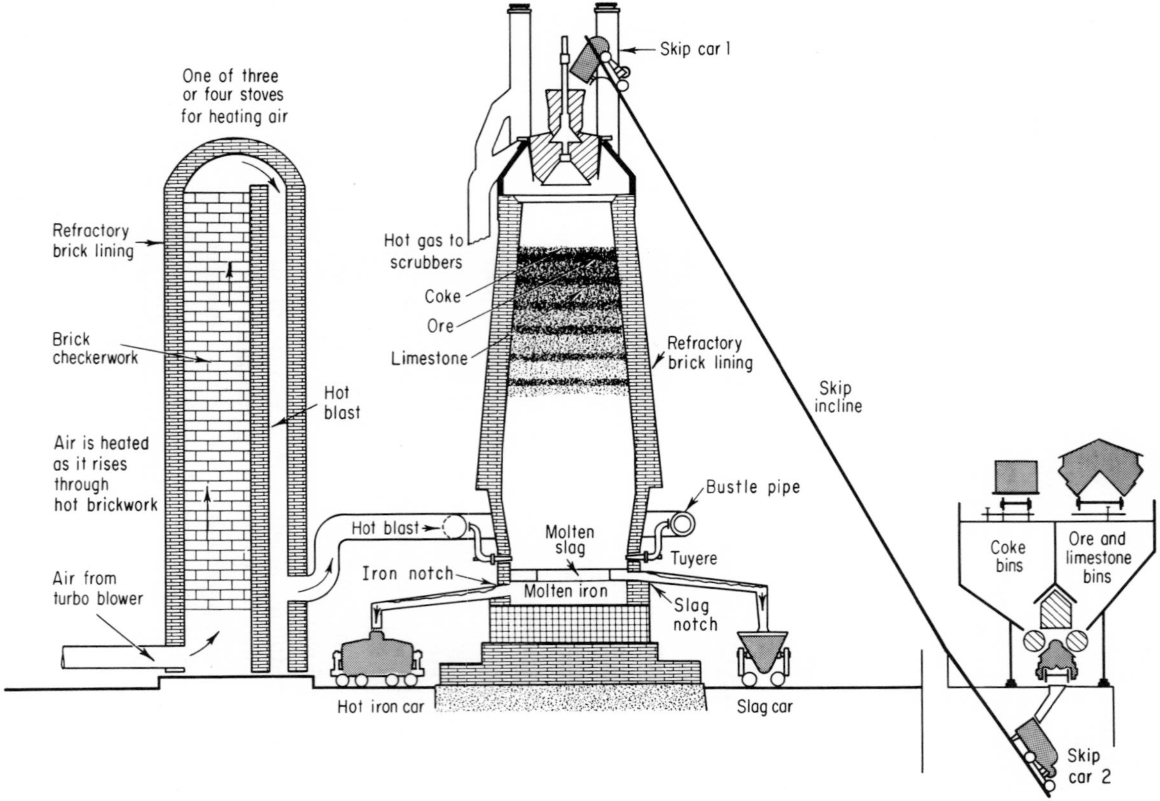

Fig. 17·20 Cross section of blast furnace and heating stove. (*Bethlehem Steel Company*)

Skip car 1

Skip incline

Ore and limestone bins

Coke bins

Skip car 2

Hot gas to scrubbers

Refractory brick lining

Coke
Ore
Limestone

Bustle pipe

Tuyere

Slag notch

Molten slag

Molten iron

Slag car

Hot blast

Iron notch

Hot iron car

Hot blast

One of three or four stoves for heating air

Refractory brick lining

Brick checkerwork

Air is heated as it rises through hot brickwork

Air from turbo blower

100 ft high and lined with firebrick. The lower cylindrical portion, about 10 ft high and 26 ft in diameter, called the *hearth*, contains the tuyeres, the slag notch, and the iron notch. The tuyeres are a ring of holes in the upper part of the hearth lining through which the hot blast of air is driven into the furnace. The slag notch or cinder notch for tapping off the liquid slag is located about 3 ft below the tuyeres. The iron notch for tapping off the liquid pig iron is located about 2 ft above the bottom of the hearth. Above the hearth is the *bosh*, a conical portion about 10 ft high, whose walls diverge to a diameter of about 30 ft. The bustle pipe, which conducts the hot blast from the hot-blast main to the tuyeres, encircles the bosh. Above the bosh extends the stack, converging to a diameter of about 20 ft at the throat at a height of 50 to 60 ft above the bosh. An inclined track or skipway is used to haul the buckets of raw material to the top of the furnace. The top of the stack is equipped with two cone-shaped bells for charging the materials without losing hot gases from the furnace. The materials are dumped into the upper bell, which is then lowered, causing them to fall into the lower bell. The upper bell is closed and the lower bell opened, allowing the materials to fall into the stack.

Each furnace is equipped with three to four hot-blast stoves. The function of the stoves is to preheat the air blast before its admission into the furnace through the tuyeres. The stove is a vertical steel cylinder, 26 to 28 ft in diameter and about 120 ft high, containing two firebrick chambers (Fig. 17·20). The large open chamber is the com- bustion chamber, in which the exhaust gases from the blast furnace are mixed with a definite proportion of air and allowed to burn. The combusted gases rise to the dome and then pass downward through a checkerwork of firebrick containing many small passageways. The large part of their heat is absorbed by the firebrick. After being "on gas" for about 3 hr, the gas is diverted to another stove while air from the turboblower is introduced at the bottom of the checkerwork. The air absorbs heat from the hot firebrick before entering the furnace. With three stoves to a furnace, one stove is "on blast" at a time when the other two stoves are "on gas," with the result that each stove is "on gas" twice as long as it is "on blast."

Numerous chemical reactions take place in the blast furnace, and only the most important ones will be discussed. The ore, limestone, and coke upon being charged into the top of the furnace come in contact with an ascending current of hot gases at about 300°F. The first effect is a physical one of drying in which included water is driven off. The materials slowly descend to the reducing zone, where the temperature ranges from 700 to 1600°F. Here they are in contact with the reducing gas, carbon monoxide (CO), and the following reactions take place with increasing temperature:

$$3Fe_2O_3 + CO \rightarrow 2Fe_3O_4 + CO_2 \tag{17·9}$$

$$Fe_3O_4 + CO \rightarrow 3FeO + CO_2 \tag{17·10}$$

$$FeO + CO \rightarrow Fe + CO_2 \tag{17·11}$$

$$CO_2 + C \rightarrow 2CO \tag{17·12}$$

The materials now descend to the heat-absorption zone, where the temperature varies from 1600°F to about 2400°F at the top of the bosh. In this zone, water and limestone are decomposed, some carbon is absorbed by the spongy iron, and part of the manganous oxide is reduced according to the following reactions:

$$H_2O + C \rightarrow H_2 + CO \tag{17·13}$$

$$CaCO_3 \rightarrow CaO + CO_2 \tag{17·14}$$

$$MnO + C \rightarrow Mn + CO \tag{17·15}$$

In the bosh region, known as the *melting* or *fusion zone*, the temperature rises to about 3000°F. In this zone, many of the reactions take place that form the slag. Some typical ones are

$$CaO + SiO_2 \rightarrow CaSiO_3 \tag{17·16}$$

$$FeS + CaO + C \rightarrow CaS + Fe + CO \tag{17·17}$$

$$Ca_3P_2O_8 + 3SiO_2 + 5C + 6Fe \leftarrow 3CaSiO_3 + 5CO + 2Fe_3P \tag{17·18}$$

$$P_2O_5 + 5C \rightarrow 2P + 5CO \tag{17·19}$$

$$3Fe + P \rightarrow Fe_3P \tag{17·20}$$

Reactions (17·18) and (17·20) result in the formation of iron phosphide, which is soluble in iron and becomes part of the metallic bath; therefore, the phosphorus in pig iron can be controlled only by the selection of proper raw materials.

Just above the tuyeres is the combustion zone. Here the temperature is about 3600°F. Oxygen and water of the hot-air blast combine with carbon of the coke to form hydrogen and carbon monoxide [reactions (17·13 and (17·12)]. The slag and the iron, both now in the liquid state, trickle down through the interstices of the coke to the hearth, where they become separated by gravity, forming two layers. The lower metallic layer contains all reduced substances, while the upper slag layer contains all unreduced matter. It is probable that at the surface, where the molten slag and pig iron are in contact, there will be some reduction of silica forming iron silicide or silicon, as follows:

$$SiO_2 + 2C + Fe \rightarrow FeSi + 2CO \qquad (17\cdot21)$$

or $$SiO_2 + 2C \rightarrow Si + 2CO \qquad (17\cdot22)$$

the ordinary amounts of silicon dissolving in the iron.

With the furnace in continuous operation, slag is tapped off about every 2 hr, while the iron is tapped off four or five times a day. The pig iron is run into ladles and transported to the steel furnaces, which are usually nearby, or it may be cast into bars or *pigs*.

The impurities in pig iron will vary considerably depending upon the ore but are usually within the following ranges: total carbon, 3 to 4.5 per cent; silicon, 1 to 4 per cent; sulfur, 0.04 to 0.2 per cent; phosphorus, 0.1 to 2 per cent; manganese, 0.2 to 2.5 per cent.

The reverberatory furnace is used extensively in the reduction and refining of many nonferrous metals, particularly for matte smelting of copper. The furnace is about 100 ft long and may handle up to 2,000 tons of copper concentrate a day. It consists of a shallow hearth with side and end walls covered by an arch roof (see Fig. 17·40). Heating is usually by pulverized fuel or gas injected into the furnace by burners in the rear wall. Hot roasted concentrates or calcines and molten slag from the converters, which is too high in copper to discard, are charged into the furnace either through holes in the roof or through openings in the side walls. The roasted ore charged into a reverberatory furnace may contain Cu_2S, Cu_2O, CuO, $CuSO_4$, FeS, $FeSO_4$, Fe_2O_3, Fe_3O_4, SiO_2, and various complex silicates. Under a temperature of about 2600°F, the copper compounds are converted to cuprous sulfide (Cu_2S), and most of the iron becomes ferrous sulfide (FeS). These two sulfides dissolve in each other to form the matte, which being the heaviest product settles to the bottom of the furnace. The precious metals, and any nickel, arsenic, antimony, lead, and zinc present, appear in the matte as sulfides. The matte is tapped, as needed, for the converter department, through a taphole in the side of the furnace.

The iron which does not enter the matte as sulfide is oxidized or reduced to FeO and, together with lime, alumina, magnesia, etc., unites with the silica present to enter the slag. The slag is continuously tapped through a taphole near the flue end of the furnace.

An important part of copper smelting is the conversion of the copper matte to blister copper. The process is essentially one of oxidation similar to the manufacture of steel from pig iron in a bessemer converter. The converter is a cylindrical steel vessel lying in a horizontal plane on rollers so that it may be rotated for charging and emptying (Fig. 17·21).   Air for oxidation is admitted, along the length of the converter, about 1 ft above the bottom by tuyeres so that the air is forced by pressure through the matte.   The charge consists of liquid matte,

Fig.· 17·21   Skimming slag from a copper converter. (*Phelps Dodge Corporation*)

mainly copper and iron sulfides from the reverberatory furnace, and silica flux.   The blow is turned on, oxidation of the iron starts, and the slag begins to form.   The oxidation generates enough heat to maintain the charge in a molten condition.   The reactions in the first stage are

$$2FeS + 3O_2 \rightarrow 2FeO + 2SO_2 \tag{17·23}$$

$$FeO + SiO_2 \rightarrow FeSiO_3 \tag{17·24}$$

The operator judges the progress of the reaction by the color of the flame coming out of the mouth of the converter.   When the color is violet, this indicates that the iron has entered the slag. At this point the air blast is turned off. The converter is tilted, and the molten slag is poured off and returned to the reverberatory furnace to recover the 2 to 5 per cent copper in the slag.

The converter is righted, the air blast is turned on, and the second stage begins. The Cu_2S is oxidized by the following reaction:

$$Cu_2S + O_2 \rightarrow 2Cu + SO_2 \qquad (17 \cdot 25)$$

When the color of the flame has passed from yellow to nearly colorless it indicates that the sulfur has been burned off, leaving metallic copper. The molten copper is poured into ladles and then cast in cakes for shipment to a refinery. The gas given off when the copper solidifies causes surface irregularities; hence the name *blister copper*.

17·11 Distillation. Distillation is a pyrometallurgical method used to separate volatile metals from nonvolatile impurities. This method is used in the production of zinc. Preliminary operations of concentration and roasting have converted the zinc sulfide ore to zinc oxide (ZnO). Zinc may now be recovered in a distillation process by reduction with carbon, or by an electrolytic process.

Before reduction with carbon, the roasted concentrates are usually sintered to remove excess sulfur left by the roasting step and may drive off volatile metallic impurities.

Zinc boils at 1706°F, but ZnO is not completely reduced by carbon until about 2000°F. Zinc is therefore generated as a vapor mixed with other gases from which it must be condensed. The two most widely used furnaces are the horizontal retort and the vertical retort.

In the horizontal-retort process, clay retorts about 5 ft long and 9 in. in diameter are set in four to six horizontal rows in a gas-fired furnace. The retort is filled with a mixture of coal and sintered ZnO, and a clay condenser is attached to the open end of the retort, which extends from the furnace. Being exposed to the air, the condenser temperature is about 900°F. Zinc oxide is reduced by carbon to form zinc vapor and carbon monoxide. The zinc vapor passing into the cool condenser is condensed while the carbon monoxide is ignited at the mouth of the condenser. Figure 17·22 shows the front end of a horizontal-retort zinc furnace. Liquid zinc is tapped from the condenser three times during a 24-hr cycle. At the end of the cycle, the condensers are removed, the spent charge is blown out of the retorts, and a new cycle is started.

In contrast to the horizontal-retort process, which is batch-type, the vertical-retort process allows continuous production of zinc. The charge is made up of briquettes consisting of a mixture of sintered concentrates and coal which have been coked. The furnace is kept full of briquettes which are charged at the top. As they pass down through the retort, the zinc vapor released passes up through the charge and to a large condenser near the top of the furnace, where it is condensed to liquid zinc. The accompanying carbon monoxide is prepared for use as fuel. The spent briquettes are continuously discharged from the bottom. Heat for the reaction is supplied externally by gas-fired burners. Figure 17·23 shows a vertical retort.

Fig. 17·22   The front end of a horizontal-retort zinc furnace. (*American Smelting & Refining Company*)

17·12   Treatment of flue gas. Many of the pyrometallurgical processes generate large quantities of dust and fume which pass out of the furnace with the flue gas. Since these smokes may contain metal particles, methods have been developed for the recovery and collection of such material. Separation of dust from flue gas may be achieved by an automatic bag house, a dust catcher, or an electrostatic precipitator.

An automatic bag-type dust arrester may contain 80 or more cloth filters or bags, each filter being about 6 in. in diameter and 8 ft long. The bags with closed tops are suspended from a framework which can be agitated. The open bottom ends of the bags are fitted over collars opening to a lower compartment. Flue gases containing suspended solids enter at the bottom and pass upward and through the cloth filters into the space surrounding the bags. The clean gas is drawn through a manifold at the top. The bags are shaken every few minutes, and the dust drops into a hopper at the bottom of the unit and is removed. An automatic bag house always contains several of the units described above, which allows one to be shut down for repair while the others are operating. Life of the bags is increased by

Fig. 17·23 Vertical retort. (*St. Joseph Lead Co.*)

lowering the entering temperature of the flue gas. This may be done by automatically admitting cold air or by water spraying the inlet gas main. Where the flue gas contains acid constituents, bag life is considerably shortened and other methods of dust recovery must be used.

The dust catcher is used to remove larger dust particles from the flue gas. It is about 35 to 40 ft in diameter, usually lined with brick to prevent cooling. The flue gas enters a vertical conical-shaped section with its widest end near the bottom of the dust catcher. The decrease in velocity of the gas and the sudden change in gas direction when it hits bottom promote separation of the heavier dust particles, which are collected at the bottom. The cleaner gas rising along the sides is removed at the top and usually sent to an electrostatic precipitator for further dust recovery.

The electrostatic (Cottrell) method of dust precipitation is in wide use. The principle involved in this method is that a gas becomes charged when it is passed through a high-voltage field. The gas ions are carried from the discharging electrode to the collecting electrode. Suspended solids between the electrodes are caught up by the gas ions, become charged, and are attracted to the collecting electrode (cathode), where they give up their charge and are deposited. The usual Cottrell treater consists of a series of vertical iron pipes (collecting electrodes) with a wire or chain (discharge electrode) suspended at the center of each. The wire or chain receives direct current of 30,000 to 80,000 volts. Dust particles deposited on the inside of the pipe may be removed by periodic rapping with weights attached on the outside or by a thin film of water which flows over the inside edge of each tube.

The dust collected by any of the above methods is usually sintered and then returned for further processing.

HYDROMETALLURGICAL PROCESSES

17·13 Leaching. This is a process of extraction of the valuable mineral from a solid mixture by chemical reaction and solution in a solvent. Leaching requires a reagent which dissolves most of the values and little or no gangue. It is used for oxidized copper, manganese, gold, and silver ores and preroasted zinc ores. Hydrometallurgical methods are also used for preliminary treatments such as the digestion of bauxite with caustic soda to produce alumina (see Fig. 17·17) and the treatment of sea water for precipitation of magnesium hydrate and conversion to chloride before electrolysis. Leaching lends itself to large-scale production and to the treatment of low-grade ores.

Preliminary crushing is necessary to reduce the material to a suitable size. Roasting is necessary to convert sulfide ores to oxides. Leaching may be carried out either by percolation or by agitation. Leaching by percolation is used when the ore is sufficiently permeable to allow the solvent free access to the mineral. Copper is recovered from copper sulfate ores by percolation with dilute sulfuric acid as the solvent. When the particle size is too fine, leaching by percolation is too slow and agitation must be employed. The liquid and solid are agitated together either by mechanically driven stirrers or by introducing compressed air at the bottom of the tank.

Ammonia may also be used as a copper solvent dissolving the metal with the formation of cupric ammonium compounds. These compounds decompose on heating to yield ammonia by distillation which is reused. The remaining black copper oxide may be smelted for copper. The leaching process for zinc is similar to that for copper. Sodium cyanide is used for the leaching of low-grade gold and silver ores.

The metal must now be recovered from the solution. This may be accomplished by either chemical precipitation or electrolytic methods. Chemical precipitation or cementation is based on the fact that a metal is displaced from its solution by another metal that is higher in the electromotive series. In the recovery of copper, scrap or pig iron is placed in rotating *tumblers* and the leached copper sulfate solution is passed over the iron. Copper is replaced in solution by the reaction

$$CuSO_4 + Fe \rightarrow FeSO_4 + Cu \qquad (17 \cdot 26)$$

The precipitated copper falls continuously from the tumbler into a pit which is periodically emptied. Zinc dust and activated charcoal have been used to precipitate gold from cyanide solutions.

ELECTROMETALLURGICAL PROCESSES

17·14 Electrolysis. Prior treatment of the ore or concentrate has isolated the metal in a purified solution or in a solid chemical compound, such as a chloride or an oxide. There are therefore two methods of metal extraction by electrolysis. In one, typified by copper and zinc, the metal is obtained from solution. For a solid chemical compound, electrolysis takes place in a fused-salt bath. The latter method is used for the extraction of aluminum and magnesium.

The extraction of copper is done in an electrolytic cell consisting of an insoluble anode of lead or lead alloy, a thin starting sheet of copper as a cathode, and the leached solution as the electrolyte. Under the influence of an electric current, the following reaction takes place:

$$2CuSO_4 + 2H_2O \rightarrow 2Cu + 2H_2SO_4 + O_2 \qquad (17 \cdot 27)$$

Copper is plated out of solution on the cathode. It is important to note that sulfuric acid formed in the above reaction is the same chemical that is used as a solvent in the leaching process. When the metal content of the solution has been reduced sufficiently, the solution is returned to the leaching tanks to become enriched in copper sulfate, and the cycle is repeated. Electrodeposition of copper from solution turns out to be more economical than chemical precipitation with iron.

The more active metals, such as aluminum and magnesium, react with water to form hydroxides. Therefore, they cannot be extracted from water solutions. Instead, electrolysis takes place in a fused-salt bath.

The diagram of an electrolytic cell in which aluminum is made is shown in Fig. 17·24. Pure alumina (Al_2O_3) is dissolved in molten cryolite, sodium aluminum fluoride ($AlF_3·3NaF$), in large electrolytic furnaces or cells, called *reduction pots*. By means of a carbon anode suspended in the bath, electric current is passed through the fused-salt bath, causing metallic aluminum to be deposited on the cathode,

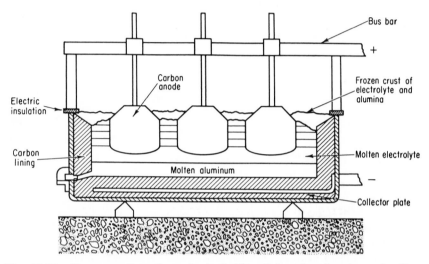

Fig. 17·24   Cross section of an electrolytic cell for aluminum production. (*Aluminum Company of America*)

the carbon lining of the pot, where it settles to the bottom of the cell. Two reactions are involved, first, the decomposition of cryolite:

$$2(AlF_3·3NaF) \rightarrow 2Al + 3F_2 + 6NaF \qquad (17·28)$$

to produce molten aluminum which settles to the bottom, and secondly, the reaction of fluorine gas and sodium fluoride with alumina on the surface:

$$Al_2O_3 + 3F_2 + 6NaF \rightarrow 2(AlF_3·3NaF) + 3O \qquad (17·29)$$

Oxygen combines with the carbon anodes and is released as carbon dioxide gas, while cryolite is re-formed for further production of aluminum. The heat generated by the passage of electric current keeps the bath molten so that alumina can be added as necessary to make the process continuous. Periodically, aluminum is siphoned from the pots and cast into pigs or transferred to holding furnaces for removal of impurities or for alloying.

In the case of magnesium, the electrolyte is molten sodium chloride and calcium chloride. Magnesium chloride, suitably prepared from sea water (Fig. 17·25) or magnesium ores, is dissolved in the electrolyte. Anodes of graphite and cathodes of steel project through the covering of the cell. The passage of electric current liberates magnesium at the cathode, and by the use of cathode baffles, the liquid metal is diverted to a pool in front from which it is withdrawn by the use of ladles. Chlorine, liberated at the anode, is collected and used in the preparation of magnesium chloride. Unlike aluminum, the graphite anodes are not consumed in the process. Usually, the cell is set in a gas-fired furnace instead of depending upon the passage of the electric current to provide the heat necessary to keep the bath molten. This allows for greater flexibility in operation. The cross section of an electrolytic cell for the production of magnesium is shown in Fig. 17·26.

17·15 Electrothermic processes. The principle involved in electrothermic processes is that, when electric current flows through a conductor, the energy required to overcome the resistance appears as heat.

This method is used for the vertical-retort process in the production of zinc described earlier. The charge consists of properly sized sinter and coke. The charge is heated by three independent single-phase circuits flowing between three carbon electrodes near the top and a similar set near the bottom. The coke-sinter charge carries the current between each pair of upper and lower electrodes, thereby heating it by resistance. The residue is continuously withdrawn from the bottom. The vapor-gas mixture is removed from the top, and the zinc is condensed.

REFINING

17·16 General. The metal obtained from the smelting operations is usually not pure enough for many purposes. Very rarely is it more than 95 per cent pure. In some cases, where the purity is higher, such as blister copper (about 99 per cent copper), the presence of certain impurities exerts a harmful influence on its properties. Arsenic drastically lowers the electrical conductivity of copper, and sulfur reduces the workability of copper.

The purity required is determined by the ultimate use of the metal. Copper for electrical conductors must be 99.99+ per cent pure. Chemical-grade lead requires a minimum lead content of 99.99 per cent. Zinc for die casting must be very pure, since impurities reduce corrosion resistance and may cause fracture in the metal due to shrinkage stresses. Metals used for alloying purposes may contain impurities that do not have any adverse effect on the properties of the alloy.

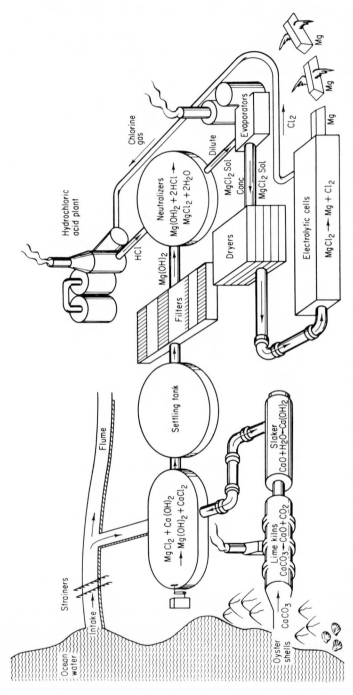

Fig. 17·25 Flow sheet for magnesium production from sea water. (*The Dow Chemical Company, Metals Dept.*)

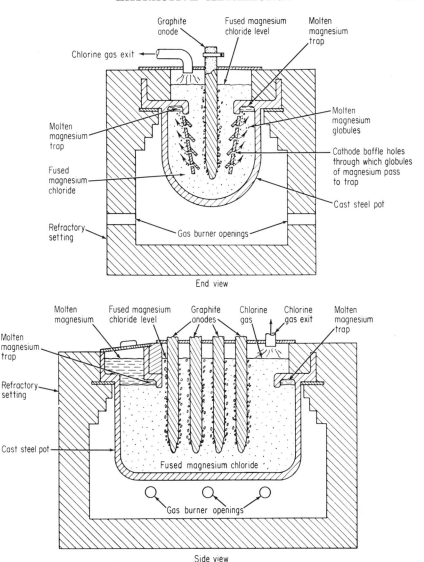

Fig. 17·26 Cross section of an electrolytic cell for the production of magnesium. (*The Dow Chemical Company, Metals Dept.*)

Refining processes are employed to obtain the desired purity.   Like the processes used for metal extraction, refining may be done by pyrometallurgical (fire-refining), hydrometallurgical (chemical-refining), and electrometallurgical (electrothermic- and electrolytic-refining) methods.

17·17 Fire refining.   Fire refining removes impurities by selective oxidation.   Impurities may be removed from the molten metal by either the application of air or the use of oxidizing agents which are slagged off. If the metal is volatile, it may be recovered by distillation.

To return to the manufacture of steel (Fig. 17·19), pig iron, obtained from a blast furnace, contains impurities which are mainly carbon, manganese, silicon, sulfur, and phosphorus. These impurities may be

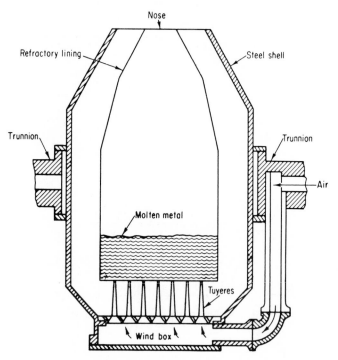

Fig. 17·27   Cross section of a Bessemer converter. (By permission from M. Nord, "Textbook of Engineering Materials," John Wiley & Sons, Inc., New York, 1952)

removed by several processes: bessemer converter, basic oxygen furnace, open-hearth furnace, electric-arc furnace. In each process the furnace may be lined with acid (siliceous) material or basic material (magnesite or dolomite).

The bessemer converter consists of a pear-shaped steel shell with a refractory lining (Fig. 17·27). Molten pig iron from the blast furnace is charged into the converter while it is in a horizontal position. Air for oxidation, under about 30 psi pressure, is forced through the hollow trunnion to the wind box and up through the tuyeres into the charge. The oxygen in the air first oxidizes the iron, which in turn oxidizes the silicon and manganese that combine to form the slag according to the following reactions:

$$2Fe + O_2 \rightarrow 2FeO \tag{17·30}$$

$$2FeO + Si \rightarrow 2Fe + SiO_2 \tag{17·31}$$

$$FeO + Mn \rightarrow Fe + MnO \tag{17·32}$$

$$MnO + SiO_2 \rightarrow MnSiO_3 \tag{17·33}$$

Fig. 17·28   Bessemer converter in operation.   (*A. M. Byers Company*)

After silicon and manganese are oxidized, carbon will combine with oxygen to form carbon monoxide, which burns at the mouth of the converter.

The character of the refractory lining determines the type of slag produced.   An acid (silica) lining has no effect on phosphorus and sulfur, which can be removed only by a basic slag.   Therefore, in the acid bessemer process, which is exclusively used in the United States, the pig iron must be low in phosphorus and sulfur.   The oxidation of silicon is the principal source of heat in the acid converter.   The pig iron used should contain 1 to 2 per cent silicon not only to act as "fuel" but to provide a suitable slag.

The progress of the oxidation is judged by the appearance of the flame at the mouth of the converter.   A few minutes after the blow is started, silicon and manganese have been removed and carbon begins to oxidize by the appearance of a reddish-yellow flame at the mouth of the converter. This rapidly changes to a white-hot flame 25 ft high. Figure 17·28 shows a bessemer converter in the middle of the blow. Soon the flame begins to shorten and becomes less luminous, indicating that the carbon is practically burned out. The converter is turned down, the blast is shut off, and the purified iron is poured into a ladle.

Fig. 17·29 Pouring or "teeming" molten steel from the ladle into ingot molds. (*Bethlehem Steel Company*)

Since all the carbon originally in the pig iron has been removed, calculated additions are made to the ladle to deoxidize and recarburize the purified iron to steel of the desired composition. The material usually added for this purpose is ferromanganese, which contains about 80 per cent manganese, 5 to 7 per cent carbon, and 0.5 to 1 per cent silicon. Manganese and silicon are good deoxidizers and reduce any iron oxide that is present. For high-carbon steels, spiegeleisen (18 to 22Mn, 5 to 6C, 1Si) is used instead of ferromanganese. Small amounts of ferrosilicon (47 to 52Si) may also be added as an additional deoxidizer. The molten steel is transferred by pouring or *teeming* from the ladle into ingot molds for further processing into desired shapes (Fig. 17·29).

The bessemer process is rapid and cheap, taking 10 to 15 min to produce 20 tons of steel, but the product contains more nonmetallic impurities than steel produced by the other processes.

The introduction of the bessemer process in 1864 ushered in large-scale commercial production of steel. Most of the steel manufactured in the last half of the nineteenth century was made by this process.

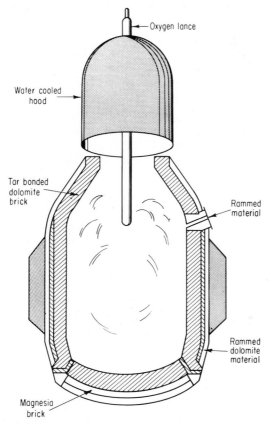

Fig. 17·30 Cross section of a basic oxygen-process furnace. (*Bethlehem Steel Company*)

In the last 50 years the open-hearth process has replaced the bessemer process as the largest producer of steel, the latter process being mainly confined to the production of pipe, tin-plate stock, and to some extent wire. The recent development of the basic oxygen process has completed the decline of the acid bessemer process.

The basic oxygen-process furnace, shown in Fig. 17·30, is similar in construction to a basic bessemer converter except that it has no tuyeres, wind box, or removable bottom. The basic refractory lining is approximately 40 in. thick, consisting of a permanent outer layer of magnesia brick, an intermediate layer of rammed dolomite material, and a working layer of tar-bonded dolomite brick. The furnace is designed to turn out steel at the rate of approximately one 200-ton heat per hour.

The charge is made up of iron ore, steel scrap, and molten pig iron combined with a small amount of lime as a flux. During the blow, additional fluxing materials such as burnt lime and fluorspar are usually added. After the furnace has been charged and righted, a water-cooled vertical lance is lowered to within 5 ft of the bath. The lance directs a stream of high-purity oxygen under 100 to 150 psi pressure at the surface of the bath. The temperature at the surface of the bath reaches approximately 4000°F. The same reactions take place as in the bessemer process except that, under the influence of the higher temperature, the oxidation is more rapid. Violent boiling action throughout the bath results from the carbon monoxide formed. Since the lining is basic, most of the sulfur and phosphorus will appear in the slag. A clearly visible drop in the flame at the mouth of the furnace indicates completion of the process. The lance is withdrawn; the furnace is tilted to skim off the slag, then rotated back on its side, and the purified iron pours through a hole into a ladle. The usual additions are made in the ladle to produce the steel of desired composition. The quality of the steel produced by the basic oxygen process is as good as or better than that produced by the open-hearth process.

The open-hearth process developed more slowly than the bessemer process, and it was only after 1908 that it became the major steel-production method. Depending upon the type of refractory lining, the open-hearth process may be either acid or basic, but by far the largest steel tonnage is produced by the basic process.

The open-hearth furnace shown in Fig. 17·31 employs the regenerative principle with fuel. Air for combustion is preheated in a brick checker chamber before combining with the fuel. There are two checker chambers with each furnace, one on either side. While air is preheated by passing through one chamber, the hot exhaust gases pass through the opposite chamber, heating the brick checkerwork. About every 20 min the direction of flow is reversed. This system allows for greater thermal efficiency, and a more constant temperature may be maintained in the melting chamber.

In charging the basic open-hearth furnace a layer of light scrap is first placed in the furnace. This melts quickly and forms a protective covering for the hearth bottom from the limestone flux. Limestone lumps are then added, followed by iron ore and finally steel scrap. Iron ore and steel scrap supply iron oxide, which is the source of oxygen for oxidation of impurities. The refining reactions are essentially the same as those which take place in the bessemer converter but they occur more slowly. The open-hearth process requires 10 to 15 hr whereas the bessemer process requires 10 to 15 min.

The solid charge is fused by heating for about 2 to 4 hr, and then molten pig iron is added through a spout inserted in one of the charging doors. After the charge is melted, there are three periods during the refining of the metal: the ore boil, the lime boil, and the working period.

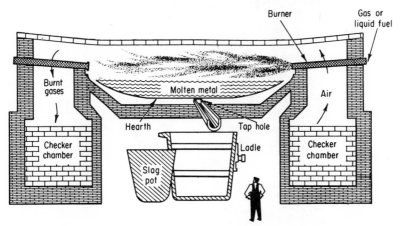

Fig. 17-31   Cross section of an open-hearth furnace.   (Bethlehem Steel Company)

During the ore boil, the reaction between the ore and iron oxides in the slag and carbon of the metal causes rapid evolution of carbon monoxide gas, which bubbles up through the liquid charge. Silicon, manganese, and phosphorus are oxidized and enter the slag.

During the lime boil, carbon dioxide released from the decomposing limestone on the bottom of the hearth bubbles up through the molten charge and assists the oxidation. Most of the lime also comes to the surface during this period to form a more basic slag.

After boiling has ended, most of the impurities other than carbon have been oxidized and slagged. During the working period, the carbon content is adjusted to the desired range. If the carbon content of the metal is too low, some additional pig iron is added; if too high, some additional ore is charged. When tests indicate that the composition of the metal and slag is correct, and the temperature is right, the charge is tapped. Final break-through of the tap hole is made by a long bar inserted through the center charging door and through the bath. The metal then runs through the tapping spout into the ladle, followed by the slag. As the molten steel fills the ladle, the lighter slag rises to the top and flows into an adjacent slag pot (Fig. 17·32). Deoxidation additions are usually made in the ladle while the furnace is being tapped.

As compared with the acid bessemer process, the principal advantages of the basic open-hearth process are:

1. A solid charge may be used.

Fig. 17·32 Tapping an open-hearth furnace. (*Bethlehem Steel Company*)

2. Phosphorus and sulfur may be removed.

3. A better-quality steel may be produced since the process is slower.

4. Closer control of steel composition allows the production of alloy steels.

A duplex process is one in which the raw materials for producing steel are treated in one type of furnace, and the liquid product is then transferred to another type of furnace for finishing. The most common duplex process is acid bessemer–basic open hearth. It takes advantage of the rapid removal of silicon and most of the carbon from the pig iron in the bessemer process, leaving a relatively high-phosphorus product which can be quickly finished in the basic open hearth.

17·18 Electrothermic refining. The electric-arc furnace is an electrothermic method for the production of steel. There are two types of electric-arc furnaces. In one type, the direct-arc, the arc is formed between the carbon electrodes and the metal being refined. In the indirect-arc type the arc is formed above the bath between the electrodes, the metal being heated by radiation. Most installations are of the direct-arc type, with the height of the electrodes adjusted so that there is some arcing between electrodes above the bath. Figure 17·33 shows a cross section of an electric-arc furnace. Like the bessemer and open-hearth processes, electric-arc furnaces may be either basic- or acid-lined.

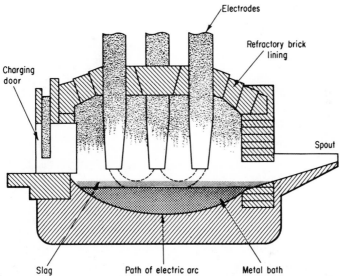

Fig. 17·33   Cross section of an electric-arc furnace. (*Bethlehem Steel Company*)

Since the electric-arc furnace requires no fuel, any desired atmosphere, neutral or reducing, may be used. There is no contamination from fuel oil or combustion gases. Because of atmospheric control and the possibility of producing first a strongly oxidizing slag followed by a reducing slag, a high-quality product may be obtained.

The charge is usually solid steel scrap of known composition. The first step requires an oxidizing basic slag to remove phosphorus and other oxidizable constituents. Lime and iron ore are charged on the molten steel for this purpose. When the phosphorus content in the metal has been reduced to the desired point, the slag may be skimmed or poured off. The second step is for desulfurization and deoxidation of the metal. This step requires a reducing basic slag which is obtained by the addition of lime, powdered coke, and fluorspar. The high lime and reducing conditions favor the removal of sulfur from the bath and its absorption by the slag as calcium sulfide. Proper alloy additions may be made to produce the desired composition of alloy steel.

When analysis indicates that the steel composition is correct, the furnace is tilted and the steel is poured into a ladle (Fig. 17·34). The tilting mechanism and charging side of the electric furnace are shown in Fig. 17·35.

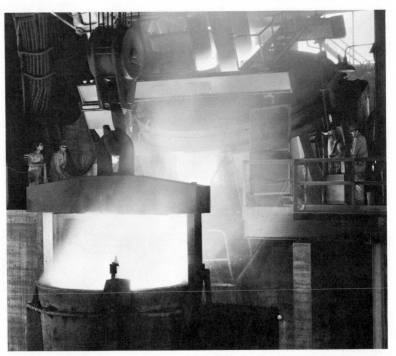

Fig. 17·34 Tapping an electric-arc furnace. (*Bethlehem Steel Company*)

17·19 Electrolytic refining. Electrolytic refining is similar to electrolysis, described earlier, and is used to produce metals of very high purity. It is also possible to recover silver, gold, and the precious metals from the anode mud that settles to the bottom of the tank (Sec. 17·20).

In electrolytic refining, the metal to be refined is the anode, a starting sheet of pure metal forms the cathode, and a salt solution of the metal is the electrolyte. When an external source of electricity is connected across the cell, it is found that the anode will decrease in weight and the cathode will increase at the same rate while the solution remains unchanged.

Copper produced by fire refining is of sufficient purity for most applications except for use as an electrical conductor. All electrical copper is refined electrolytically. Molten copper, after fire refining, is cast into anodes. The cathodes are thin sheets of electrolytic copper prepared by deposition on a rolled copper plate. The electrolyte consists of copper sulfate and sulfuric acid. When a new set of starting

Fig. 17·35 Front end of an electric-arc furnace during tapping. (*Bethlehem Steel Company*)

sheets (cathodes) is put in a tank, they tend to curl or warp and may cause short circuits. They are therefore inspected shortly after insertion. Figure 17·36 shows the insertion and straightening of cathodes.

At the anode, the copper atoms give up two electrons and go into solution as copper ions according to the following reaction:

$$Cu^0 - 2e \rightarrow Cu^{++} \tag{17·34}$$

At the cathode, the copper atoms take on two electrons and copper is deposited as follows:

$$Cu^{++} + 2e \rightarrow Cu^0$$

The impurities in copper are insoluble in the solution. They drop off the anode and settle out at the bottom of the tank as *anode mud*. The anodes usually last 20 to 30 days, and the cathodes are usually changed every 10 to 15 days. Figure 17·37 shows the pulling of electrolytic copper in cathode form from a refinery tank. The 38 cathodes shown are the entire cathode load of one refining tank. There are also 37 anodes in each tank. Notice that a refinery plant consists of

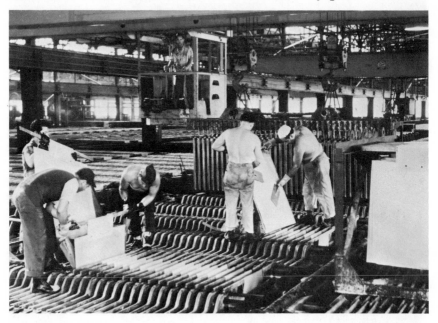

Fig. 17·36   Insertion and straightening of copper cathodes.   (*Phelps Dodge Corporation*)

an enormous number of cells. The picture also shows anodes being hosed down to remove adhering slime.

Cathode copper is charged into a refining furnace (Fig. 17·38), melted, further refined, and cast into ingots, cakes, wire bars, and billets for fabrication into desired shapes. These operations differ only slightly from those previously described under Fire Refining.

Nickel, lead, and tin are sometimes electrolytically refined for special applications.

17·20   Chemical refining.   Chemical refining is a process in which impurities are dissolved by chemical means. This method is possible only when the reagent has a selective action on the impurity.

The anode mud or slimes obtained in electrolytc reifining of copper contain silver, gold, and other precious metals of the platinum group.

Fig. 17·37 Pulling electrolytic copper in cathode form from a refinery tank. (*Phelps Dodge Corporation*)

Fig. 17·38 Charging cathodes into a refinery furnace. (*Phelps Dodge Corporation*)

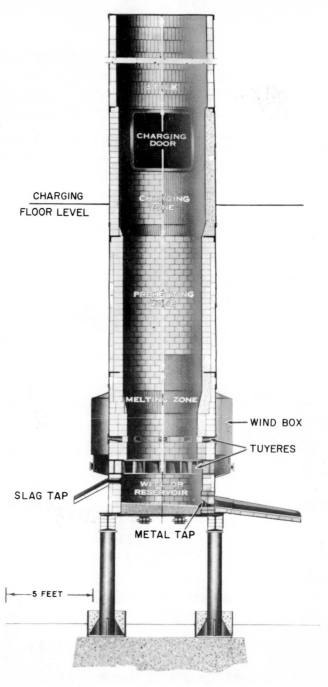

Fig. 17·39 Cross section of a cupola furnace. (*Harbison-Walker Refractories Company*)

These slimes are usually roasted and leached, and the silver is removed by electrolytic parting. The gold slime from the electrolytic parting may be boiled with sulfuric acid. This dissolves any remaining silver together with the platinum metals. The gold residue is fused and cast into bars.

Soda ash is used to remove arsenic from copper during the refining of copper. Chlorine gas is used to treat desilverized lead to remove zinc.

17·21 Melting of cast iron. Castings are usually made from melted pig iron. The furnaces used are either the cupola or the air furnace.

The cupola furnace (Fig. 17·39) is essentially a small blast furnace. It is operated under much smaller blast pressures. Before the pig iron is charged, a proper bed of fuel must be prepared. A bed of kindling wood is placed on the bottom, followed by heavier wood, fine coke, and a layer of the regular fuel. Charging is begun when all the fuel is well lighted. Pig-iron scrap and coke are charged in alternate layers until the height of the charging door. A small amount of limestone may be charged on top of each bed of iron to flux the coke ash. The cupola is never run continuously. When the desired amount of metal has been melted, charging ceases, and tapping is continued until all the iron has been removed. The bottom is then dropped and the furnace emptied.

The air furnace uses the reverberatory principle of heat reflection from the roof upon the metal. A longitudinal section of the furnace is shown in Fig. 17·40. The furnace is charged, when cold, by placing pigs of iron and scrap closely together on the hearth. The burner is fired by either powdered coal or oil. When the charge is melted, its composition may be adjusted by suitable additions, after which it is tapped into ladles for use. The air furnace is widely used for the production of malleable cast iron.

Since the metal does not come in contact with the fuel, the product of the air furnace is purer than cupola iron. There is less absorption of sulfur and carbon, resulting generally in a better grade and stronger cast iron. A wider range of scrap material may be used and the process is under better control, so that any desired composition can be more closely approached in an air furnace. The cupola, however, is a cheaper installation and cheaper to operate. It may be started and stopped more readily, fuel efficiency is greater, and there is less loss of metal through oxidation and consequent removal in the slag.

17·22 Vacuum metallurgy. Recent advances in electronics and jet engines have created a demand for materials and alloys of very high purity. This has led to the development of vacuum metallurgy.

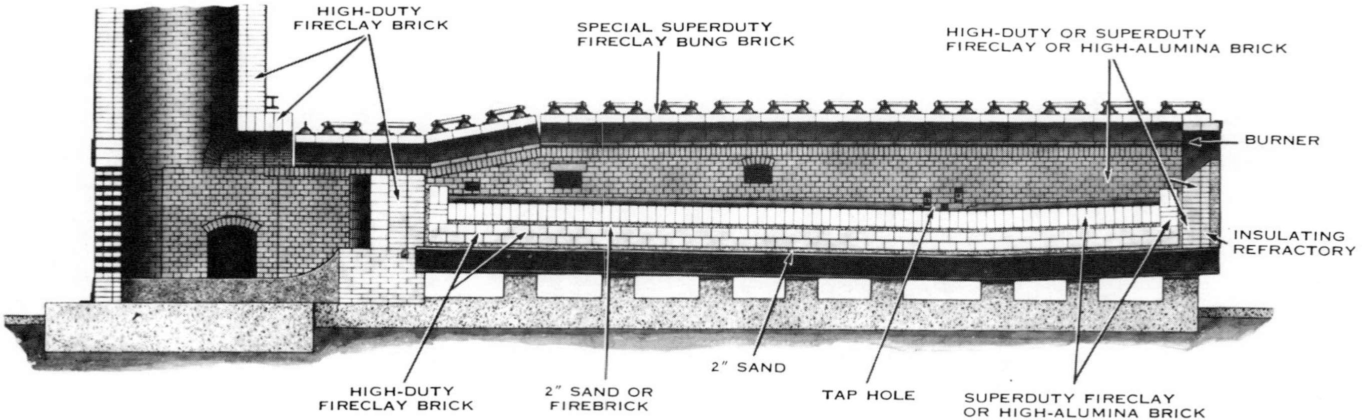

HIGH-DUTY OR SUPERDUTY
FIRECLAY OR HIGH-ALUMINA BRICK

BURNER

INSULATING
REFRACTORY

SUPERDUTY FIRECLAY
OR HIGH-ALUMINA BRICK

SPECIAL SUPERDUTY
FIRECLAY BUNG BRICK

TAP HOLE

2" SAND

2" SAND OR
FIREBRICK

HIGH-DUTY
FIRECLAY BRICK

HIGH-DUTY
FIRECLAY BRICK

Fig. 17·40 Longitudinal section of an air furnace. (*Harbison-Walker Refractories Company*)

520

The presence of small amounts of dissolved gases such as oxygen, hydrogen, and nitrogen often decreases strength and other properties, especially at high temperatures. These gases may also adversely affect subsequent working operations.

Much of the difficulty arises from the greater solubility of the gases in the liquid metal than in the solid metal. The excess gas liberated during solidification may produce blowholes in castings, blistering of sheet material, and embrittlement of the material if it is precipitated at the grain boundaries. The solubility of the gases may be reduced by a reduction in pressure as in a vacuum furnace.

One application of vacuum melting has been in the production of metals for use in atomic reactors such as uranium, thorium, and zirconium. Vacuum techniques are also used for processing ductile titanium, tantalum, and molybdenum. High-purity silicon and germanium are widely used in the electronics industry. Vacuum distillation has been applied to the recovery of magnesium, calcium, barium, and strontium. The harmful effects of dissolved oxygen and hydrogen are avoided by vacuum casting of copper.

The use of a vacuum furnace for heat treating of steel is also a rapidly developing field. A typical application is for the bright hardening of stainless steel. Loads may be as high as 500 lb of steel, and the entire cycle is automatic. After charging, the furnace is pumped down to a predetermined vacuum before the heat is applied. Outgassing of the steel and pumping continue while the temperature is raised. After soaking at the desired temperature, the steel may be rapidly quenched by the introduction of liquid nitrogen into the furnace. Vacuum-hardened stainless seems to have a cleaner surface, higher hardness, and better corrosion resistance.

17.23 Zone refining. This is another method of producing metals and alloys of ultrahigh purity for special applications. Zone refining is based on the fact that impurities are generally more soluble in liquid metal than they are in solid metal. If a short portion of a bar of metal is melted and this molten zone is moved along the bar, impurities will be carried by the molten portion toward one end of the bar while pure metal will concentrate in the cooling portion. This is shown schematically in Fig. 17·41. The zones are usually produced by induction heaters. The zone traverse may be repeated a number of times until the necessary purity is obtained.

Zone refining may be applied to any crystalline material, provided there is sufficient difference in impurity solubility in the liquid and solid states. It has been used to produce ultrapure germanium, silicon, zirconium, titanium, molybdenum, tungsten, and other metals.

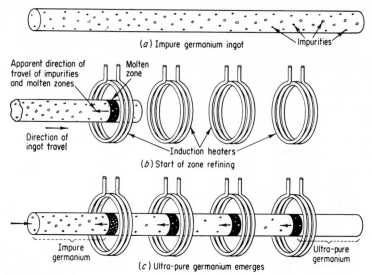

(a) Impure germanium ingot

Impurities

Apparent direction of travel of impurities and molten zones

Molten zone

Direction of ingot travel

Induction heaters

(b) Start of zone refining

Impure germanium

Ultra-pure germanium

(c) Ultra-pure germanium emerges

Fig. 17·41   Schematic representation of zone refining.   (*Bell Telephone Laboratories, Inc.*)

QUESTIONS

17·1   List the countries that are the world's major producers of the following metals and give the percentage for average production over a recent 5-year period: nickel, copper, tin, iron, aluminum, and magnesium.

17·2   Why is gold sometimes found in the free state?

17·3   Most metals are found in combination with certain elements.   Why?

17·4   Define the following terms: ore deposit, values, and gangue.

17·5   In the flow sheet of nickel, copper, and magnesium (Figs. 17.1, 17.2, 17.25), list the operations that fall under ore dressing, concentration, metal extraction, and refining.

17·6   Why is it necessary to use a classifier in conjunction with a ball mill?

17·7   Explain *closed-circuit grinding*.

17·8   Describe two different types of classifiers.

17·9   Explain the operation of a flotation cell.

17·10   Why is the principle involved in flotation different from that in gravity concentration methods?

17·11   Why is bubble size important in flotation?

17·12   Explain the principle of an electrostatic separator.

17·13   List and explain the three classifications of metal-extraction processes.

17·14   Why does flotation work best with fine particles?

17·15   Why is it sometimes desirable to increase particle size by sintering?

17·16   What is the difference between calcination and roasting?

17·17   Why is it not necessary to provide much fuel for roasting?

17·18   Discuss the advantages and disadvantages of leaching as compared with smelting.

17·19   List the raw materials that make up the charge of a blast furnace, and discuss the part played by each in the manufacture of pig iron.

17·20   Although air is blown into a blast furnace, why is it considered a reducing process rather than an oxidizing process?

17·21   Draw a cross section of the blast furnace and indicate the approximate location of the reducing zone, heat-absorption zone, fusion zone, combustion zone, and crucible.   Indicate the approximate temperature in each zone.

17·22   What is the function of the hot-blast stoves and how do they work?

17·23   Why are phosphorus and sulfur not removed from iron in the acid bessemer process?

17·24   Why is solid pig iron not used as the charge in the bessemer converter?

17·25   How is heat provided in the bessemer converter?

17·26   Why is it necessary to deoxidize and recarburize at the end of the bessemer or open-hearth processes?   What additions are used for this purpose?

17·27   What are the advantages of the basic open-hearth process compared with the acid bessemer process?

17·28   What are the advantages of the basic oxygen process compared with the acid bessemer process?

17·29   Why are sulfur and sometimes lead added to steel?

17·30   What are the differences in construction and operation between the basic oxygen furnaces and the bessemer converter?

17·31   What is a duplex process?   What are its advantages?

17·32   Explain the regenerative principle and its use in the open-hearth process.

17·33   Explain what happens during the ore boil, lime boil, and working periods of the open-hearth process.

17·34   Why is distillation possible with only certain metals?

17·35   In the extraction of zinc, what is the difference between the horizontal-retort and vertical-retort processes?

17·36   Name two electrothermic processes and give the application of each.

17·37   What are the advantages of the electric-arc furnace?

17·38   What are the differences and similarities between the cupola and blast furnace?

17·39   What are the advantages and disadvantages of the cupola compared with the air furnace?

17·40   What are the advantages of vacuum melting?   Give some applications.

17·41   Explain why aluminum and magnesium are produced by electrolysis of a fused-salt bath.

17·42   What is the difference between electrolysis and electrolytic refining?

REFERENCES

American Society for Metals: "Metals Handbook," 1948 edition, Metals Park, Ohio.

Bray, J. L.: "Ferrous Process Metallurgy," John Wiley & Sons, Inc., New York, 1954.

————: "Non-ferrous Production Metallurgy," John Wiley & Sons, Inc., New York, 1947.

Camp, J. M., and C. B. Francis: "The Making, Shaping and Treating of Steel," U.S. Steel Company, Pittsburgh, Pa., 1951.

Dennis, W. H.: "Metallurgy of the Non-ferrous Metals," Pitman Publishing Corporation, New York, 1961.

Gaudin, A. M.: "Principles of Mineral Dressing," McGraw-Hill Book Company, Inc., New York, 1939.

Haywood, C. R.: "An Outline of Metallurgical Practice," D. Van Nostrand Company, Inc., Princeton, N.J., 1942.

Liddell, D. M.: "Handbook of Non-ferrous Metallurgy," vol. 1, "Principles and Processes"; vol. 2, "Recovery of the Metals," McGraw-Hill Book Company, Inc., New York, 1945.

Nord, M.: "Textbook of Engineering Materials," John Wiley & Sons, Inc., New York, 1952.

Richards, R. H., and C. E. Locke: "Textbook of Ore Dressing," 3d ed., McGraw-Hill Book Company, Inc., New York, 1940.

Stoughton, B., A. Butts, and A. M. Bounds: "Engineering Metallurgy," 4th ed., McGraw-Hill Book Company, Inc., New York, 1953.

Van Arsdale, G. D.: "Hydrometallurgy of Base Metals," McGraw-Hill Book Company, Inc., New York, 1953.

Young, G. J.: "Elements of Mining," 4th ed., McGraw-Hill Book Company, Inc., New York, 1946.

APPENDIX

°C	°F	°C	°F	°C	°F	°C	°F	°C	°F
−273	−459	400	752	1000	1832	1600	2912	−268	−450
−250	−418	410	770	1010	1850	1610	2930	−240	−400
−200	−328	420	788	1020	1868	1620	2948	−212	−350
−150	−238	430	806	1030	1886	1630	2966	−184	−300
−100	−148	440	824	1040	1904	1640	2984	−157	−250
− 50	− 58	450	842	1050	1922	1650	3002	−129	−200
− 40	− 40	460	860	1060	1940	1660	3020	−101	−150
− 30	− 22	470	878	1070	1958	1670	3038	− 73	−100
− 20	− 4	480	896	1080	1976	1680	3056	− 46	− 50
− 10	+ 14	490	914	1090	1994	1690	3074	− 40	− 40
0	32	500	932	1100	2012	1700	3092	− 34	− 30
5	41	510	950	1110	2030	1710	3110	− 29	− 20
10	50	520	968	1120	2048	1720	3128	− 23	− 10
15	59	530	986	1130	2066	1730	3146	− 18	0
20	68	540	1004	1140	2084	1740	3164	− 15	5
25	77	550	1022	1150	2102	1750	3182	− 12	10
30	86	560	1040	1160	2120	1760	3200	− 9	15
35	95	570	1058	1170	2138	1770	3218	− 7	20
40	104	580	1076	1180	2156	1780	3236	− 4	25
45	113	590	1094	1190	2174	1790	3254	− 1	30
50	122	600	1112	1200	2192	1800	3272	+ 2	35
55	131	610	1130	1210	2210	1810	3290	4	40
60	140	620	1148	1220	2228	1820	3308	7	45
65	149	630	1166	1230	2246	1830	3326	10	50
70	158	640	1184	1240	2264	1840	3344	13	55
75	167	650	1202	1250	2282	1850	3362	16	60
80	176	660	1220	1260	2300	1860	3380	18	65
85	185	670	1238	1270	2318	1870	3398	21	70
90	194	680	1256	1280	2336	1880	3416	24	75
95	203	690	1274	1290	2354	1890	3434	27	80
100	212	700	1292	1300	2372	1900	3452	29	85
110	230	710	1310	1310	2390	1910	3470	32	90
120	248	720	1328	1320	2408	1920	3488	35	95
130	266	730	1346	1330	2426	1930	3506	38	100
140	284	740	1364	1340	2444	1940	3524	43	110
150	302	750	1382	1350	2462	1950	3542	49	120
160	320	760	1400	1360	2480	1960	3560	54	130
170	338	770	1418	1370	2498	1970	3578	60	140
180	356	780	1436	1380	2516	1980	3596	65	150
190	374	790	1454	1390	2534	1990	3614	71	160
200	392	800	1472	1400	2552	2000	3632	76	170
210	410	810	1490	1410	2570	2050	3722	83	180
220	428	820	1508	1420	2588	2100	3812	88	190
230	446	830	1526	1430	2606	2150	3902	93	200
240	464	840	1544	1440	2624	2200	3992	121	250
250	482	850	1562	1450	2642	2250	4082	149	300
260	500	860	1580	1460	2660	2300	4172	177	350
270	518	870	1598	1470	2678	2350	4262	204	400
280	536	880	1616	1480	2696	2400	4352	232	450
290	554	890	1634	1490	2714	2450	4442	260	500
300	572	900	1652	1500	2732	2500	4532	288	550
310	590	910	1670	1510	2750	2550	4622	316	600
320	608	920	1688	1520	2768	2600	4712	343	650
330	626	930	1706	1530	2786	2650	4802	371	700
340	644	940	1724	1540	2804	2700	4892	399	750
350	662	950	1742	1550	2822	2750	4982	427	800
360	680	960	1760	1560	2840	2800	5072	454	850
370	698	970	1778	1570	2858	2850	5162	482	900
380	716	980	1796	1580	2876	2900	5252	510	950
390	734	990	1814	1590	2894	3000	5432	538	1000

INDEX